Pobell · Matter and Methods at Low Temperatures

Frank Pobell

Matter and Methods at Low Temperatures

With 192 Figures

Springer-Verlag

Berlin Heidelberg New York
London Paris Tokyo
Hong Kong Barcelona
Budapest

Professor Dr. Frank Pobell

Physikalisches Institut, Universität Bayreuth, Postfach 10 12 51
W-8580 Bayreuth, Fed. Rep. of Germany

PHYSICS

o4624841

ISBN 3-540-53751-1 Springer-Verlag Berlin Heidelberg New York
ISBN 0-387-53751-1 Springer-Verlag New York Berlin Heidelberg

Library of Congress Cataloging-in-Publication Data. Pobell, Frank, 1937– Matter and methods at low temperatures / Frank Pobell. p. cm. Includes bibliographical references and index. ISBN 0-387-53751-1 (U.S.) 1. Matter--Thermal properties. 2. Low temperatures. 3. Cryostats. I. Title. QC192.P63   1992   536.1'2--dc20

© Springer-Verlag Berlin Heidelberg 1992
Printed in Germany

This text was prepared using the PS^{TM} Technical Word Processor and printed by a Hewlett-Packard Laser Jet III

54/3140-543210 – Printed on acid-free paper

Preface

The aim of this book is to provide information about performing experiments at low temperatures, as well as basic facts concerning the low temperature properties of liquid and solid matter. To orient the reader, I begin with chapters on these low temperature properties. The major part of the book is then devoted to refrigeration techniques and to the physics on which they are based. Of equal importance, of course, are the definition and measurement of temperature; hence low temperature thermometry is extensively discussed in subsequent chapters. Finally, I describe a variety of design and construction techniques which have turned out to be useful over the years.

The content of the book is based on the three-hour-per-week lecture course which I have given several times at the University of Bayreuth between 1983 and 1991. It should be particularly suited for advanced students whose intended masters (diploma) or Ph.D. subject is experimental condensed matter physics at low temperatures. However, I believe that the book will also be of value to experienced scientists, since it describes several very recent advances in experimental low temperature physics and technology, for example, new developments in nuclear refrigeration and thermometry.

My knowledge and appreciation of low temperature physics have been strongly influenced and enhanced over the years by many colleagues. In particular, I wish to express my thanks to my colleagues and coworkers at the Institut für Festkörperforschung, Forschungszentrum Jülich and at the Physikalisches Institut, Universität Bayreuth. Their enthusiasm for low temperature physics has been essential for the work in our groups, and for many achievements described in this book. Among them I wish to mention especially R.M. Mueller, Ch. Buchal, and M. Kubota from the time at Jülich (1975-1983), K. Gloos, R. König, B. Schröder-Smeibidl, P. Smeibidl, P. Sekowski, and E. Syskakis in Bayreuth (since 1983).

Above all, I am deeply indebted to my colleague and friend Girgl Eska, who shares with me all the joys and sorrows of our low temperature work in Bayreuth. He and Bob Mueller read the entire manuscript and made many important comments on it. I am also very grateful to Dierk Rainer for so often sharing with me his deep insight into the physics of many low temperature phenomena.

It is a pleasure for me to thank Mrs. G. Pinzer for her perfect typing of the manuscript and Ms. D. Hollis for her careful copy-editing. Likewise, I gratefully acknowledge the very thorough and time-consuming checking of the whole manuscript by Dr. H. Lotsch.

V

Finally, I thank the Institute for Physical Problems, USSR Academy of Sciences, where part of the manuscript was written, for the hospitality extended to me, and the "Volkswagen Stiftung" for a stipend which I held for some time while writing this book.

Bayreuth   F. Pobell
September 1991

Contents

1. Introduction 1

2. Properties of Cryoliquids 6
   2.1 Liquid Air, Liquid Oxygen, Liquid Nitrogen 7
   2.2 Liquid Hydrogen 7
   2.3 Liquid Helium 11
       2.3.1 Some Properties of the Helium Isotopes 11
       2.3.2 Latent Heat of Evaporation and Vapour Pressure 15
       2.3.3 Specific Heat 18
       2.3.4 Transport Properties of Liquid ^{4}He:
             Thermal Conductivity and Viscosity 21
       2.3.5 Superfluid Film Flow 23
       2.3.6 Liquid ^{3}He at Millikelvin Temperatures 25

3. Solid Matter at Low Temperatures 30
   3.1 Specific Heat 31
       3.1.1 Insulators 31
       3.1.2 Metals 33
       3.1.3 Superconducting Metals 37
       3.1.4 Non-Crystalline Solids 38
       3.1.5 Magnetic Specific Heat 40
       3.1.6 The Low-Temperature Specific Heat of Copper 43
   3.2 Thermal Expansion 44
   3.3 Thermal Conductivity 48
       3.3.1 Lattice Conductivity: Phonons 49
       3.3.2 Electronic Thermal Conductivity 54
       3.3.3 Thermal Conductivity at Low Temperatures 55
             a) Insulators/Phonons 55
             b) Metals/Conduction Electrons 55
       3.3.4 Superconducting Metals 56
       3.3.5 Relation Between Thermal and Electrical Conductivity:
             The Wiedemann-Franz Law 57
       3.3.6 Influence of Impurities on Conductivity 59
             a) Electron Scattering by Non-Magnetic Impurity Atoms 60
             b) Scattering of Electrons by Magnetic Impurity Atoms
                (in Particular in Copper) 60

4. Thermal Contact and Thermal Isolation 64
 4.1 Selection of the Material
   with the Appropriate Cryogenic Thermal Conductivity 64
 4.2 Heat Switches 66
   4.2.1 Gaseous and Mechanical Heat Switches 66
   4.2.2 Superconducting Heat Switches 67
 4.3 Thermal Boundary Resistance 70
   4.3.1 Boundary Resistance Between Metals 70
   4.3.2 Boundary Resistance Between Liquid Helium and Solids . 73
     a) Acoustic Mismatch 73
     b) Acoustic Coupling Between Liquid Helium
       and Metal Sinters 76
     c) Magnetic Coupling Between Liquid ^{3}He and Solids
       Containing Magnetic Moments 77

5. Helium-4 Cryostats 81
 5.1 Use of Liquid ^{4}He in Low-Temperature Equipment 82
   5.1.1 Cool-Down Period 82
   5.1.2 Running Phase of the Experiment 83
     a) Heat Conduction 83
     b) Heat Radiation 83
     c) Conduction by Gas Particles
       Remaining in the Vacuum Space 84
 5.2 Helium-4 Cryostats 85
   5.2.1 Double-Walled Glass Dewars 85
   5.2.2 Metal Dewars 87
   5.2.3 Cryostats for T > 5 K 88
   5.2.4 Cryostats with Variable Temperature at $1.3K \leq T \leq 4.2K$ 88
     a) Pumping on the Main ^{4}He Bath 89
     b) Continuously Operating ^{4}He Evaporation Cryostat . . 89
   5.2.5 Auxiliary Equipment 92
     a) Storage Vessel 92
     b) Transfer Tube 92
     c) Level Detector 94
       Acoustic Level Detection 94
       Resistive Level Detection 95

6. Helium-3 Cryostats 97
 6.1 Helium-3 Cryostats with External Pumps 98
 6.2 Helium-3 Cryostats with Internal Adsorption Pumps 100

7. The ^{3}He-^{4}He Dilution Refrigerator 105
 7.1 Properties of Liquid ^{3}He-^{4}He Mixtures 106
   7.1.1 Phase Diagram and Solubility 106
   7.1.2 ^{3}He-^{4}He Mixtures as Fermi Liquids 109
   7.1.3 Finite Solubility of ^{3}He in ^{4}He 110
     a) ^{3}He in Pure ^{3}He (x = 1) 110

          b) One ^{3}He Atom in Liquid ^{4}He ($x \simeq 0$) 110
          c) Many ^{3}He Atoms in Liquid ^{4}He ($x > 0$) 111
    7.1.4 Cooling Power of the Dilution Process 113
    7.1.5 Osmotic Pressure 116
  7.2 Realization of a ^{3}He-^{4}He Dilution Refrigerator 118
  7.3 Properties of the Main Components of a ^{3}He-^{4}He Dilution
     Refrigerator 121
    7.3.1 Mixing Chamber 121
    7.3.2 Still 122
    7.3.3 Heat Exchangers 123
  7.4 Examples of ^{3}He-^{4}He Dilution Refrigerators 131

8. Refrigeration by Solidification of Liquid ^{3}He:
   Pomeranchuck Cooling 138
  8.1 Phase and Entropy Diagrams of ^{3}He 139
  8.2 Entropies of Liquid and Solid ^{3}He 140
  8.3 Pomeranchuk Cooling 142

9. Refrigeration by Adiabatic Demagnetization
   of a Paramagnetic Salt 148
  9.1 The Principle of Magnetic Refrigeration 148
  9.2 Thermodynamics of Magnetic Refrigeration 150
         a) Heat of Isothermal Magnetization 150
         b) Adiabatic Demagnetization 150
         c) Warming up due to External Heating 151
  9.3 Non-Interacting Magnetic Dipoles in a Magnetic Field ... 152
  9.4 Paramagnetic Salts and Magnetic Refrigerators 154

10. Refrigeration by Adiabatic Nuclear Demagnetization 158
  10.1 Some Equations Relevant for Nuclear Refrigeration 162
  10.2 Differences in the Experimental Procedure for Nuclear
      and Electronic Demagnetization 163
  10.3 Interaction Between Conduction Electrons and Nuclei ... 165
    10.3.1 Electron-Phonon Coupling 165
    10.3.2 Nucleus-Electron Coupling 168
  10.4 Influence of an External Heat Load and the Optimum Final
      Magnetic Field 171
  10.5 Heat Leaks 174
    10.5.1 External Heat Leaks 174
    10.5.2 Eddy Current Heating 177
    10.5.3 Internal, Time-Dependent Heat Leaks 178
  10.6 Nuclear Refrigerants 181
  10.7 Hyperfine Enhanced Nuclear Refrigeration 184
  10.8 Nuclear Demagnetization Refrigerators 186

11. Temperature Scales and Temperature Fixed Points 198
  11.1 Thermodynamic Temperature 198

11.2 The International Temperature Scale ITS-90 199
11.3 Practical but Not Officially Accepted Low-Temperature
Fixed Points 204
    11.3.1 Fixed Points of EPT-76 204
    11.3.2 The NBS Superconducting Fixed-Point Device . . . 204
    11.3.3 Fixed Points of Liquid and Solid ^{3}He 207

12. **Low-Temperature Thermometry** 210
12.1 Gas Thermometry 211
12.2 Helium Vapour Pressure Thermometry 212
12.3 Helium-3 Melting Pressure Thermometry 214
12.4 Thermoelectricity 216
12.5 Resistance Thermometry 219
    12.5.1 Metals 219
    12.5.2 Semiconductors, Carbon Resistors and RuO_2 220
        a) Doped Germanium 222
        b) Carbon Resistance Thermometers 222
        c) Thick-Film Chip Resistors Based on RuO_2 . . . 233
12.6 Noise Thermometry 234
12.7 Dielectric-Constant Thermometry 237
12.8 Magnetic Thermometry with Electronic Paramagnets 239
12.9 Magnetic Thermometry with Nuclear Paramagnets 248
    12.9.1 Non-Resonant, Integral Detection of Nuclear
        Magnetization 249
    12.9.2 Selective Excitation but Non-Resonant Detection
        of Nuclear Magnetization 250
    12.9.3 Resonant Excitation and Resonant Detection
        of Nuclear Magnetization 252
        a) Continuous Wave Nuclear Magnetic Resonance 252
        b) Pulsed Nuclear Magnetic Resonance 253
12.10 Magnetic Thermometry via Anisotropy of Gamma Rays
    (Nuclear Orientation Thermometry) 260
12.11 Summary 265

13. **Miscellaneous Cryogenic Design Aids** 267
13.1 Cryogenic Capacitive Transducers for Thermometry and
Manometry 267
13.2 Cold Valves 271
13.3 Coaxial Cables and Feedthroughs 273
13.4 Small Superconducting Magnets and Magnet Leads 274
13.5 Shielding Against Magnetic Fields and Magnetic Fields
Inside of Shields 276
    13.5.1 Normal-Conducting Shields 276
    13.5.2 Superconducting Shields 277
    13.5.3 Magnetic Fields Inside of Shields 278
13.6 Sintered Metal Heat Exchangers 278
13.7 Optical Windows 282

Appendix 284
   Magnetic Susceptibilities of Some Selected Materials 284

List of Symbols 285
   Conversion Factors 286

References 287

Subject Index 309

1. Introduction

The importance of temperature is very often not fully recognized, the reason probably being that our life is restricted to an extremely narrow range of temperatures. This can be realized if we look at the temperatures existing in nature or accessible in laboratories (Fig.1.1). These temperatures range from about 10^9 K, the temperature at the centre of the hottest stars and necessary to form or destroy atomic nuclei, to about 10^{-5} K, the lowest temperatures accessible today in the laboratory in condensed matter physics experiments. This lower limit means that we have been able to refrigerate matter to within about 10 μK of absolute zero (0K = -273.15° C). Indeed, nuclei have been investigated at nuclear-spin temperatures which are an-

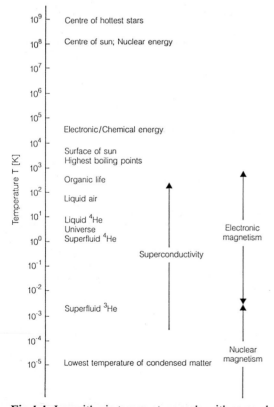

Fig.1.1. Logarithmic temperature scale with some characteristic phenomena

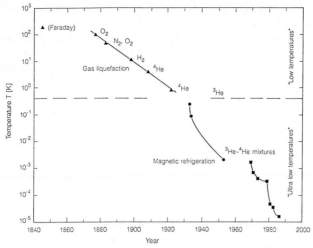

Fig.1.2. Historical development of refrigeration temperatures of matter, starting about 150 years ago with Faraday's gas liquefaction. The low temperature range was made accessible by liquid air, liquid H_2 and liquid ^{4}He. Ultralow temperatures were attained by magnetic refrigeration with electronic magnetic moments (•) and later with nuclear magnetic moments (■). Refrigeration with liquid ^{3}He and liquid ^{3}He-^{4}He mixtures developed as the rare helium isotope became available in sufficient quantities

other four orders of magnitude lower, in the low nanokelvin temperature range. With these achievements, low-temperature physics has surpassed nature by several orders of magnitude, because the lowest temperature in nature and in the universe is 2.7 K. This background temperature exists everywhere in the universe because of the photon energy which is still being radiated from the "big bang". If we compare low-temperature physics to other branches of physics, we realize that it is actually one of the very few branches of science where mankind has surpassed nature, an achievement which has not yet proved possible, for example, in high-pressure physics, high-energy physics or vacuum physics. The very wide range of temperatures accessible to experiments has made temperature probably the most important among the parameters which we can vary in the laboratory in order to change the properties of matter, to obtain a better understanding of its behaviour, and to make practical use of it.

The historical development of refrigeration to lower and lower temperatures is illustrated in Fig.1.2. Air, N_2 and O_2 were liquefied and eventually solidified over one hundred years ago, in 1883. This was the first time that mankind reached temperatures below 100 K. The scientists and engineers involved in this venture had two aims. A very practical one was to devise a means of refrigerating meat for its journey from other continents to Europe. The scientific aim was to discover whether permanent gases exist, in other words, are there any substances which do not exist in the liquid and/or solid state? This latter aim led to the liquefaction and solidification of hydrogen by James Dewar in 1898; he reached temperatures of 20 K and later 13 K. At about that time the last gaseous element to be discovered, helium, was detected first in spectroscopic investigations of solar protuberances and then as a gas escaping from various minerals on earth. The Dutch scientist Heike Kamerlingh-Onnes won the race to liquefy this last element; he liquefied helium-4 at 4.2 K in 1908. Kamerlingh-Onnes' work opened up the Kelvin temperature range to science, and scientists at his low-temperature laboratory at the University of Leiden dominated low-temperature physics for at least 20 years, making many fundamental investigations in helium physics, in the physics of metals, and in the physics of magnetism, for example. Today H. Kamerlingh-Onnes is considered "the father of low-temperature physics".

In 1926, H. Kamerlingh-Onnes reached 0.7 K by pumping on the vapour above a bath of boiling ^{4}He. The development of a fundamentally different technology, magnetic refrigeration, was necessary to attain temperatures appreciably below 1 K. By adiabatic demagnetization of paramagnetic salts, a method proposed in the 1920s, we can approach absolute zero to within a few millikelvin (Fig.1.2). An advanced version of this magnetic refrigeration method, adiabatic demagnetization of nuclear magnetic moments, is the only method known today by which we can reach temperatures far into the microkelvin temperature range. While these "one-shot" magnetic cooling methods were being perfected, another refrigeration technique, again based on the properties of liquid helium, the dilution of the rare isotope ^{3}He by the common isotope ^{4}He, enabled the development of a continuous refrigeration method to reach the low millikelvin temperature range. This method was proposed in the 1960s and put into practice in the early 1970s. Today it is very well developed and has probably approached its limits; it has largely replaced adiabatic demagnetization of paramagnetic salts. Therefore, I shall discuss dilution refrigeration at length and devote only a short chapter to electronic paramagnetic refrigeration. Nuclear magnetic refrigeration - the only method for the microkelvin temperature range - will, of course, be discussed in detail. I shall also briefly describe two additional refrigeration methods based on the properties of ^{3}He that are of minor importance today: refrigeration by evaporation of liquid ^{3}He and refrigeration by solidification of liquid ^{3}He (Pomeranchuk cooling).

As a result of these developments, three refrigeration methods dominate low-temperature physics today (Table 1.1). Temperatures in the Kelvin range down to about 1 K are obtained by evaporation of liquid ^{4}He, the evaporation of pure ^{3}He for cooling is now only of minor importance. The millikelvin temperature range is completely dominated by the ^{3}He-^{4}He dilution refrigeration method, which in a simple apparatus can reach minimum temperatures of about 20 mK and in a more complicated apparatus 5 mK; the present record is about 2 mK. The other two millikelvin refrigeration methods, Pomeranchuk cooling and adiabatic demagnetization of electronic magnetic moments, are of minor importance today. Finally, in the microkelvin temperature range, we have only one method, nuclear adiabatic demagnetization. This method has opened up the microkelvin temperature range (with a present minimum of $12 \mu K$) to condensed-matter physics, and

Table 1.1. Refrigeration techniques. The methods which dominate in the three temperature ranges are in italics

Temperature range	Refrigeration technique	Available since	Typical T_{min}	Record T_{min}
I Kelvin	Universe			2.74 K
	Helium-4 evaporation	1908	1.3 K	0.7 K
	Helium-3 evaporation	1950	0.3 K	0.25 K
II Milli-kelvin	*^{3}He-^{4}He dilution*	1965	10 mK	2 mK
	Pomeranchuk cooling	1965	3 mK	2 mK
	Electronic magnetic refrigeration	1934	3 mK	2 mK
III Micro-kelvin	*Nuclear magnetic refrigeration*	1956	50 μK	12 μK [a]

[a] The given minimum temperature for the microkelvin temperature range is the *lattice (electronic) equilibrium* temperature measured with a thermometer attached to the refrigeration stage. *Nuclear spin* temperatures as low as about 1 nK have been reached (Table 10.2)

the nanokelvin temperature range to nuclear-spin physics. At these extremely low temperatures it makes sense, as we will see, to distinguish between a temperature of the nuclear magnetic spin system and a temperature of the electrons and of lattice vibrations. When I speak about "temperature" in this textbook, I always mean the latter, unless I explicitly state otherwise.

Low-temperature physics and technology are not possible without knowledge of the relevant properties of liquid and solid matter at low temperatures. And many fundamental properties of matter were only found and/or understood after matter had been cooled to the Kelvin range or to even lower temperatures. Among these properties are the quantization of lattice vibrations (phonons), the electronic excitations leading to the linear temperature dependence of the specific heat of conduction electrons, superconductivity, superfluidity and many aspects of magnetism. Hence, this textbook begins with chapters on the properties of liquid and solid matter at low temperatures relevant for the performance and design of low-temperature experiments. But even though a major part of the book will deal with solid-state physics, it is not intended to replace more general textbooks on this subject. Indeed, readers are assumed to have a basic knowledge of condensed-matter physics as found in [1.1-4], for example.

Experiments at low temperatures make no sense without thermometry. In fact, the measurement of a low or very low temperature and its relation to the thermodynamic temperature scale are as important as the attainment of that temperature itself, and very often just as difficult. This has become increasingly apparent in the last two decades as lower and lower temperatures have been reached. Hence, after discussion of the various refrigeration techniques, I shall discuss temperature scales and the various thermometric methods at low temperatures. The book closes with a chapter on various "cryogenic design aids", a discussion of various tools and tricks helpful for low-temperature investigations.

There are several excellent books on the properties of matter at low temperatures [1.5] and on the technology of cryogenics above about 1 K [1.6,7] and below 1 K [1.8-11]. The reader should consult them for subjects not included in this book, in particular the chapter on SQUID technology in *Lounasmaa*'s book [1.8] or in [1.12-15], or for information on the state of the art at the time of writing of those books. The two most comprehensive monographs [1.8,9] on the subject of this book were written about 15 years ago, but the field of experimental physics at milli- and microkelvin temperatures has been rapidly expanding since then, and therefore a new monograph devoted to this field seemed to be appropriate. The present textbook was written in the last two years, and it reflects largely the state of the art of experimental low-temperature physics at that time. Endeavours in low-temperature physics and technology have been rewarded by a great number of fundamental discoveries that are important for our understanding of matter, in particular of its quantum behaviour, and for practical applications. These achievements were only possible by overcoming substantial experimental difficulties, in particular when the range below 1 K was entered, and the (slightly modified) statement from the first page of *Lounasmaa*'s book [1.8] provides a good summary of the essentials:

"An experimentalist wishing to pursue research at low temperatures faces four technical difficulties: how to reach the low temperature, how to measure it, how to reduce the external heat leak so that the low temperature can be maintained for a sufficiently long time, and how to transfer cold from one place to another. Many experimental methods have been developed to provide a satisfactory solution to these problems."

The progress in these areas will be discussed in the present book. I shall restrict the discussion of the properties of matter and experimental techniques to temperatures below about 10 K; higher temperatures will only be considered if we need them in order to understand what is going on at temperatures of interest in this book.

References are made preferentially to books or to review articles. Original papers are cited only when I consider them necessary for obtaining more details than can be given in a monograph, in particular for fields which are still under development, like thermal boundary resistance, nuclear refrigeration or thermometry at very low temperatures. In many instances I cite according not to priority but to pertinence for the purpose of this book. References are mostly made to work published after 1970. Naturally, many more publications are available than are given in the list of references. I will use cgs and/or SI units, whatever seems appropriate and as is typical for practical work in today's low-temperature laboratories. Equations - as for specific heat or susceptibility - are given for one mole.

2. Properties of Cryoliquids

In this chapter I shall discuss properties of cryoliquids important for the design and performance of low-temperature experiments. Of course, cryoliquids are very important for low-temperature physics because they are the simplest means of achieving low temperatures. In particular, the properties of liquid helium are essential because all refrigeration methods to $T < 10$ K use liquid helium as a final or intermediate refrigeration stage. I shall not discuss the technology of liquefaction [2.1,2]. For liquifaction the gas has to be isothermally compressed and then expanded to let it perform "external" work (for example in an expansion engine), or perhaps using the well-known Joule-Thomson effect, which means letting the gas expand and perform "internal" work against the mutual attraction of its atoms or molecules. This latter effect leads to cooling if the starting temperature is below the inversion temperature T_i, which is $6.75 T_c$, where T_c is the critical temperature for a van der Waals gas. Various properties of cryoliquids are summarized in Table 2.1 and are compared there to the relevant properties of water. Of particular importance for refrigeration are the boiling point T_b (defining the accessible temperature range), the latent heat of evaporation L

Table 2.1. Properties of some liquids (T_b: boiling point at $P = 1$ bar, T_m: melting point at $P = 1$ bar, $T_{tr}(P_{tr})$: triple-point temperature (pressure), $T_c(P_c)$: critical temperature (pressure), L: latent heat of evaporation at T_b). The date have mostly been taken from [2.3,12]

Substance	T_b [K]	T_m [K]	T_{tr} [K]	P_{tr} [bar]	T_c [K]	P_c [bar]	Latent heat L [kJ/ℓ]	Vol.% in air
H_2O	373.15	273.15	273.16	0.06	647.3	220	2252	--
Xe	165.1	161.3	161.4	0.82	289.8	58.9	303	$0.1\cdot10^{-4}$
Kr	119.9	115.8	114.9	0.73	209.4	54.9	279	$1.1\cdot10^{-4}$
O_2	90.2	54.4	54.36	0.016	154.3	50.4	245	20.9
Ar	87.3	83.8	83.81	0.67	150.9	48.7	224	0.93
N_2	77.4	63.3	63.15	0.12	126.0	33.9	160	78.1
Ne	27.1	24.5	24.56	0.43	44.5	27.2	110	$18\cdot10^{-4}$
D_2	23.7	18.7	18.72	0.17	38.3	16.6	50	--
H_2	20.3	14.0	13.80	0.07	33.3	13.0	31.8	$0.5\cdot10^{-4}$
^{4}He	4.21	--	--	--	5.20	2.28	2.56	$5.2\cdot10^{-4}$
^{3}He	3.19	--	--	--	3.32	1.16	0.48	--

(defining the cooling power) and - last but by no means least important - the price (defining the availability).

2.1 Liquid Air, Liquid Oxygen, Liquid Nitrogen

Today liquid oxygen is not in common use as a refrigerant because it is extremely reactive. An explosive oxidation reaction can occur if oxygen comes into contact with organic liquids, like oil used in pumps, or with solid matter having a large surface area, like metal powder. The boiling temperature of oxygen lies above the boiling temperature of nitrogen. Therefore, if one keeps liquid air in a container, the nitrogen evaporates first, resulting in an enrichment of liquid oxygen, and thus eventually leading to this dangerous liquid again.

For these reasons, today air is liquefied and separated into oxygen and nitrogen in large liquefaction and separation plants. Liquid nitrogen (LN_2) is then sold as a refrigerant at roughly 0.5 DM/ℓ when delivered in large quantities. Very few research organisations still use their own liquefaction plant as was common until the 1960s.

Evaporating nitrogen can cause suffocation if it displaces much of the oxygen in an enclosed volume. Therefore, rooms in which evaporating liquid nitrogen is kept have to be fitted with an appropriate ventilation system.

2.2 Liquid Hydrogen

In liquid hydrogen the pair of atoms forming an H_2 molecule are bound by a strong covalent force. The interactions between H_2 molecules, which lead to the liquid and solid states, are the weak van der Waals forces. These weak dipolar forces, as well as the large zero-point motion of the light H_2, result in rather low boiling and melting points (Table 2.1). Because of the large difference in strength between chemical bonds and dipolar forces, liquid and solid H_2 are true molecular fluids and crystals in which the molecules retain many of the properties of free H_2 [2.4].

The dangerous feature of hydrogen is its exothermic reaction with oxygen to form water. Therefore, liquid hydrogen should be used in a closed system. However, sometimes the danger associated with hydrogen is overestimated because the reaction needs a critical concentration in order to occur.

Whereas at one time liquid hydrogen was frequently used as a refrigerant (and its use may become more common in hydrogen energy technologies in the future), it is not often used in laboratories these days because the temperature range between the boiling point of nitrogen (77K) and the boiling point of helium (4.2K) is now accessible by means of helium cryogenerators, helium evaporation cryostats (Sect. 5.2.3) or by performing the experiment in helium gas above a liquid helium bath.

In spite of the minor importance of hydrogen as a refrigerant I shall discuss one of its properties which is important in various low temperature experiments and which demonstrates some rather important atomic and statistical physics: the ortho-para conversion of H_2 [2.4-8].

The proton H has a nuclear spin I = 1/2. In a H_2 molecule the two nuclear spins can couple to a total spin I = 0 or I = 1, depending on their relative orientation. Thus the H_2 molecule can have a symmetric nuclear state (I = 1), so-called ortho-H_2. This system has a degeneracy of 2I+1 = 3, which means that it can exist in three different spin orientational states, namely m = -1, 0, +1. For the other total-spin situation (I = 0) we have an antisymmetric state, so-called para-H_2, with a degeneracy 2I+1 = 1, which means that this system can only exist in one spin state, m = 0.

In addition, the non-spherical H_2 molecule can rotate and we have the H_2 rotator with the rotational quantum numbers J = 0, 1, 2, 3, ... Because of the weak interaction between H_2 molecules, the behaviour of the rotator is free and J remains a good quantum number. The various rotational states are separated by rotational energies

$$E_R = (\hbar^2/2\Theta)J(J + 1) , \tag{2.1}$$

where $\Theta = 4.59 \cdot 10^{-48}$ kg·m^2 is the moment of inertia of the H_2 rotator.

Protons are Fermi particles (fermions). As a result, the total wave function of the H_2 molecule has to be antisymmetric under an exchange of particles. In other words, it has to change its sign if the two nuclei are exchanged. The total wave function is a product of the spin wave function and the rotator wave function. To get an antisymmetric total wave function either the spin or the rotator wave function has to be antisymmetric and the other one has to be symmetric. This results in two possibilities for the hydrogen molecule, which are summarized in Table 2.2.

The energy states of para- and ortho-hydrogen are depicted in Fig.2.1. The total degeneracy of each rotational state is given by d = (2J+1)(2I+1). Because of the rather large energies ΔE_R separating the various rotator states, only the lowest rotational energy states are populated at room temperature or lower temperatures. Owing to this fact and because of the different rotational degeneracies we have 25% para-hydrogen and 75% ortho-

Table 2.2. Properties of ortho- and para-hydrogen

Molecule	Nuclear spin I	Symmetry	Degeneracy	Rotator quantum number J	Symmetry	Degeneracy
Ortho-H_2	1	Symmetric	3	1, 3, ...	Anti-symmetric	3, 7, ...
Para-H_2	0	Anti-symmetric	1	0, 2, ...	Symmetric	1, 5, ...

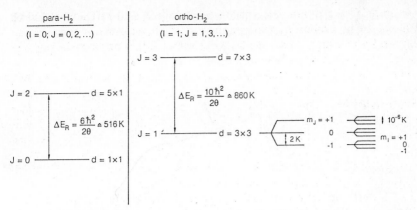

Fig.2.1. Rotational energy states of para- and ortho-H_2. The degeneracy of the rotational states of ortho-H_2 is lifted by an electric quadrupole interaction between the H_2 molecules which is of order 2 K. A nuclear magnetic dipole interaction of order 10^{-6} K lifts the nuclear magnetic degeneracy of the m_J states

hydrogen in thermal equilibrium at room temperature. Because para-H_2 (J = 0) has lower energy than ortho-H_2 (J = 1) (the difference is 172 K if expressed in terms of temperature), a conversion from ortho- to para-hydrogen occurs if we cool hydrogen to low temperatures. At 77 K the equilibrium ratio is 1:1, but at 20 K we should have 99.8% para-H_2 in thermal equilibrium.

We have to take into account two important aspects of this conversion [2.5,6]. First of all, it is an exothermic reaction giving rise to the rather large heat release of U = 1.06 (1.42) kJ/mol H_2 for a starting ortho concentration of 75% (100%). Secondly, the conversion between different rotational states is connected with a change of the nuclear spin orientation. For this change of the nuclear quantum state we need an interaction of the nuclear magnetic moments with each other or with their surroundings. Because of the smallness of the nuclear moments this interaction is rather weak. It can only occur in the collision of two H_2 molecules if there is no other magnetic partner available. We then have an autocatalytic reaction and, due to its weakness, the conversion is slow with a rate constant of k = 1.9% per hour for solid H_2 at melting pressure [2.7], leading to interesting time effects.

Let us calculate the heat release due to this conversion. The change of the concentration x of the ortho molecules with time t for this autocatalytic reaction is given by

$$\frac{dx}{dt} = -kx^2 , \qquad (2.2)$$

resulting in

$$x(t) = \frac{x_0}{1 + x_0 kt} , \qquad (2.3)$$

where x_0 is the starting ortho concentration, which is 0.75 for T = 300 K. This gives rise to a molar heat release

$$\dot{Q} = - U \frac{dx}{dt} = U \frac{kx_0^2}{(1 + x_0 kt)^2} \ . \tag{2.4}$$

There are two situations in which this heat release can give rise to problems in experiments at low or ultralow temperatures. Firstly, we have to keep in mind that the heat release due to ortho-para conversion is quite large. Therefore if one has a liquid consisting mainly of ortho-hydrogen it will evaporate due to the ortho-para conversion even without any extra external heat being introduced. As a result, one has first to convert the ortho-H_2 to para-H_2 before the liquid can be used as a refrigerant. The conversion is accelerated if the H_2 is brought into contact with a catalyst containing electronic magnetic moments, e.g., ferric hydroxide, iron or chromic oxide [2.2, 8].

The second problem became apparent in recent years in ultralow temperature physics, where the refrigeration power of refrigerators can become rather small (it is in the microwatt range for low millikelvin temperatures and in the nanowatt range for microkelvin temperatures; see later chapters). Many metals, such as palladium and niobium, can dissolve hydrogen in atomic form in their lattice. However many others such as Cu, Ag, Au, Pt and Rh, cannot dissolve hydrogen in a noticeable quantity in their lattice. If these metals contain traces of hydrogen, hydrogen molecules collect in small

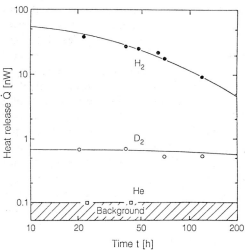

Fig.2.2. Heat release at $T \leq 0.1$ K from 19 g Cu samples charged at 930° C in 3.05 bar of the indicated gases as a function of time after cooling to T < 4 K. The upper curve represents (2.4) for 23 μmol H_2 (76ppm H_2/Cu). The curve through the D_2 data is the corresponding equation for deuterium [2.5b] for 25 μmol D_2 (83ppm D_2/Cu). The Cu sample heated in a He atmosphere did not give a heat release above the indicate background value of the calorimeter [2.10]

10

gas bubbles with a typical diameter of some 0.1 μm [2.9]. In practice, many of these metals contain hydrogen at a typical concentration of $10\div100$ ppm due to their electrolytic production or from a purification process. The hydrogen pressure in these small bubbles is so high that the hydrogen becomes liquid or solid if the metal is cooled to low temperatures. This then results again in a conversion from ortho- to para-hydrogen in the small bubbles, and therefore gives rise to heat release in these metals (Fig.2.2) [2.10,11]. The heat release is small, typically of order 1 nW/g, but it can be very detrimental if such a metal is used in an apparatus designed for ultralow temperature physics experiments, such as a nuclear refrigerator for the microkelvin temperature range (Sect.10.5.3).

In addition to its importance for low and ultralow temperature physics and its nice demonstration of atomic and statistical physics, the ortho-para conversion also demonstrates in a rather impressive way how a very little energy, in this case the nuclear magnetic interaction energy (which is of the order of microkelvins if expressed in temperatures), due to the existence of nuclear spins and in combination with the Pauli principle, can result in rather dramatic effects involving much higher energies, in this case the rotational energy of order 100 K.

2.3 Liquid Helium

2.3.1 Some Properties of the Helium Isotopes

In 1868 the two scientists J. Janssen and N. Lockyer detected new spectral lines in the optical spectrum of solar protuberances. First it was suggested that these lines might belong to an unknown *isotope* of hydrogen, but very soon it became evident that the spectral lines belonged to a new *element*, later called "helium". In 1895 the British scientist W. Ramsey detected these lines on earth, in a gas escaping from the mineral Clevite. Two of the most eminent physicsts of that time, J. Dewar in London and H. Kamerlingh-Onnes in Leiden, began a race to liquefy this newly discovered element of the periodic table. Kamerlingh-Onnes won this race, liquefying helium at a temperature of 4.2 K in 1908. The first commercial helium liquefier built by S.C. Collins in 1947 had a profound impact on the spread of low-temperature experiments because liquid helium is the most important substance for low-temperature physics. All refrigeration methods for temperatures below about 10 K either use liquid helium exclusively or, if they go to very low temperatures, use liquid helium in the pre-cooling stages. At first liquid helium was employed only as a tool, but research in the following decades made it very obvious that liquid helium is a most exotic and interesting liquid exhibiting many unique properties.

Whereas in the first years of helium research the ^{4}He gas was obtained from minerals, today helium is obtained exclusively from helium-rich natural gas sources. In both cases it is a product of radioactive alpha decay. The gas sources, particularly in the USA, North Africa, Poland, the Netherlands, and the USSR, can contain up to about 10% helium.

The common stable helium isotope is ^{4}He. Its nucleus contains two protons and two neutrons, each with antiparallel nuclear spin orientation. Therefore the total nuclear spin of ^{4}He I = 0; it is a Bose particle (boson). The rare helium isotope ^{3}He constitutes a fraction $(1 \div 2) \cdot 10^{-7}$ of helium gas from natural gas sources and about $1.3 \cdot 10^{-6}$ of the helium gas in the atmosphere. Obtaining ^{3}He in a reasonable amount from these two sources by separating it from ^{4}He is very costly. The ^{3}He in use today for low-temperature physics experiments is a byproduct of tritium manufacture in a nuclear reactor:

$$\begin{aligned} ^6_3\text{Li} + ^1_0\text{n} &\rightarrow ^3_1\text{T} + ^4_2\text{He} , \\[1em] ^3_1\text{T} \; &\overset{12.3\text{y}}{\rightarrow} \; ^3_2\text{He} + ^{\,0}_{-1}\text{e} + \bar{\nu} . \end{aligned}$$

$$(2.5)$$

where $\bar{\nu}$ is the electron anti-neutrino. The helium isotopes are separated from tritium by diffusion processes. Due to this method of production, ^{3}He has only been available in the necessary quantities since the late 1950s, and it is expensive (about 400 DM/ℓ of gas at standard temperature and pressure). The ^{3}He nucleus again contains two protons, but only one neutron. Therefore its total nuclear spin I = 1/2, and ^{3}He is a fermion. The different statistics for the boson ^{4}He and for the fermion ^{3}He cause substantial differences in their low-temperature behaviour, some of which will be discussed in the following pages. Details can be found in [2.12-19].

Besides the stable isotopes ^{3}He and ^{4}He, there exist two unstable helium isotopes with relatively long lifetimes: ^{6}He ($\tau_{1/2}$ = 0.82s), and ^{8}He ($\tau_{1/2}$ = 0.12s); they have not yet been liquified.

In Table 2.3 some important properties of the two stable helium isotopes are summarized and their pressure-temperature phase diagrams are shown in Fig.2.3. The table and the figure demonstrate some of the

Table 2.3. Properties of liquid helium

	^{3}He	^{4}He
Boiling point T_b [K]	3.19	4.21
Critical temperature T_c [K]	3.32	5.20
Superfluid transition temperature T_c [K]	0.0025	2.177
Density[a] ρ [g/cm^3]	0.082	0.145
Classical molar volume[a] V_m [cm^3/mol]	12	12
Actual molar volume[a] V_m [cm^3/mol]	36.84	27.58
Melting pressure[b] P_m [bar]	34.39	25.36

[a] At saturated vapour pressure and T = 0K
[b] At T = 0K

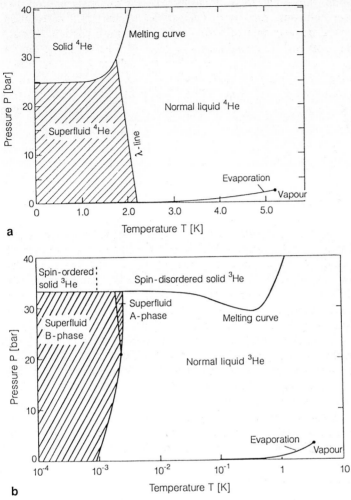

Fig.2.3. Phase diagrams of (a) ⁴He and (b) ³He. Note the different temperature scales

remarkable properties of these so-called quantum substances. First there are their rather low boiling points and critical temperatures. Then, unlike all other liquids these two isotopes do not become solid under their own vapour pressure even when cooled to absolute zero. One has to apply at least about 25 bar or 34 bar (for $T \rightarrow 0K$), respectively, to get these two isotopes in their solid state. The melting pressure of ⁴He is constant to within 10^{-4} below 1 K but for ³He it shows a pronounced minimum at 0.32 K (Chap.8). Then the two liquids have a rather small density or large molar volume. The molar volume V_m of ⁴He (³He) is more than a factor of two (three) larger than one would calculate for a corresponding classical liquid.

The origin for all these observations are two essential properties of helium. Firstly, the binding forces between the atoms are very weak. They are van der Waals forces and are weak because of the closed electronic s-shell of helium, giving rise to the absence of static dipole moments and to the smallest known atomic polarizibility $\alpha = 0.1232$ cm^3/mol (the resulting dielectric constants for the two helium isotopes are $\epsilon_4 = 1.0572$ and $\epsilon_3 = 1.0426$). For example, these binding forces are more than an order of magnitude smaller than for hydrogen molecules with their larger polarizibility, which leads to a much higher boiling point of H_2. Because the electronic structure of the two helium isotopes is identical, they have identical van der Waals forces and behave identically chemically. - Secondly, due to the small atomic mass m, the two helium isotopes have a large quantum mechanical zero-point energy E_0, given by

$$E_0 = \frac{h^2}{2ma^2} ,$$ (2.6)

where $a = (V_m/N_0)^{1/3}$, the distance between the atoms, and N_0 is Avogadro's number, $6.022 \cdot 10^{23}$ atoms/mol.

The large zero-point energy (which is larger than the latent heat of evaporation of liquid helium, see Table 2.1) gives rise to a zero-point vibration amplitude which is about 1/3 of the mean separation of the atoms in the liquid state. Figure 2.4 illustrates the influence of the zero-point energy on the total energy as a function of distance between the atoms and demonstrates why helium - in contrast to all other substances - will remain in the liquid state under its own vapour pressure even when cooled to absolute zero. Of course, due to its smaller mass the influence of the zero-point energy is more pronounced for ^{3}He, giving rise to its lower boiling

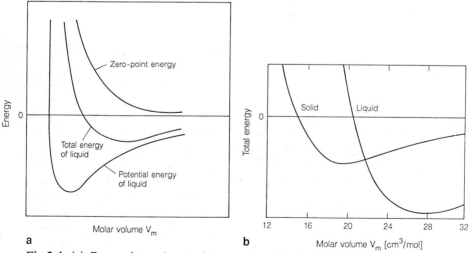

Fig.2.4. (a) Zero-point and potential energies of liquid ^{4}He as a function of molar volume. The total energy is the sum of these two energies. (b) Illustration of why the liquid state is the stable one for helium at saturated vapour pressure even at T = 0 K

14

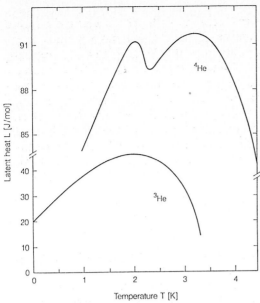

Fig.2.5. Latent heats of evaporation of ^{3}He and ^{4}He. Note the change of vertical scale

point, smaller density, smaller latent heat of evaporation and larger vapour pressure (Sect.2.3.2).

Because of the strong influence of quantum effects on their properties, the helium liquids are called "quantum liquids". In general, this term is used for any liquid whose kinetic (or zero-point) energy is larger than its potential (or binding) energy. To distinguish these liquids from classical liquids one introduces a quantum parameter $\lambda = E_{kin}/E_{pot}$. These parameters λ for some cryoliquids are

liquid:	Xe	Kr	Ar	N_2	Ne	H_2	^{4}He	^{3}He
λ:	0.06	0.10	0.19	0.23	0.59	1.73	2.64	3.05

indicating that hydrogen and the helium isotopes are quantum liquids in this sense.

2.3.2 Latent Heat of Evaporation and Vapour Pressure

The latent heat of evaporation L and the vapour pressure P_{vap} are important properties that determine whether a liquid is suitable for use as a refrigerant. For the helium isotopes both these properties are dramatically different from the values of the corresponding classical liquids due to the large zero-point energy. For example, for ^{4}He the latent heat of evaporation is only about one quarter of its value for the corresponding classical liquid. Due to the small heat of evaporation of helium (Fig.2.5), liquid helium baths have a rather small cooling power (it is very easy to evaporate them). Therefore, all low-temperature experiments require efficient shielding aga-

15

inst introduction of heat from the surroundings, e.g. heat due to radiation, heat along supports to the experiments, or heat due to the measurements one wants to perform at low temperatures. This will be discussed later when we discuss the design of low-temperature equipment. The dip in L for ^{4}He at 2.2 K is due to the superfluid transition occurring at this temperature, which will be discussed in the next section.

The vapour pressure can be calculated, at least to a first approximation, from the Clausius-Clapeyron equation

$$\left(\frac{dP}{dT}\right)_{vap} = \frac{S_{gas} - S_{liq}}{V_{m,gas} - V_{m,liq}} , \tag{2.7}$$

where S is the entropy and V_m the molar volume.

If we take into account that the difference in the entropies of the liquid and gaseous phases is L/T, that the molar volume of the liquid is much smaller than the molar volume of the gas, and that in a rough approximation the molar volume of helium gas is given by the ideal gas equation $V_{gas} \simeq RT/P$, then we obtain

$$\left(\frac{dP}{dT}\right)_{vap} \simeq \frac{L(T)P}{RT^2} , \tag{2.8}$$

and eventually arrive at our result for the vapour pressure

$$P_{vap} \propto \exp(-L/RT) , \tag{2.9}$$

if we make the further approximation that L $\simeq$ constant (Fig.2.5). Therefore, the vapour pressure decreases roughly exponentially with decreasing temperature, as shown in Fig.2.6 for the helium isotopes and in Fig.2.7 for several cryoliquids.

One can take advantage of this pronounced temperature dependence of the vapour pressure in several ways. In the Kelvin temperature range the vapour pressures of all substances except helium are extremely low (Fig. 2.7). Therefore, the surfaces in a low-temperature apparatus cooled to Kelvin temperatures, e.g. by liquid helium, are extremely efficient "pumps". If one has pumped on the vacuum space of a low-temperature apparatus at high temperatures, the valve to the pumping system should be closed when the apparatus has reached the Kelvin temperature range by introducing liquid helium because the cold surfaces can improve the vacuum by several orders of magnitude by condensing the remaining gas molecules. Usually it is much better to do this than to keep the valve to the pumping system open, because after a while the cold surfaces may pump molecules from the pumping system (such as crack products of the pump oil) into the cryostat. This "cryopumping" is utilized commercially in so-called cryopumps available from various suppliers.

Secondly, one can pump on the vapour above a liquid, for example above a liquid-helium bath, to obtain temperatures below the normal (1 bar)

16

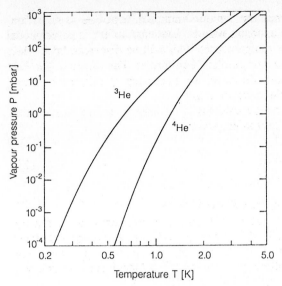

Fig.2.6. Vapour pressures of liquid ^{3}He and liquid ^{4}He

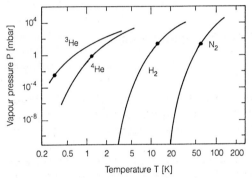

Fig.2.7. Vapour pressures of various cryoliquids. The dots indicate the practical lower limits for the temperatures which can be obtained by reducing the vapour pressure above these liquids

boiling point. If one pumps away atoms from the vapour phase, the most energetic ("hottest") atoms will leave the liquid to replenish the vapour. Therefore the mean energy of the liquid will decrease; it will cool. For a pumped-on liquid bath where $\dot{n}$ particles/time are moved to the vapour phase, the cooling power is given by

$$\dot{Q} = \dot{n}[H_{liq} - H_{vap}] = \dot{n}L .\tag{2.10}$$

Usually a pump with a constant volume pumping speed $\dot{V}$ is used and therefore the mass flow $\dot{n}$ across the liquid-vapour boundary is proportional to the vapour pressure

$$\dot{n} \propto P_{vap}(T) \, ,$$

giving a cooling power

$$\dot{Q} \propto L P_{vap} \propto \exp(-1/T) \, . \tag{2.11}$$

This last equation demonstrates that the cooling power decreases rapidly with decreasing temperature because the vapour pressure decreases rapidly with decreasing temperature and pumping becomes less and less efficient. Eventually there is almost no vapour left, resulting in a limit for the minimum temperature obtainable by pumping on a bath of an evaporating cryoliquid. This limit is reached when the refrigeration due to evaporation of atoms is balanced by the external heat flowing to the bath. The practical low-temperature limits determined by experimental parameters are typically about 1.3 K for ^{4}He and 0.3 K for ^{3}He (Fig.2.7).

The temperature dependence of the vapour pressure of liquid helium is well known and can be used for vapour pressure thermometry (Sect.12.2). By measuring the vapour pressure above a liquid helium bath (or other liquids at higher temperatures) one can read the temperature from the corresponding vapour pressure table. In fact, the helium vapour pressure scale represents the low-temperature part of the recently ratified international temperature scale ITS-90 (Sect.11.2).

2.3.3 Specific Heat

Many of the basic properties of a material, including liquid helium, are revealed by its specific heat. First of all, the specific heat of liquid helium is very large compared to the specific heat of other materials at low temperatures (Fig.2.8). For example, at about 1.5 K the specific heat of 1 g of ^{3}He or ^{4}He is of the order of 1 J/K whereas the specific heat of 1 g of Cu is only about 10^{-5} J/K at this temperature. This remarkable fact is of great cryotechnical importance for low-temperature physics. It means that the thermal behaviour, for example the thermal response time, of low-temperature apparatus is in most cases determined by the amount and thermal behaviour of the liquid helium it contains. In addition, the latent heat of evaporation of liquid helium - even though it is rather small compared to the latent heat of other materials - is large compared to the specific heat of other materials at low temperatures, enabling us to cool other materials, e.g. a metal, by liquid helium. Both properties mean that the temperature of an experiment rapidly follows any temperature change of its refrigerating helium bath.

At low temperatures the properties of materials are strongly influenced by statistical or quantum effects. This is particularly important for the specific heat of the helium isotopes. As Fig.2.9 demonstrates, the specific heat

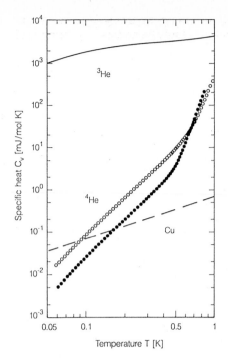

Fig.2.8. Specific heat of liquid ^{4}He at vapour pressure (27.58 cm^3/mol, ○) and at about 22 bar (23.55 cm^3/mol, •) [2.20] compared to the specific heats of liquid ^{3}He at vapour pressure [2.21] and of Cu

of ^{4}He has a pronounced maximum at about 2 K, indicating a phase transition to a new state of this liquid. The detection of this phase transition came as a great surprise to scientists. It was not expected that anything interesting could happen at low temperatures with this rather simple liquid composed of inert spherical atoms. Therefore, when L.J. Dana and H. Kamerlingh-Onnes measured the specific heat of liquid helium in the 1920s and saw an "anomalous" increase of the specific heat at about 2 K, they did not publish the data points at those temperatures, believing that they resulted from some experimental artefacts. Later W.H. Keesom and K. Clusius (1932) in the same laboratory of the University of Leiden measured the specific heat of liquid helium again and again saw the pronounced peak of the specific heat. They did believe in their data and realized that a phase transition occurred in this liquid at that temperature, the transition to the unique "superfluid state" of ^{4}He. W.H. Keesom introduced the names *He I* for the normal liquid above the transition temperature and *He II* for the superfluid liquid below it. The history of the specific heat of liquid ^{4}He is one of the important examples in physics that one should never disregard any apparently "anomalous" data or data points unless one has good reason not to trust one's own measurements. The specific heat maximum of liquid ^{4}He near 2.2 K has been measured with increasing temperature resolution over the past decades (Fig.2.9). Today it is known with a temperature resolution of some nanokelvins and these very precise measurements are one of the most important testing grounds for modern theories of phase transitions [2.22-24]. It is a demonstration of the model character of the superfluid

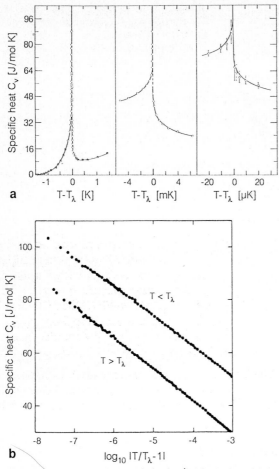

Fig.2.9a,b. Specific heat of liquid ^{4}He at temperatures close to its superfluid transition. (a) With increasing T-resolution on a linear temperature scale [2.22] and (b) on a logarithmic temperature scale [2.23]

transition of liquid helium for phase transitions and the very advanced state of low-temperature thermometry (Chaps.11,12). Helium is an extremely good system for the study of properties with a very high temperature resolution near a critical temperature due to its extreme purity (all other materials are "frozen-out") and therefore the sharpness of the transition. The characteristic shape of the specific heat maximum has led to the term "λ-transition" for the superfluid transition of ^{4}He occurring at the "λ-temperature" $T_\lambda = 2.1768$ K at saturated vapour pressure. The λ-temperature decreases with increasing pressure to a value of 1.7673 K at the melting line (Fig.2.3a).

Above the λ-transition, ^{4}He behaves essentially like a classical fluid or in some respects - because of its low density - almost like a classical gas (Fig.2.10). But below T_λ due to its (Bose-Einstein like) condensation in

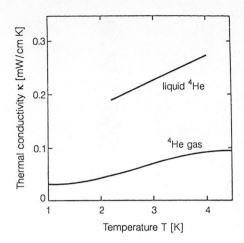

Fig.2.10. Thermal conductivities of gaseous and liquid ^{4}He

momentum space, its entropy and specific heat decrease rapidly with temperature (Fig. 2.8). Between 1 K and about 2 K the specific heat of ^{4}He has a strong temperature dependence due to so-called roton excitations. Finally, below 0.6 K, the specific heat decreases with T^3 due to phonon-like excitations, as for an insulating Debye solid (Sect.3.1.1) [2.12–18].

The isotope ^{3}He has a nuclear spin $I = 1/2$. It is therefore a Fermi particle and has to obey Fermi statistics and the Pauli principle. This liquid has many properties in common with the "conducting Fermi liquid" composed of electrons in metals, which are also spin-1/2 particles. For example, the specific heat of ^{3}He obeys $C \propto T$ at low enough temperatures. This result and some other properties of ^{3}He will be discussed in Sect.2.3.6 and in Chaps.7,8.

2.3.4 Transport Properties of Liquid ^{4}He: Thermal Conductivity and Viscosity

In its normal fluid state above $T = 2.2$ K, liquid ^{4}He, due to its low density, shows transport properties almost like a classical gas (Fig.2.10). The same applies to liquid ^{3}He at temperatures above 0.1 K. Due to its low thermal conductivity *above* 2.2 K [it is about a factor of 10 (10^4) lower than the thermal conductivity of stainless steel (Cu), see Sect.3.3] liquid ^{4}He I boils with strong bubbling. When one pumps on liquid ^{4}He I (or liquid ^{3}He), bubbles of vapour form within the liquid and the liquid is agitated when they rise to the surface. The bubbles form because the bulk of the liquid is hotter than its pumped surface. In an experiment employing liquid helium it is very likely that there are large thermal gradients in the liquid at these temperatures. This is of importance, for example, when the vapour pressure of liquid helium is used for thermometry (Sect.12.2). Conversely, *below* 2.2 K, in the superfluid state, under ideal experimental conditions (heat flow $\dot{Q} \rightarrow 0$) the thermal conductivity of ^{4}He II is infinite; for realistic conditions it is finite but quite large (Fig.2.11). The very high thermal conductivity of superfluid helium makes this material a very efficient medium

21

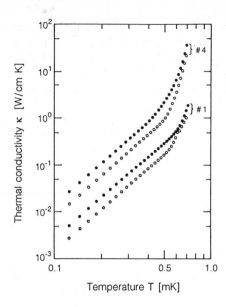

Fig.2.11. Thermal conductivity of liquid ^{4}He at 2 bar (•) and 20 bar (○) in tubes of 1.38 mm (#1) and 7.97 mm (#4) diameter [2.25]

for establishing temperature homogeneity or for transporting heat. For example, at these temperatures the liquid does not boil as other liquids do if heated from the bottom or if they are pumped, because for boiling by creation of bubbles and their transport to the surface it is necessary that a temperature gradient is established. This is impossible in liquid helium below T_λ if the heat current is not so large that it "destroys" the superfluid state. In the superfluid state helium atoms evaporate exclusively from the surface and the liquid is "quiet" because no more bubbles are formed. The thermal conductivity of superfluid ^{4}He below 0.4 K, in the phonon regime, and at $P \le 2$ bar is given by

$$\kappa_4 \sim 20 d T^3 \quad [\text{W/K·cm}] , \tag{2.12}$$

where d is the diameter of the ^{4}He column in centimetres (Fig.2.11) [2.25]. As a result, the thermal conductivity of superfluid ^{4}He is quite high under most experimental conditions, comparable to that of a metal. For the physics of heat transport in superfluid ^{4}He, the reader should consult the literature specializing on this quantum liquid [2.12-19].

Because the thermal conductivity of superfluid helium can be very large (or ideally infinitely large), temperature waves or entropy waves can propagate in this unusual liquid. This wave propagation is called *second sound* to distinguish it from the usual *first sound*, the density waves. The velocity of second sound in ^{4}He II is about an order of magnitude smaller than the velocity of first sound at $1K < T < 2K$ [2.12-19].

In the superfluid state, liquid helium has a vanishing viscosity, $\eta_s = 0$, for flow through fine capillaries or holes; it is indeed "superfluid" if the flow velocity does not exceed a critical value (corresponding to a critical current in metallic superconductors). The vanishing viscosity allows superfluid helium to flow in a persistent mode as the persistent supercurrents in a metallic superconductor do. Apparatus which seems to be leak-tight at T > T_λ may show a leak at lower temperatures if it comes into contact with superfluid helium because this liquid can flow through minute cracks or holes which are impermeable to viscous materials. This is a very efficient way of detecting extremely small leaks. On the other hand, it is, of course, a nuisance because apparatus which seems to be leak-tight at higher temperatures may suddenly develop a so-called superleak when in contact with superfluid helium.

The transport properties of liquid [3]He will be briefly discussed in Sect. 2.3.6.

2.3.5 Superfluid Film Flow

The walls of a container which is partly filled with liquid helium are coated with a film of helium via the adsorption of atoms from the vapour phase. Due to the rather strong van der Waals interaction which a substrate exerts on helium atoms, this film is relatively thick, typically 30 nm at SVP (see below). Usually, due to its viscosity, such a film is immobile. However, in the superfluid state with $\eta_s = 0$, the film can move. If two containers which are partly filled with liquid He II to different levels are connected, their levels will equalize by means of frictionless flow of the He II film from one container to the other one driven by the difference in gravitational potential (Fig.2.12); the film acts as though being siphoned. This superfluid film flow [2.12, 26] will lead to an enhanced evaporation rate from [4]He baths at $T < T_\lambda$ because the superfluid film flows to hotter places and evaporates there.

Here, I will calculate the thickness d of a helium film at a height h above the bulk liquid level (Fig.2.13). The chemical potentials in equilibrium are

$$\mu_{\text{film}} = \mu_{\text{gas}} .$$
(2.13)

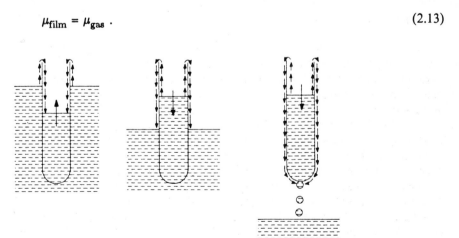

Fig.2.12. Due to its superfluid properties [4]He II can leave a container via superfluid film flow over the walls

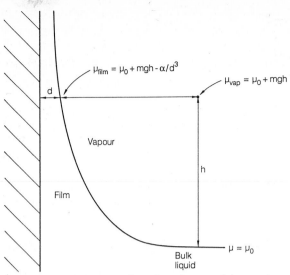

Fig.2.13. Profile of a helium film on a vertical wall in equilibrium with its bulk liquid and with its saturated vapour. The chemical potential is given for the bulk liquid (μ_0), for the vapour (μ_{vap}) and for the liquid film (μ_{film}) at a height h above the bulk liquid

For the film we have

$$\mu_{film} = \mu_0 + mgh - \alpha/d^n , \qquad (2.14)$$

where μ_0 is the chemical potential of the bulk liquid, and mgh is the gravitational term. The third term in the above equation is the van der Waals potential which the substrate supplies to the film (with n = 3 for d $\leq$ 5nm; n = 4 for d > 10nm). For thin films, the van der Waals constant is α = (10 to 200 [K])$\times$(no. of helium layers)^3 for various solid substrates [2.26]. In thermal equilibrium we find for the film with the condition that the chemical potential is the same everywhere, in particular $\mu = \mu_{liq}$ everywhere (for d $\leq$ 5nm)

$$d = (\alpha/mgh)^{1/3} . \qquad (2.15)$$

A typical value is

$$d \simeq 30h^{-1/3} \qquad (2.16)$$

with h in cm and d in nm; but, of course, d strongly depends on the cleanliness and structure of the surface of the substrate.

If there is gas but no bulk liquid present we have an "unsaturated film", whose thickness depends on the gas pressure P. The gas pressure at height h is

$$P(h) = P_{sat} e^{-mgh/k_B T} . \qquad (2.17)$$

24

Therefore the film thickness is

$$d = \left[\frac{-\alpha}{k_B T \ln(P/P_{sat})} \right]^{1/3} . \tag{2.18}$$

For a typical critical superfluid velocity of a ^{4}He film, $v_{s,crit} \sim 30$ cm/s, we find a volume flow rate out of a beaker of radius R = 5 mm

$$\dot{V}_{liq} = 2R\pi d v_{s,crit} \sim 1 \text{ cm}^3/\text{h} , \quad \text{or} \quad \dot{V}_{gas} \sim 1 \ \ell/\text{h} . \tag{2.19}$$

We then find for a pump with a volume pumping rate $\dot{V}_{pump} = 10^4 \ \ell/\text{h}$ at P =1 bar that the minimum pressure to which this pump can pump such a helium bath from which a superfluid film is creeping is

$$P_{min} = P\dot{V}_{gas}/\dot{V}_{pump} \sim 10^{-4} \text{ bar} \quad (10^{-3} \text{bar if R = 50mm}) . \tag{2.20}$$

Correspondingly, the minimum helium bath temperature will be about 1 K, showing that one has to consider the film flow rate quite carefully and possibly has to reduce it, for example by a constriction of about 1 mm diameter in the pumping tube (Chap. 7).

2.3.6 Liquid ^{3}He at Millikelvin Temperatures

Because ^{3}He atoms are Fermi particles, single ^{3}He atoms cannot undergo the analogue of a Bose momentum condensation into a superfluid state as the bosons ^{4}He do at T_λ. However, there exists a weak attractive interaction between ^{3}He atoms in the liquid which gives rise to pairing of two ^{3}He atoms. Like the paired conduction electrons in a superconducting metal, the paired ^{3}He atoms then behave like bosons and can undergo a transition into a superfluid state. Because the pairing forces are rather weak, this transition occurs only at 2.5 (0.93) mK for P = $P_{melting}$ (P_{svp}). The exciting properties of superfluid ^{3}He have been the driving force for the development of refrigeration techniques to T < 3 mK over the last 15 years and they have been the object of intense investigations since the detection of superfluid ^{3}He in 1972 [2.27, 28]. They are discussed in several recent publications [2.15-17, 19, 29-38]. As for ^{4}He, where the experiments on the superfluid properties in the late 1920s and 1930s were restricted to the few laboratories which had access to the low Kelvin temperature range, particularly Leiden, the experiments on the superfluid properties of ^{3}He in the 1970s were restricted to the few laboratories which then had access to the low millikelvin temperature range, particularly Cornell, San Diego, and Helsinki. Because we are interested in this book in the cryotechnological aspects of materials, I will not discuss superfluid ^{3}He but just remind you of those properties of liquid ^{3}He above its superfluid transition that are of importance in cryotechnical applications of this Fermi liquid.

Liquid ^{3}He, due to its smaller mass, has a larger zero-point energy than liquid ^{4}He. It therefore has an even lower density and in the almost "classical" regime, at T > 0.1 K, behaves even more like a dense classical gas. For example, its specific heat is almost T-independent, as it should be according to the Dulong-Petit law (Sect.3.1.1), at T ~ 0.5 K (Fig.2.15). Liquid ^{3}He is a spin-1/2 particle; it is a fermion with an antisymmetric wave function. At lower temperatures, its properties then become in many respects increasingly similar to the well-known Fermi liquid composed of the conduction electrons in metals, obeying Fermi statistics, too. The properties of liquid ^{3}He at low temperatures are therefore fundamentally different from those of ^{4}He. From about 0.1 K down to the superfluid transition temperature they can be accounted for by Landau's Fermi liquid theory [2.12, 15-17, 29, 37-42]. This theory describes the liquid as a system of free fermions with its properties rescaled by the interatomic interactions. Due to the Pauli principle the ^{3}He atoms have to fill energy states up to the Fermi energy E_F (Fig.3.3). Because E_F/k_B ~ 1 K for ^{3}He but E_F/k_B ~ 10^4 K for electrons, and because the specific heat $C \propto T/T_F$ for a Fermi liquid (Sect.3.1.2), the specific heat of ^{3}He at low temperatures is very large compared to the specific heat of metals (Fig.2.8). This linear T-dependence of C is obeyed by ^{3}He only up to some ten millikelvin (Fig.2.14, Sect.7.1). At higher temperatures, the specific heat of ^{3}He shows a plateau and then increases again with increasing temperature (Fig.2.15). In the low millikelvin temperature range when ^{3}He enters its superfluid state, the specific heat, of course, deviates from a linear temperature dependence.

The transport properties of liquid ^{3}He in the Fermi-liquid temperature range, too, show a distinct T-dependence. For example, the thermal conductivity κ_3 increases as T^{-1} at $T \ll T_F$ (Figs.2.16, 17), and its viscosity η_3

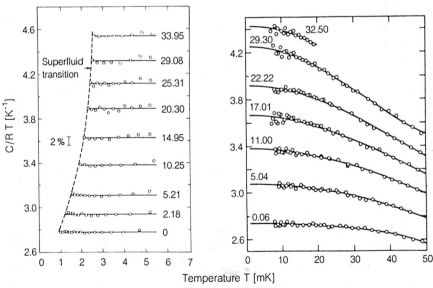

Fig.2.14. Specific heat C divided by the gas constant R times temperature T of liquid ^{3}He at millikelvin temperatures at the given pressures (in bar). Note the different scales [2.21]

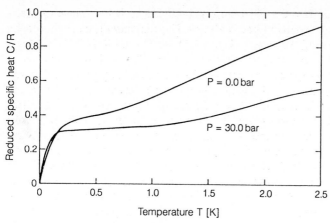

Fig.2.15. Specific heat C (divided by the gas constant R) of liquid ^{3}He at two given pressures (after data from [2.21])

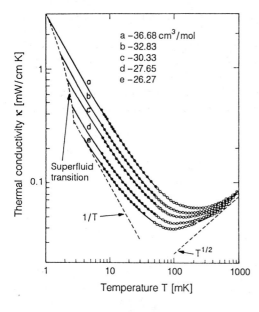

a –36.68 cm^3/mol
b –32.83
c –30.33
d –27.65
e –26.27

Fig.2.16. Thermal conductivity of liquid ^{3}He at the given molar volumes [2.43]

increases as T^{-2} in the low millikelvin temperature range (Fig.2.18), making ^{3}He a very viscous but well-conducting fluid at low temperatures above its superfluid transition. These temperature dependences can easily be understood. The mean free path λ of ^{3}He particles in the liquid is limited by scattering with other ^{3}He particles. The probability of a two-body collision for Fermi particles is proportional to $(T/T_F)^2$, because the number of particles and the number of empty states into which they can scatter near to the Fermi energy are both proportional to temperature. Hence, we have $\lambda \propto T^{-2}$, and with $C \propto T$ and $v_F = $ const. we find from (3.27) that $\kappa_3 \propto T^{-1}$ (and $\eta_3 \propto T^{-2}$) for $T \ll T_F$. The behaviour of κ_3 and η_3 at higher temper-

27

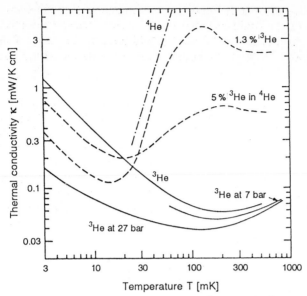

Fig.2.17. Thermal conductivities of liquid ^{3}He, liquid ^{4}He, and dilute ^{3}He-^{4}He mixtures; unless otherwise indicated, the data are taken at SVP [2.44]. (This reference should also be consulted for references to the original literature). More-recent data for the thermal conductivities of ^{4}He and ^{3}He are given in Figs.2.11,16

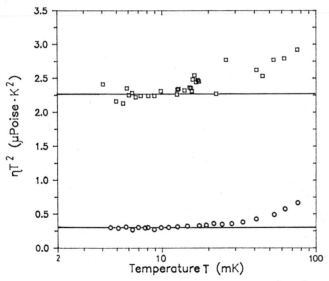

Fig.2.18. Viscosity η of liquid ^{3}He ($\square$) and of a 6.8% ^{3}He-^{4}He mixture ($\circ$) at 0.4 bar multiplied by T^2 as a function of temperature. The solid lines represent the Fermi liquid behaviour $\eta \propto T^2$ [2.45]

tures is more complicated. - It is important to remember that the thermal conductivity of this Fermi liquid becomes equal to the thermal conductivity of good metallic conductors at about 2 mK! In addition, the viscosity of liquid ^{3}He increases to that of light machine oil just above its superfluid transition temperature!

This short discussion of the properties of liquid helium relevant for its application in low-temperature experiments, in particular as a refrigerant, should be sufficient for our purpose. For a general discussion of the properties of liquid, in particular, superfluid helium, whose properties can be phenomenologially understood in terms of a "two-fluid model", the reader should consult the special literature on this subject given in the list of references for this chapter. Some of the properties of liquid ^{3}He will be discussed again in connection with Pomeranchuk cooling in Chap.8, and liquid mixtures of the two helium isotopes will be considered in Chap.7 when we discuss the dilution refrigerator.

3. Solid Matter at Low Temperatures

The purpose of this chapter is to summarize the basic properties of solid materials at low temperatures [3.1-5] that are relevant for the design and construction of low-temperature apparatus and for performing experiments with such apparatus. These properties are, in particular, the specific heat, thermal expansion, and thermal conductivity; some magnetic properties of solids will be discussed in later chapters in connection with magnetic cooling and thermometry.

Quite generally one can say that the properties of materials can be better understood the further the temperature is reduced (except for some exotic cases like solid ^{3}He), because as the temperature is lowered the properties of materials become more and more "ideal" or "simpler"; they approach their theoretical models more closely. At low temperatures the number of excitations decreases and the vibrations of the atoms can be described in the harmonic approximation, which means that the potential V^* as a function of distance $r-r_0$ from the equilibrium position r_0 of the atom can be written as

$$V^*(r-r_0) \propto (r-r_0)^2 . \tag{3.1}$$

In this approximation there is no thermal expansion because thermal expansion results from the anharmonic parts of the potential, for which we would have to introduce higher-order terms in the above equation. As a result, the thermal expansion coefficient becomes smaller and smaller, as we approach lower and lower temperatures (Sect.3.2). A further advantage of low temperatures for the description of the properties of materials is the fact that various "parts" of a material can be treated independently. For example, in many cases one can consider the nuclear spin system (which is of great importance at ultralow temperatures) independently of the electrons and the lattice vibrations (Chap.10). Of course, this is not true for all the "parts" of a material. For example, the temperature dependence of the electrical resistivity of a metal just results from the interaction of conduction electrons with the lattice. The fact that the specific heat and the thermal conductivity due to lattice vibrations and due to conduction electrons in a metal can be treated independently and can then just be added is a consequence of the large mass difference of nuclei and electrons. To a very good approximation, their motions are independent, and the Schrödinger equation for the whole crystal can be separated into an electronic part and a lattice part. This is known as the Born-Oppenheimer approximation.

3.1 Specific Heat

The specific heat is a measure of the energy content of a material. In other words, it tells us how much energy we have to transfer to the material in order to heat it to a particular temperature or how much energy we have to extract from it to cool it to a particular temperature. To calculate the specific heat of a material we have to consider the various excitations that can be excited if we transfer thermal energy to it [3.1-7].

3.1.1 Insulators

For non-magnetic, crystalline insulators the most important, and in most cases only possible, excitations are vibrations of the atoms, the so-called phonons [3.7]. At high temperatures all possible vibrational states of the atoms are excited. Considering each atom to behave as an independent, classical harmonic oscillator results in the Dulong-Petit law for the high-temperature specific heat of a material of N_0 atoms per mole, each of which has three degrees of freedom for its potential energy and for its kinetic energy. Because each degree of freedom contributes $k_B/2$ to the specific heat (at constant volume of the material),

$$C_v = \frac{6}{2} N_0 k_B = 3R = 24.94 \quad [\text{J/mol·K}] . \tag{3.2}$$

However, when the thermal energy $k_B T$ becomes of the order of the energy necessary for excitation of lattice vibrations one sees deviations from the Dulong-Petit law, because not all of the lattice vibrations will then be excited. The limit for the applicability of the Dulong-Petit law is given by

$$T \sim \hbar \omega_{ph}/k_B , \tag{3.3}$$

where ω_{ph} is the phonon frequency. The limiting temperature is of order 100 K.

In 1907 A. Einstein showed that a reasonable description of the specific heat of lattice vibrations below this temperature is obtained if the lattice vibrations are considered to be quantized. He performed a calculation of the phonon specific heat by describing the lattice vibrations as quantized phonon "particles", but gave them all the same frequency ω_E. In this Einstein model the material is considered as being composed of independent oscillators with energies

$$E_n = \hbar \omega_E (n + 1/2) , \tag{3.4}$$

where $n = 0, 1, 2, ...$ is the excitation number of the modes or of the phonons. M. Planck then showed that the mean excitation number $\langle n \rangle$ of each oscillator or the mean number of phonons at temperature T is given by the Boson distribution function

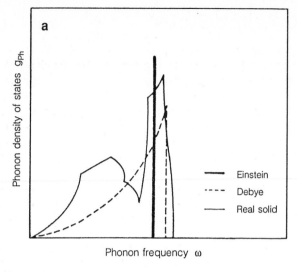

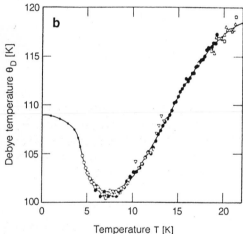

Fig.3.1. (a) The phonon density of states g_{ph} used in the Einstein and Debye theories compared with that for a typical real solid. (b) Variation in the Debye temperature θ_D of indium due to the influence of deviations from $g_{ph} \propto \omega^2$ [3.8]

$$\langle n \rangle = f_{ph}(\omega) = \frac{1}{\exp(\hbar\omega/k_B T) - 1} . \tag{3.5}$$

This model, of course, deviates from reality because the vibrational frequencies of the atoms in a crystal are not equal but are distributed over a spectrum, which can have a rather complicated structure as a function of energy (Fig.3.1a). Again, at low temperatures the situation becomes simpler because the frequency dependence of the phonon density of states goes as ω^2 at low energies. As P. Debye showed, at low temperatures the phonon density of states g_{ph} can then be described by the following parabolic energy or frequency dependence (Fig.3.1a):

$$g_{ph}(\omega) = \begin{cases} (3V_m/2\pi^2 v_s^3)\omega^2 = 9\,N_0\omega^2/\omega_D^3\,, & \omega < \omega_D\,, \\ 0\,, & \omega > \omega_D\,, \end{cases} \qquad (3.6)$$

V_m being the molar volume, and v_s the average value of the velocities of sound of a crystal: $v_s^{-3} = (v_{long}^{-3} + 2v_{trans}^{-3})/3$.

Of course, this spectrum does not extend to infinity but is cut off at a maximum frequency that is given by the condition that g_{ph} contains all the phonon frequencies. This limiting frequency is called the Debye frequency ω_D. The corresponding temperature, the Debye temperature θ_D of the material, is a measure of the temperature below which phonons begin to "freeze out". Values for several metals are given in Table 10.1. These parameters are material constants with large values for a lattice composed of light atoms which are strongly bound, as in diamond ($\theta_D = 2000$K), and with small values for a lattice composed of heavy atoms bound by weak forces, as in lead ($\theta_D = 95$K).

If we apply the Debye model to calculate the internal energy of the lattice vibrations and take its temperature derivative to arrive at the specific heat, we find [3.1-7][1]

$$C_{ph}(T) = \frac{12}{5}\pi^4 N_0 k_B \left(\frac{T}{\theta_D}\right)^3 = 1944 \left(\frac{T}{\theta_D}\right)^3 \left[\frac{J}{mol\cdot K}\right] \qquad (3.7)$$

for temperatures $T < \theta_D/10$. A deviation of the phonon density of states from the ω^2 dependence can be taken into account by letting $\theta_D = f(T)$, see Fig.3.1b. The cubic dependence of the phonon specific heat on temperature demonstrates its rather strong decrease with decreasing temperature. Therefore, insulators such as rare gas crystals very often have a very small specific heat at low temperatures. Examples are illustrated in Fig.3.2.

3.1.2 Metals

Besides the lattice vibrations, in a metal we also have (nearly free moving) conduction electrons, which can be thermally excited. Electrons have a spin 1/2, are fermions and obey the Pauli principle. Therefore each energy state can be occupied by at most two electrons with antiparallel spin orientation. Putting all our electrons into energy states, we will fill these states up to a limiting energy, the Fermi energy, given by

$$E_F = k_B T_F = \frac{\hbar^2}{2m}\left(\frac{3\pi^2 N_0}{V_m}\right)^{2/3} = 3.0\cdot 10^5 k_B V_m^{-2/3} \quad [erg]\,. \qquad (3.8)$$

---

[1] In the following I do not distinguish between C_p and C_v, the specific heats at constant pressure and constant volume, respectively; the difference is negligible at low temperatures, approaching about 1% at $T \sim \theta_D/2$

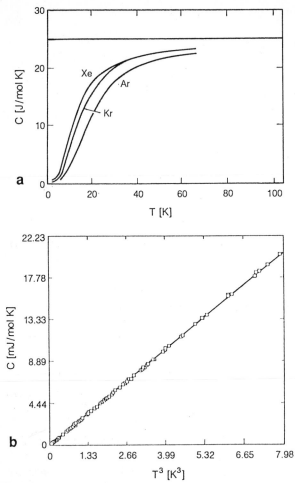

Fig.3.2. (a) Specific heat of Ar, Kr and Xe. The horizontal line is the classical Dulong–Petit value [3.9]. (b) Specific heat of Ar as a function of T^3 [3.1, 10]

A typical value for this energy is 1 eV, corresponding to the rather high temperature of about 10^4 K. The Fermi-Dirac distribution function for the occupation of energy states of electrons at temperature T is (Fig.3.3)

$$f_e(E) = \frac{1}{\exp[(E-\mu)/k_B T] + 1} \tag{3.9}$$

with the chemical potential $\mu = E_F$ at T = 0. Because of the high value of the Fermi temperature $T_F = E_F/k_B$, room temperature is already a "low temperature" for the electron gas, in the sense that here the electron gas is already pretty well in its ground state. And indeed, the properties of metals at low temperatures are determined exclusively by electrons in energy states very close to the Fermi energy.

34

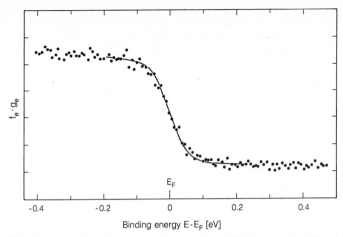

Binding energy E-E_F [eV]

Fig.3.3. Occupied electronic states of Ag at 300 K near the Fermi energy E_F obtained from photoelectron spectroscopy. The full line is the Fermi distribution function (3.9) [3.11]

To fill energy states we first have to have them. That means, we have to calculate the density $g_e(E)$ of states for conduction electrons. This is rather simple within the "free-electron model", which describes many of the electronic properties of metals rather well [3.1-6]. The result is

$$g_e(E) = \frac{3N_0}{2E_F^{3/2}}E^{1/2} = \frac{V_m}{2\pi^2}\left[\frac{2m}{\hbar^2}\right]^{3/2}E^{1/2} . \tag{3.10}$$

To calculate properties of conduction electrons in a metal we have to multiply the two quantities $g_e(E)$ and $f_e(E)$.

At a temperature T one can thermally excite only electrons near the Fermi energy, within an energy range from about $E_F - k_B T$ to about $E_F + k_B T$; the thermal energy is not enough to excite electrons out of energy states further below the Fermi energy. At a temperature T the number of "thermally involved" electrons is then approximately given by $g_e(E_F) k_B T \propto T/T_F$. If we raise the temperature from 0 to T, these electrons experience an energy change $\Delta E \simeq g_e(E_F)k_B^2 T^2 \propto T^2/T_F$ corresponding to an electronic specific heat of $C_e \simeq 2g_e(E_F)k_B^2 T$. If we do the calculation more rigorously, we have to take into account the Fermi-Dirac distribution (3.9) at finite temperatures, which modifies our result for the electronic specific heat only slightly to

$$C_e(T) = \frac{\pi^2}{2}N_0 k_B \frac{T}{T_F} = \gamma T , \tag{3.11}$$

where T_F is given by (3.8). The γ-values (Sommerfeld constants) for some metals are listed in Table 10.1. The result (3.11) is in good agreement with

35

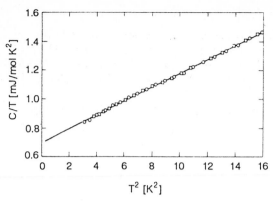

Fig.3.4. Specific heat C of copper divided by temperature T as a function of T^2 [3.4]

experimental data (Fig.3.4) and was a great triumph for quantum mechanics, for the free-electron model, and for the Fermi theory of spin-1/2 particles.

Of course, for a real metal we have to give up the free-electron model. We have to consider the mutual interactions of the electrons, their interactions with the ions, and the symmetry of the crystal. This can be taken into account by going from the free-electron model to a so-called quasi-particle model [3.1-6]. In this model each electron has an effective mass m^* that deviates from the mass m of bare electrons because the electrons in a metal behave "heavier" or "lighter" than bare electrons owing to their interactions. We still obtain the same equations for the specific heat, in particular $C_e \propto T$; we just have to replace the mass of bare electrons by the effective mass of interacting electrons. For the specific heat, e.g., it means that we have to multiply (3.11) by m^*/m.

With these results we arrive at the following equation for the total specific heat of a metal at "low" temperatures:

$$C = \gamma T + \beta T^3 . \tag{3.12}$$

"Low" means "small compared to the Debye temperature" if we consider the phonons and "small compared to the Fermi temperature" if we consider the electrons. If we introduce the appropriate material constants, we find that at room temperature the specific heat of a metal is dominated by the phonon specific heat and usually only at temperatures below 10 K is the electronic specific heat important; it dominates at temperatures below 1 K. The results for the electronic and lattice specific heats of copper are shown in Fig.3.4, where C/T versus T^2 is plotted for low temperatures. The figure demonstrates how well the data are described by the theory discussed above. It also demonstrates that it is very often rather important to choose the right coordinates to get a sensitive indication of whether data follow an expected behaviour.

3.1.3 Superconducting Metals

Many metals - elements, alloys and compounds - enter a new state below a critical temperature T_c. In this so-called superconducting state [3.12-15] they can carry an electric current without dissipation and they show several other new properties. As an example I discuss here the specific heat of a metal in its superconducting state, at $T < T_c$. Data for the specific heat of superconductors are presented in Fig.3.5. Examining these data we arrive at the following conclusions. The specific heat C_{ph} of the lattice vibrations is not influenced by the transition to the superconducting state. It still follows

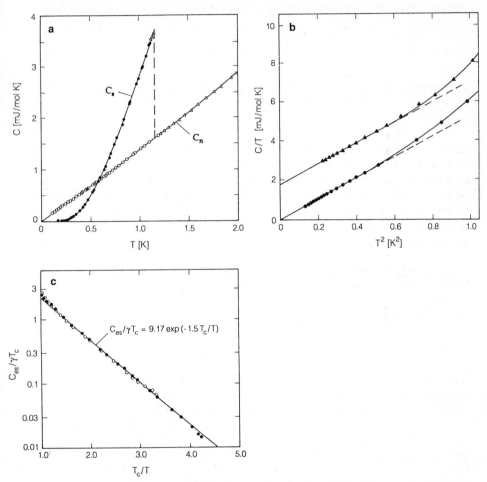

Fig.3.5. (a) Specific heat of Al in the superconducting (C_s) and normal-conducting (C_n) states [3.16]. (b) Specific heat C of Hg divided by temperature T as a function of T^2 in the normal ($\triangle$) and superconducting ($\bullet$) states. The straight lines correspond to (3.7,11) with $\theta_D = 72$ K and $\gamma = 1.82$ mJ/mol·K^2 [3.17]. (c) Electronic specific heat C_{es} of superconducting V ($\bullet$) and Sn ($\circ$) divided by γT_c as a function of T_c/T. The full line represents (3.15) [3.18]

37

a T^3 law with the same coefficient as one finds in the normal-conducting state (3.7)

$$C_{ph,s} = C_{ph,n} = \beta T^3 .$$ (3.13)

The new behaviour evident from Fig.3.5 is entirely due to the altered specific heat of the electrons. First of all, there is a jump of the electronic specific heat at the critical temperature, but no latent heat (the transition is a second-order phase change when the external magnetic field is zero). The jump in C occurs because the metal now has - one might say - a new "degree of freedom" corresponding to the possibility of entering the superconducting state. In the discussion of the Dulong-Petit law for the specific heat at high temperatures we have already seen that each degree of freedom enhances the specific heat. For simple superconductors such as aluminium and tin, which follow the Bardeen, Cooper, Schrieffer (BCS) theory of superconductivity [3.12-15, 19], the jump of the specific heat is given by

$$\Delta C = 1.43 \gamma T_c ,$$ (3.14)

where γT_c is the normal-state electronic specific heat (3.11) at T_c.

Below the transition temperature the electronic specific heat in the superconducting state vanishes much more rapidly than the electronic specific heat in the normal-conducting state of the metal. Its temperature dependence is given by

$$C_{e,s} \propto \exp(-bT_c/T) .$$ (3.15)

An exponential temperature dependence of the specific heat is indicative of an energy gap ΔE in the density of states, as occurs for the electrons in a superconductor (and in a semiconductor). This reflects the number of electrons thermally excited across the energy gap.

3.1.4 Non-Crystalline Solids

In non-crystalline or disordered solids [3.20-23] like vitreous silica or metallic glasses the atoms are not arranged in a periodic order; these solids can be visualized as supercooled liquids. As an example, Fig.3.6 depicts a possible arrangement of silicon and oxygen atoms in vitreous silica. In such a disordered structure many atoms have more than one possible position and these positions can be distinguished by rather small energy differences. Even at low temperatures the atoms can "tunnel" from one position to another. Again, we have a new "degree of freedom" for the material: the possibility of performing structural rearrangements. As a result, we observe an additional contribution to the specific heat caused by the tunneling transitions or structural relaxations in a disordered or glassy material. At low temperatures this additional contribution is given by

$$C_a = aT^n$$ (3.16)

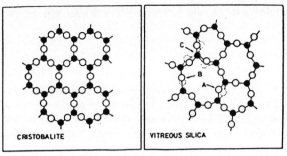

Fig.3.6. Schematic two-dimensional representation of the structure of cristobalite, a crystalline modification of SiO_2, and of vitreous silica, the amorphous modification of SiO_2. Full circles represent silicon atoms and open circles oxygen atoms. Three possible types of defects are indicated by arrows [3.24]

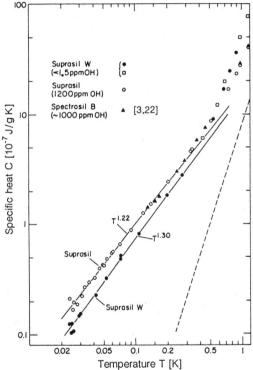

Fig.3.7. Specific heats of three types of vitreous SiO_2 containing different concentrations of OH^- (as well as metal ions, chlorine and fluorine). The dashed line is the phonon specific heat of crystalline SiO_2 [3.25]

with an exponent n which is very close to 1 [3.20-23,25]. (In addition, one often observes an enhancement of the T^3 specific heat contribution). This is illustrated for vitreous silica in Fig.3.7. Disordered insulators, therefore, show an almost linear contribution (from the tunneling transitions between various positions of the atoms) and a cubic contribution (from the vibrations of the atoms) to the specific heat. The same is observed for a metallic glass, but here we have two contributions to the linear part of the specific heat, one from the tunneling transitions and the other one from the conduction electrons. It is very remarkable that the contributions to the specific heat from the non-crystallinity are of very similar size even for quite dissimilar materials [3.20-23], indicating that the additional excitations in a disordered material are associated with the disorder and do not depend on the type of material very much. Because the specific heat contributed by disorder decreases linearly with decreasing temperature instead of as T^3 as for lattice vibrations, the specific heat of a dielectric in its glassy state is much higher than in its crystalline state at low temperatures (Fig.3.7). Often, below about 1 K, glasses have a specific heat which is even larger than that of a metal. In fact, at 10 mK the heat capacity of a dielectric glass can be a factor of 10^3 larger than the heat capacity of the corresponding crystal, which can be of great importance for the design of low temperature apparatus containing non-crystalline components.

3.1.5 Magnetic Specific Heat

When a magnetic field is applied to a material whose atoms have magnetic moments, there are $(2I+1)$ ways the magnetic moments can orient themselves with respect to the magnetic field, where I is the spin associated with the magnetic moment. Again, a new "degree of freedom" results in an additional contribution to the specific heat. Let us consider the simplest case, a spin-1/2 system so that there are two possible spin orientations. At very low temperatures most of the magnetic moments will be in the lower energy state. If the temperature increases, transitions from the lower to the upper level will occur, giving the following contribution to the specific heat [3.1-3]:

$$C_m = k_B N_0 \left(\frac{\Delta E}{k_B T} \right)^2 \frac{e^{\Delta E/k_B T}}{(1 + e^{\Delta E/k_B T})^2} . \tag{3.17}$$

This contribution, shown in Fig.3.8, is called a "Schottky anomaly". Very often the energy splitting ΔE is small compared to the thermal energy $k_B T$. In this "high-temperature" approximation the magnetic contribution to the specific heat is given by

$$C_m \rightarrow k_B N_0 \left(\frac{\Delta E}{2k_B T} \right)^2 \quad \text{for} \quad \Delta E \ll k_B T . \tag{3.18}$$

For a metal with such a T^{-2} contribution we have for the specific heat (at T < 1K where the lattice specific heat is negligible)

$$C = \gamma T + \delta T^{-2} . \tag{3.19}$$

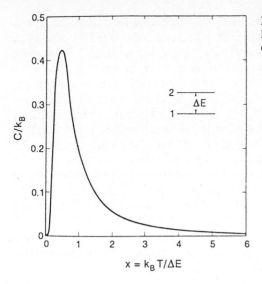

Fig.3.8. Specific heat C (divided by k_B) of a two-level system with energy separation ΔE

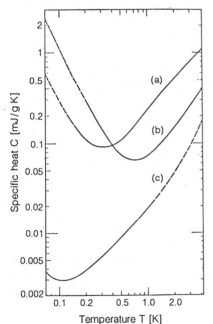

Fig.3.9. Specific heats of (a) Constantan (57%Cu, 43%Ni), (b) Manganin (87% Cu, 13% Mn) and (c) a 9% W, 91% Pt alloy [3.26]

The magnetic specific heats of some commercial alloys containing paramagnetic atoms and often used as thin wires for low-temperature equipment are exhibited in Fig.3.9. Again, at T < 1K, the specific heat can be strongly enhanced compared to the simple electronic and lattice specific heats. The data in Fig.3.9 demonstrate that one has to be very cautious in using wires of Manganin (87% Cu, 13% Mn) or Constantan (57% Cu, 43% Ni) at T <

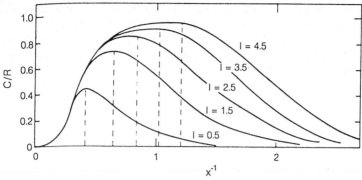

Fig.3.10. Molar heat capacities C divided by the gas constant R as a function of $1/x_e$ $= k_B T/g_e \mu_B B$ or $1/x_n = k_B T/g_n \mu_n B$ for different values of spin I (see also Table 3.1)

1K and, in fact, it would be better to resort to other commercial materials, like 92% Pt, 8% W.

Of course, in general the spin may be larger than 1/2 and we then have more than two levels. The calculation of the Schottky specific heat using (9.15b) for I = 0.5, 1.5, 2.5, 3.5 and 4.5 in Fig.3.10 reveals that this results only in quantitative changes. But for low-temperature physics it is rather important to remember that the *temperature* at which the maximum of the magnetic contribution to the specific heat occurs is determined by the energy splitting ΔE of the levels. In other words, for nuclear magnetic moments, which are about a factor of 1000 smaller than electronic magnetic moments, this maximum occurs at much lower temperatures than for the electronic magnetic moments. For example, an electronic magnetic moment of 1 μ_B in a field of 1 T leads to a maximum in C_m at about 1 K, whereas a nuclear magnetic moment in this field will have a maximum in C_m at only about 1 mK (Chaps.9, 10). But the *maximum value* of the specific heat is *independent* of the energy splitting, it is only a function of the number of degrees of freedom (2I+1); these values are listed in Table 3.1. This means that an electronic paramagnet with a spin 1/2 in an arbitrary external magnetic field will have $C_{m,max}$ = 0.439R, (occurring in the Kelvin range or possibly at even higher temperatures, depending on the magnitude of its moment and the magnetic field this moment is exposed to). On the other

Table 3.1. Position $x_e = g_e \mu_B B/k_B T$ or $x_n = g_n \mu B/k_B T$ and value (C_{max}/R) of the maximum of the magnetic specific heat divided by the gas constant, as a function of spin (or angular momentum) I.(See also Fig.3.10)

I:	1/2	3/2	5/2	7/2	9/2
x_{max}	2.399	1.566	1.193	0.976	0.831
C_{max}/R	0.439	0.743	0.849	0.899	0.927

hand, a nuclear magnetic moment, again with a spin 1/2, will have the *same maximum value* of the specific heat, but occurring at much lower temperature, in the microkelvin or millikelvin temperature range due to its smaller moment. This fact is of considerable importance for nuclear magnetic refrigeration (Chap.10).

The above considerations on specific heat contributions resulting from interactions between a magnetic moment and a magnetic field can be applied analogously to the specific heat resulting from interactions of an electric quadrupole moment with an electric field gradient (see also Sects.3.1.6 and 10.6).

3.1.6 The Low-Temperature Specific Heat of Copper

Copper is a material that is particularly important and often used in low temperature apparatus. There are several reports in the literature of an enhanced specific heat of Cu at low temperatures [3.27-36]. For $0.03K \leq T \leq 2K$ these increases have been traced to hydrogen and/or oxygen impurities, to magnetic impurities, mainly Fe and Mn, and to lattice defects [3.27-34]. On the other hand, the increased specific heat of Cu observed in the low millikelvin temperature range seems to arise from a nuclear quadrupole Schottky-type contribution, see (10.35), due to Cu nuclei (which have a nuclear quadrupole moment) being located in non-cubic neighbourhoods, which occur near lattice defects or in copper oxide [3.35, 36] (Fig.3.11). These anomalies should be considered in the wide-spread low-temperature applications of Cu in calorimetry, thermometry (Chap.12) and nuclear magnetic cooling (Chap.10), and in other applications of this very useful metal. A proper heat treatment of Cu can remove some of these anomalous increases of the specific heat.

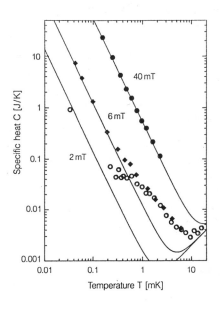

Fig.3.11. Heat capacity of 275 moles of Cu, of which 104 moles are in the given magnetic fields, as a function of temperature. The full lines are the expected values for the nuclear magnetic heat capacities of 104 moles Cu in the given fields plus - at higher temperatures - the electronic contributions of 275 moles Cu. The deviation of the measured data from the lines is attributed to a heat capacity resulting from a splitting of the $I = 3/2$ nuclear levels of Cu due to a nuclear electric quadrupole interaction, see (10.29 and 30), of 11 mmoles of Cu which are located in an electric field gradient of about 10^{18} V/cm^2. For these Cu nuclei the cubic symmetry must have been destroyed in order to create an electric field gradient [3.36]

Comprehensive compilations of references to specific heat data, including data for technical materials, can be found in [3.37-41]. Some of these data are shown in Fig.3.12.

3.2 Thermal Expansion

If the potential which an atom sees in a crystal were parabolic (the harmonic approximation) and therefore given by (3.1), there would be no thermal expansion. However, in reality the potential which an atom experiences due to the electrostatic forces of its neighbours looks more like that displayed in Fig.3.13. At low temperatures the amplitudes of the atomic vibrations around their equilibrium position r_0 are rather small and the potential can be approximated by (3.1). As a result the thermal expansion coefficient

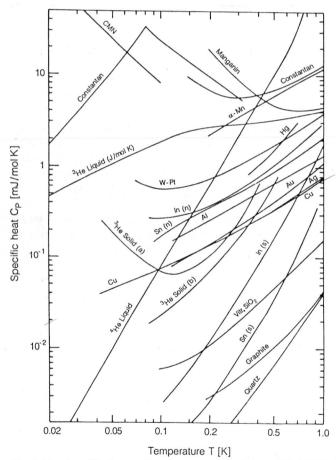

Fig.3.12. Specific heats of several materials below 1 K [3.38]. (This paper provides references to the original literature)

$$\alpha = \frac{1}{\ell}\left(\frac{\partial \ell}{\partial T}\right)_p \tag{3.20}$$

does indeed vanish for T→0 (for Cu: $\alpha = 2.9\cdot10^{-10}T+2.68\cdot10^{-11}T^3$ at 0.2K < T < 1.9K [3.42]). When the temperature is raised the thermal vibrations of the atoms grow and they increasingly experience that the potential is asymmetric: steeper for small distances and flatter for larger distances. The atoms experience the "anharmonic" part of the potential. Due to the shape of the potential the atoms spend more of their time at larger separations, leading to an increased average separation. Therefore the material expands when the temperature is increased. For a potential $V(r-r_0) = V(x)$, the mean deviation from the zero-temperature position $r = r_0$ is given by [3.1-6]

$$\langle x \rangle = \int_{-\infty}^{\infty} x\,e^{-V(x)/k_B T}\,dx \left/ \int_{-\infty}^{\infty} e^{-V(x)/k_B T}\,dx \right. . \tag{3.21}$$

The thermal contraction of various materials when cooled from room temperature to lower temperatures is displayed in Fig.3.14. Looking at this figure we can divide the materials quite generally into three groups. Firstly, there is a group of commercial alloys and glasses, which have been specially produced to exhibit an extremely small expansion coefficient. Then we have the groups of metals which contract by about $0.2\div0.4\%$ when cooled from room temperature to low temperatures. It is very important to remember that different metals have different expansion coefficients and therefore have to be joined in the proper order (see below). Finally, we have the organic materials with their large expansion coefficients of typical $1\div2\%$ length change when cooled from room temperature to the low Kelvin temperature range. These latter materials are rather important for low-temperature purposes as well, because they are used as construction materials on

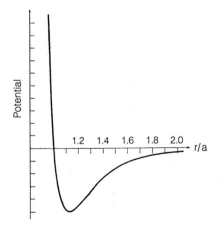

Fig.3.13. Typical potential which an atom or ion experiences in a lattice as a function of distance r between them (normalized to the lattice parameter a)

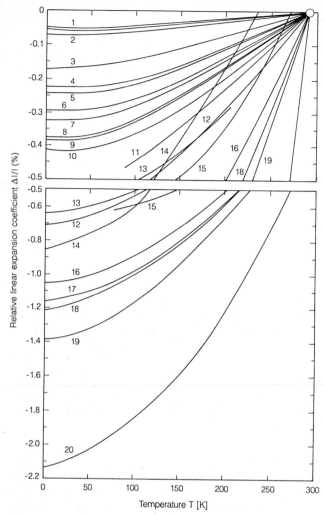

Fig. 3.14. Relative linear thermal expansion coefficient of (1) Invar (upper), Pyrex (lower), (2) W, (3) non-alloyed steel, (4) Ni, (5) $Cu_{0.7}Ni_{0.3}$, (6) stainless steel, (7) Cu, (8) German silver, (9) brass, (10) Al, (11) soft solder, (12) In, (13) Vespel SP22, (14) Hg, (15) ice, (16) Araldite, (17) Stycast 1266, (18) PMMA, (19) Nylon, (20) Teflon [3.44]. Some further data are: Pt similar to (3); Ag between (9) and (10); Stycast 2850 GT slightly larger than (10). The relative change of length between 300 and 4 K is $10^3 \Delta\ell/\ell = 11.5$, 4.2, 6.3 and 5.7 for Stycast 1266, Stycast 2850 GT, Vespel SP-22 and solders, respectively [3.43–45]

46

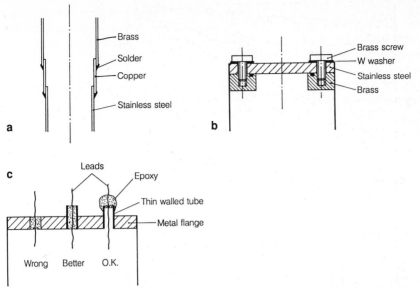

Fig.3.15. When joining different materials in a cryogenic apparatus one has to take into account the difference in their thermal expansion coefficients. For example: (a) The tube with the largest expansion coefficient should be on the outside so that the solder joint is not pulled open during cooldown. (b) In an O-ring seal the screw should have a larger expansion coefficient than the flange. The seal will tighten even further during cooldown if a washer with a very small expansion coefficient is used. (c) In an epoxy feedthrough for leads the epoxy, with its large expansion coefficient, should contract on a thin-walled metal tube during cooldown rather then pull away. It helps if the tube walls are tapered to a sharp edge. An epoxy with filler should be used to lower its thermal expansion coefficient

account of their low thermal conductivity, or for bonding, electrical insulation or making leak-tight joints. Here problems can often occur due to their rather large thermal expansion coefficients which can lead to substantial thermal stresses. For some applications the very small expansion coefficients of many glasses of $\alpha \simeq 4 \cdot 10^{-7}$ K^{-1} at 0° C may be useful. However, unlike the specific heat and other properties, α is not a universal property of glasses at low temperature; it may even have different sign for different glasses at T $\leq$ 1 K [3.46].

Joining materials of different thermal expansion in an apparatus whose temperature will repeatedly be changed requires rather careful selection of the materials and a suitable design if destruction of the joint by the severe stresses in thermal cycling is to be avoided. This is a very serious consideration because a low-temperature apparatus composed of a variety of materials usually has to be leak-tight. Figure 3.15 illustrates the correct ways of joining tubes of different metals and the design of seals, which appear in almost every piece of low-temperature equipment. (For the proper design of an insulating feedthrough of leads, see Sect.13.3). In addition, stresses due to parallel connection by parts of different materials have to be a-voided. Very often good thermal contact between different metallic parts of low-temperature apparatus is essential (Sect.4.3.1). Here again the correct selection of the materials for bolts and nuts is important. Frequently the thermal contact after cooldown can be improved by adding a washer of a material with a low thermal expansion coefficient, such as Mo or W (but they are superconductors at very low temperatures!).

A fairly comprehensive list of references and data on thermal expansion coefficients of solids can be found in [3.37,47,48].

3.3 Thermal Conductivity

Thermal conductivity is a transport property of matter similar to electrical conductivity, viscosity, diffusion, damping of sound, etc [3.1-5,49,50]. The rate of heat flow per unit area resulting from a temperature gradient in a material of cross section A is given by

$$\dot{q} = \dot{Q}/A = -\kappa\nabla T ,\qquad(3.22)$$

where κ is the thermal conductivity coefficient. Heat can be carried by conduction electrons or by lattice vibrations. These carriers of heat usually do not fly ballistically from the heated end of the material to the other, colder end. They are scattered by other electrons or phonons or by defects in the material; therefore they perform a diffusion process. To calculate thermal transport we have to apply transport theory, which in its simplest form is a kinetic gas theory. In this simplified version we consider the electrons or the phonons as a gas diffusing through the material. For the thermal conductivity coefficient this theory gives

$$\kappa = \frac{1}{3}(C/V_m)v\lambda ,\qquad(3.23)$$

where λ is the mean free path, and v the velocity of the particles. Intuitively, this is a rather convincing equation identical to those for other transport properties if we choose the corresponding parameters. It tells us that the transport property "thermal conductivity coefficient" is given by the product of: "what is transported" [here it is the specific heat C (per unit volume)], "the velocity v of the carriers performing the transport", and "how far the carriers fly before they are scattered again". The factor 1/3 comes from the fact that we are interested in the heat flow in one direction whereas the motion of the carriers is three-dimensional.

How will the thermal conductivity coefficient look like if the heat is carried either by electrons or by phonons? In the first part of this chapter we have already calculated the specific heat C of electrons and phonons as a function of temperature. The characteristic velocity of phonons is the velocity of sound v_s; this is the velocity with which "vibrations" or "phonons" move through the lattice. Typical values for solids are $v_s = (3 \div 5) \cdot 10^5$ cm/s. The electrons involved in thermal transport can only be electrons with energy near the Fermi energy (Fig. 3.3). Only these can transport heat because they are the only ones which can perform transitions to higher non-occupied energy states, which is necessary for thermal conductivity. Their velocity is the so-called Fermi velocity v_F determined by the kinetic Fermi energy E_F, see (3.8). Typical values are $v_F = (\hbar/m_e)(3\pi^2 N_0/V_m)^{1/3} = 10^7 \div 10^8$ cm/s $\gg v_s$. Both the sound velocity and the Fermi velocity are independent of temperature at low temperatures. So we know C and v, and all the problems in calculating transport properties lie in the calculation of the mean free path λ, determined by the scattering processes of the heat carriers.

The main scattering processes limiting the thermal conductivity are phonon-phonon (which is absent in the harmonic approximation), phonon-defect, electron-phonon, electron-impurity, and sometimes electron-electron interactions. The resistances of the various scattering processes are additive. Because the number of phonons increases with increasing temperature, the electron-phonon and phonon-phonon scattering are temperature dependent. The number of defects is temperature independent and correspondingly the mean free path for the phonon-defect and electron-defect scattering do not depend on temperature. As a result, we arrive at the equations for the thermal conductivity given in the following subsections.

3.3.1 Lattice Conductivity: Phonons

The lattice conductivity is given by

$$\kappa_{ph} = \frac{1}{3}(C_{ph}/V_m)v_s\lambda_{ph} \propto T^3\lambda_{ph}(T) , \quad \text{at} \quad T \le \theta_D/10 . \tag{3.24}$$

a) **Intermediate Temperatures: $T \le \theta_D/10$.** In this temperature range the phonon-phonon scattering is dominant and the phonon mean free path increases with decreasing temperature because the number of phonons decreases with decreasing temperature. A quantitative derivation [3.1-5,49,50] of the thermal conductivity for the phonon-phonon scattering regime is somewhat involved due to the anharmonicity of the potential and of the frequency dependence of the dominant phonons with temperature; it will not be given here. We just state that in this T range the thermal conductivity decreases with increasing temperature (Figs. 3.16a, 17).

b) **Low Temperatures: $T \ll \theta_D$.** In this temperature range the number of thermally excited phonons is rather small. They are no longer important for scattering, and the phonons which carry the heat are scattered by crystal defects or by crystal boundaries only. Because at low temperatures the dominant phonon wavelength is larger than the size of lattice imperfections, phonon scattering at crystallite boundaries is the important process. Now

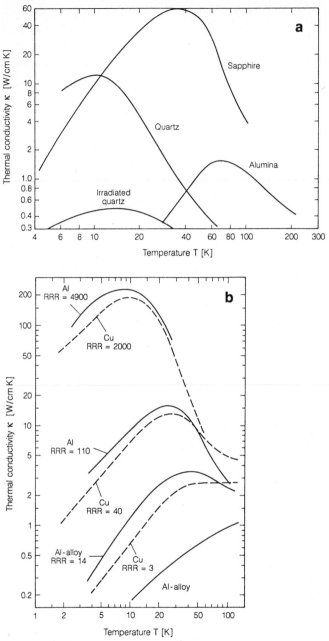

Fig.3.16. Temperature dependence of the thermal conductivities of (**a**) some dielectric solids and of (**b**) Al and Cu of varying purity (expressed as their residual resistivity ratio (3.40)) [3.51]

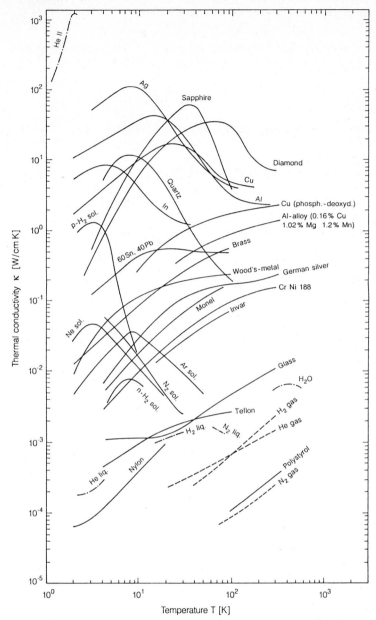

Fig.3.17. Typical thermal conductivities κ of various materials at $T > 2$ K [3.52-56]. Remember that κ depends on the purity and crystalline perfection of a material

the mean free path for phonon transport is temperature independent. The temperature dependence of the thermal conductivity is then given just by the temperature dependence of the specific heat, and decreases strongly with decreasing temperature as

51

$$\kappa_{ph} \propto C_{ph} \propto T^3 \; . \tag{3.25}$$

As a result of this consideration we find that the thermal conductivity due to phonon transport goes through a maximum, as illustrated in Figs.3.16a and 17. Due to differences in the number of defects, the low temperature thermal conductivity of nominally identical samples can vary considerably (see also Fig.3.18).

I want to mention two particularly important cases of phonon thermal conductivity. Firstly, if we have a rather perfect, large crystal with a very low density of defects and impurities, the thermal conductivity can become very large, of the order 100 W(cm·K)$^{-1}$ (Figs.3.16a, 17). This is comparable to the thermal conductivity of highly conductive metals like copper or aluminium. Secondly, if we have a strongly disordered insulator, the mean free path determined by the scattering of phonons on defects can become very small, even approaching atomic distances. In particular, if we consider a glass, the tunneling transitions between different structural arrangements of

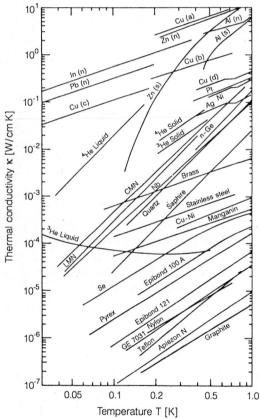

Fig.3.18. Typical thermal conductivities κ of various materials at T < 1 K [3.38]. (This paper provides references to the original literature). Remember that κ depends on the purity and crystalline perfection of a material

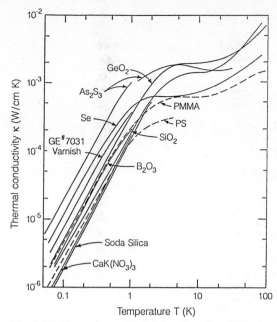

Fig.3.19. Thermal conductivities of various non-crystalline solids [3.23]

the atoms, which were discussed in the description of the specific heat of non-crystalline materials (Sect.3.1.4), limit the phonon thermal conductivity by additional scattering of phonons on tunneling states [3.20-23,57,58]. This scattering results in an almost universal T^2 dependence of the thermal conductivity of dielectric glassy materials below 1 K (Figs.3.18-20) and a plateau region for $2K \leq T \leq 20K$ (Fig.3.19). Because the heat is still carried by phonons with $C_{ph} \propto T^3$, the phonon mean-free path limited by scattering on tunneling states must vary as $\lambda \propto T^{-1}$. As for the specific heat of disordered solids, the thermal conductivities of most glasses are rather similar; for example, for commercial glasses or polymers they fall within about a factor of two of those given for Pyrex.

A detailed discussion of the lattice conductivity is rather involved due to the variation of the frequency of the dominant phonons with temperature and the various scattering processes. This is particularly true if the conductivity is limited by different lattice imperfections. The main results of such discussions are [3.1-3,49,50]

$$\lambda_{ph} = \text{const.} \quad \text{for phonon-grain boundary scattering,}$$
$$\lambda_{ph} \propto T^{-1} \quad \text{for phonon-dislocation scattering,} \qquad (3.26)$$
$$\lambda_{ph} \propto T^{-4} \quad \text{for phonon-point defect (Rayleigh) scattering.}$$

53

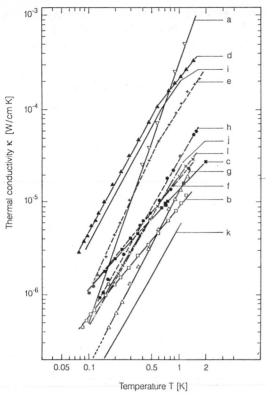

Fig.3.20. Thermal conductivities of various dielectric materials often used in cryogenic apparatus (a: sintered Al_2O_3; b: carbon BB5, c: nuclear graphite; d: Araldite CT 200; e: Araldite with talc; f: Vespel SP1; g: Vespel SP22; h: Vespel SP5; i: Epibond 100 A; j: Nylon; k: Graphite AGOT; ℓ: Vespel SP21 with 15% by weight graphite) [3.57]

3.3.2 Electronic Thermal Conductivity

For the thermal conductivity due to conduction electrons we have

$$\kappa_e = \frac{1}{3}(C_e/V_m)v_F\lambda_e \propto T\lambda_e(T) . \tag{3.27}$$

Usually, in a metal, this electronic thermal conductivity is considerably larger than the lattice thermal conductivity because the Fermi velocity v_F of the conduction electrons is much larger than the sound velocity v_s of phonons. A detailed theoretical treatment of the electronic thermal conductivity is easier than that of the lattice conductivity because the conduction electrons involved sit at the Fermi energy and therefore they all have the same energy.

a) High Temperatures. At high temperatures the thermally excited phonons are the limiting scatterers for the heat conducting electrons. Because

54

the number of thermally excited phonons increases with temperature we find for the electronic thermal conductivity in the electron-phonon scattering region a thermal conductivity which decreases with increasing temperature (Figs.3.16b, 17).

b) **Low Temperatures**. At low temperatures the number of phonons is again small and the scattering of electrons from defects and impurities dominates. We have a temperature-independent electronic mean free path resulting in the following equation for the electronic thermal conductivity:

$$\kappa_e \propto C_e \propto T .\qquad (3.28)$$

We again have two scattering processes dominating in different temperature regions and with opposite temperature dependences. As a result the electronic contribution to the thermal conductivity also goes through a maximum (Figs.3.16b, 17). The value and position of this maximum strongly depend on the perfection of the metal; for pure elements it is located at about 10 K. In a disordered alloy the scattering of electrons by the varying potential can become so strong that electronic and lattice conductivities become comparable.

3.3.3 Thermal Conductivity at Low Temperatures

For our purposes the values and temperature dependences of the thermal conductivity at low temperatures are of particular importance and will be summarized in the following. The heat carried by a material of cross section A and length L with a thermal conductivity coefficient κ is given by

$$\dot{Q} = \frac{A}{L}\int_0^L \dot{q}\,dx = \frac{A}{L}\int_{T_1}^{T_2} \kappa(T)\,dT .\qquad (3.29)$$

a) **Insulators/Phonons**. Here we have

$$\kappa_{ph} = bT^3 \quad \text{at} \quad T < \theta_D/10 \qquad (3.30)$$

and hence

$$\dot{Q} = \frac{Ab}{4L}(T_2{}^4 - T_1{}^4) .\qquad (3.31)$$

For small temperature gradients, $\Delta T = T_2 - T_1 \ll T$, we have

$$\dot{Q} \simeq \frac{Ab}{L}T^3\,\Delta T = \frac{A}{L}\kappa_{ph}(T)\,\Delta T .\qquad (3.32)$$

b) **Metals/Conduction Electrons**. Here we have

$$\kappa_e = \kappa_0 T \quad \text{at} \quad T < 10 \text{ K} \qquad (3.33)$$

55

Table 3.2 Thermal conductivity of solids frequently used in low temperature apparatus

Material	κ [mW/cm·K]	T range [K]	Ref.
Manganin	$0.94T^{1.2}$	$1 \div 4$	3.59
Nb-Ti	$0.075\,T^{1.85}$	$4 \div 9$	3.60
$Cu_{0.70}Ni_{0.30}$	$0.93T^{1.23}$	$0.3 \div 4$	3.61
$Cu_{0.70}Ni_{0.30}$	$0.64T$	$0.05 \div 0.2$	3.62
Pyrex	$0.15T^{1.75}$	$0.18 \div 0.8$	3.63
Al_2O_3	$2.7T^{2.5}$	$2 \div 8$	3.64
Al_2O_3	$0.29T^{2.7}$	$0.1 \div 2$	3.57
Stycast 1266	$0.49T^{1.98}$	$0.05 \div 0.5$	3.65
Stycast 2850 GT	$78 \cdot 10^{-3}T^{1.8}$	$1 \div 4$	3.59
Stycast 2850 FT	$53 \cdot 10^{-3}T^{1.8}$	$2 \div 10$	3.66
Vespel SP 1	$18 \cdot 10^{-3}T^{1.2}$	$0.1 \div 1$	3.57
Vespel SP 22	$17 \cdot 10^{-3}T^{2}$	$0.1 \div 2$	3.57
Teflon	$30 \cdot 10^{-3}T^{2}$	$0.2 \div 1$	3.67
Teflon	$38 \cdot 10^{-3}T^{2.4}$	$0.3 \div 0.7$	3.63
Nylon	$26 \cdot 10^{-3}T^{1.75}$	$0.2 \div 1$	3.57,63
Macor	$58 \cdot 10^{-3}T^{2.24}$	$0.4 \div 1.1$	3.68
Nuclear graphite	$15 \cdot 10^{-3}T^{1.13}$	$0.1 \div 2$	3.57
AGOT graphite	$5.1 \cdot 10^{-3}T^{1.76}$	$0.1 \div 2$	3.57
	$4.9 \cdot 10^{-3}T^{1.86}$	$0.3 \div 3$	3.69

and therefore

$$\dot{Q} = \frac{A\kappa_0}{2L}(T_2{}^2 - T_1{}^2) \, . \qquad (3.34)$$

Again, for small temperature gradients,

$$\dot{Q} \simeq \frac{A\kappa_0}{L}T\Delta T = \frac{A}{L}\kappa_e(T)\Delta T \, . \qquad (3.35)$$

Low temperature thermal conductivities of various materials are listed in Table 3.2 and plotted in Figs. 3.16-20.

3.3.4 Superconducting Metals

In superconducting metals some of the electrons are paired to so-called Copper pairs. They all sit in the same low energy state of zero entropy, which is separated by an energy gap ΔE from the states of the single, unpaired electrons [3.12-15, 19]. The Cooper pairs cannot leave this ground state to carry heat (they carry no entropy) unless they are broken up into single electrons. Therefore in a superconducting metal only the remaining unpaired electrons can carry heat. Because they are in energy states which are separated from the Cooper ground state by the energy gap $\Delta E(T)$, their number decreases exponentially with T, i.e. as $\exp(-\Delta E/k_B T)$. As a result of this qualitative discussion we find that the electronic thermal conductivity of a metal in the superconducting state is given by the product of the number of remaining unpaired single electrons and their thermal conductivity (which is identical to the electronic thermal conductivity $\kappa_{e,n} = \kappa_0 T$ in the normal-conducting state),

$$\kappa_{e,s} \propto T \exp(-\Delta E/k_B T) , \tag{3.36}$$

with $\Delta E = 1.76 \, k_B T_c$ for most elemental superconducters.

Hence the electronic thermal conductivity of a superconductor decreases very rapidly with decreasing temperature [3.70]. Indeed, at low temperatures the *electronic* thermal conductivity of a superconducting metal can even become smaller than its *lattice* conductivity, and at sufficiently low temperatures, say at $T < T_c/10$, the total thermal conductivity of a superconductor approaches the thermal conductivity of an insulator, $\kappa \propto T^3$. This is shown in Fig.4.1 for aluminium.

Because it is rather simple to "switch" a metal from the superconducting to the normal state by applying a large enough magnetic field, one can "switch" its thermal conductivity from one state to the other. We take advantage of this possibility by using a superconducting metal as a thermal switch to disconnect or to connect two parts in a low-temperature apparatus, for example in a magnetic refrigerator (Chapt.10). This application will be discussed in Sect.4.2.2.

3.3.5 Relation Between Thermal and Electrical Conductivity: The Wiedemann-Franz Law

A correct measurement of the low-temperature thermal conductivity of a metal can be rather cumbersome and, in general, a measurement of the electrical conductivity is much easier. Fortunately, due to the fact that in a metal usually both conductivities are determined by the flow of electrons and are mostly limited by the same scattering processes, a measurement of the electrical conductivity often gives reasonable information about the thermal conductivity. Let us consider a metal at low temperatures in the defect scattering limit where $\lambda_e = $ const. For the electrical conductivity the electrons conduct charge, which is temperature independent. At low temperatures in the defect scattering limit or in the residual resistivity range (see below) the electrical conductivity σ is therefore temperature independent. For the thermal conductivity κ the electrons carry heat, but the specific heat, and therefore the thermal conductivity, are proportional to temperature in this range. As a result, the ratio of thermal conductivity κ to electrical conductivity σ is proportional to temperature. One arrives at the same result for the temperature range where the conductivity due to electron transport is limited by large-angle elastic electron-phonon scattering ($T \geq \theta_D$). At, say, 4K and 300K, we then have the Wiedemann-Franz law for the ratio of these two thermal conductivities [3.1-5,71],

$$\kappa/\sigma = L_0 T , \tag{3.37}$$

where the Lorenz number L_0 is a universal constant, i.e. $L_0 = (\pi \kappa_B /e)^2 /3 = 2.45 \cdot 10^{-8}$ W·Ω/K^2.

Of course, we also arrive at (3.37) if we combine the equation for the electrical conductivity of a metal

$$\sigma = \frac{n N_0 e^2 \lambda_e V_m}{v_F m^*} , \tag{3.38}$$

where m^* is the effective mass of the conduction electrons and n is the number of conduction electrons per atom, with (3.27) for the thermal conductivity, assuming that the electronic mean free path is the same for both conductivities.

We can therefore use the measured electrical conductivity together with the Wiedemann-Franz law to calculate the thermal conductivity. In many situations this gives correct results, in particular when the electron scattering is predominantly elastic. It most often holds at low temperatures (impurity scattering; $T < \theta/10$) and at high temperatures (phonon scattering; $T \geq \theta$) but not in between, where energy losses of the order $k_B T$ are associated with electron-phonon collisions. However, cases are known in which the calculated and measured thermal conductivities differ by up to an order of magnitude at low temperatures. Usually the measured thermal conductivity is smaller than the thermal conductivity calculated with the Wiedemann-Franz law from the electrical conductivity. Particularly disturbing is the observation that this can happen at Kelvin and lower temperatures for metals of typical quality commonly used in low temperature apparatus (e.g., Al and Ag) while this deviation can be absent for other quite similar metals (e.g., Cu) [3.64], see Fig.3.21, or has even not been observed for the same metal by other investigators [3.72, 73]. The reason for this discrepancy is the fact that our above discussion is an oversimplification. In reality scattering processes may contribute with different "effectiveness" to the two conductivities [3.1-5, 49, 50]. A formula that is rather useful can be derived from the above equations, namely,

$$v_F \lambda_e = \frac{\sigma}{\gamma} \left(\frac{\pi k_B}{e} \right)^2 \tag{3.39}$$

which allows the electronic mean free path λ_e to be calculated from the measured electrical conductivity σ and specific heat coefficient γ.

In the literature the so-called Residual Resistivity Ratio (RRR) is very often given as a measure of the "purity" of a metal (Fig.3.16). This is the ratio of the electrical conductivity at low temperatures, e.g. at the boiling point of liquid helium, to the electrical conductivity at room temperature

$$RRR = \sigma_{4.2K}/\sigma_{300K} = \rho_{300K}/\rho_{4.2K} . \tag{3.40}$$

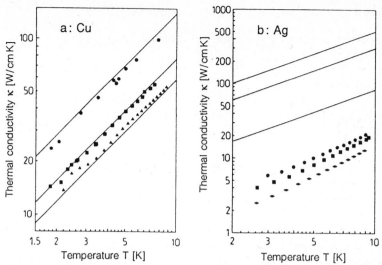

Fig.3.21. (a) Thermal conductivity of a Cu foil 60 μm thick and 20 mm wide after various treatments, resulting in RRRs of 979 (•), 540 (■) and 410 (▲). Lines correspond to thermal conductivities calculated from RRR values (3.40) by applying the Wiedemann-Franz law (3.37). (b) Thermal conductivity of a Ag rod 0.86×0.86mm² after different treatments, resulting in RRRs of 3330 (•), 1988 (■) and 553 (▲). Lines correspond to thermal conductivities calculated from RRR values (3.40) by applying the Wiedemann-Franz law (3.37) [3.64]

Because the room temperature conductivity is determined not by defect scattering but by phonon scattering, whereas the low-temperature conductivity is exclusively determined by the scattering on defects, this ratio is a direct measure of the limiting defect scattering. It indicates how good a material is by stating by what factor its conductivity increases with the vanishing of phonon scattering at low temperatures. For the important metals Cu and Ag very handy relations between the RRR and the thermal conductivity are

$$\kappa \simeq (RRR/76)T \quad [W/K\cdot cm] \quad \text{and} \quad \kappa \simeq (RRR/55)T \quad [W/K\cdot cm] , \quad (3.41)$$

respectively (but see above and Fig.3.21b).

3.3.6 Influence of Impurities on Conductivity

In the above section we have discussed how the thermal conductivity - which is so important for low-temperature experiments - can be calculated from the electrical conductivity and that both conductivities are limited at low temperatures by electron-defect scattering in a metal. In this section I will make some comments on the scattering of conduction electrons on impurity atoms. For this scattering we have to distinguish between non-magnetic and magnetic impurities.

a) Electron Scattering by Non-magnetic Impurity Atoms

The conduction electrons are scattered at the Coulomb potential of the impurity, which may have a valence difference ΔZ compared to the host lattice. The increase of the electrical resistance in this case is often not very large, and for small impurity concentrations is given by the Linde rule

$$\Delta\rho_{nm} = a + b(\Delta Z)^2 . \tag{3.42}$$

The constants a and b are determined by the host lattice and, in particular, depend on the row of the periodic table to which the host atom belongs. Examples for Cu as the host are listed in Table 3.3. These values are typically 1 $\mu\Omega\cdot$cm/at.% impurity concentration; they are comparable to the increase of ρ due to heavy cold working (several 10n$\Omega\cdot$cm) or introduction of vacancies (1 $\mu\Omega\cdot$cm/at.%) [3.38].

b) Scattering of Electrons by Magnetic Impurity Atoms (in Particular in Copper)

A magnetic or spin-flip scattering of the conduction electrons can occur at localized moments of magnetic impurities [3.74-76]. For this situation the increase of resistance can be much larger - and much more difficult to understand theoretically - than for the case of non-magnetic impurities; a theoretical discussion and a calculation of $\Delta\rho_m$ is much more involved. Examples for 3d elements as impurities in Cu are listed in Table 3.4. The strength of the scattering and the resulting resistance increase depend strongly on the properties of the magnetic impurity and it can be very different in different host lattices. For example, iron produces a very large moment in palladium whereas its moment seems to vanish in rhodium or aluminium. Furthermore, the strength of the scattering can depend very strongly on temperature due to the so-called Kondo effect, which describes an enhanced inelastic scattering of a cloud of conduction electrons "condensed" around magnetic moments that are localized on impurity atoms [3.75, 76]. The latter experience a temperature-dependent screening by the conduction electrons of the host lattice. As a result the resistivity may not approach a constant value ρ_0 at low temperatures but may rise again with

Table 3.3. Change $\Delta\rho_{nm}$ of the electrical resistance of Cu if the given non-magnetic elements with valence difference ΔZ compared to Cu are introduced as impurities, see (3.42)

Impurity	As	Si	Ge	Ga	Mg	Zn	Cd	Ag
ΔZ	4	3	3	2	1	1	1	0
$\Delta\rho_{nm}$ [n$\Omega\cdot$cm/at.ppm]	0.60	0.40	0.38	0.14	0.065	0.03	0.02	0.014

Table 3.4. Change $\Delta\rho_m$ of the electrical resistance of Cu at 1 K if the given magnetic elements are introduced as impurities

Impurity	Ti	V	Cr	Fe	Co	Ni
$\Delta\rho_m$ [nΩ·cm/at.ppm]	1.0	1.7	2.0	1.6	0.6	0.1

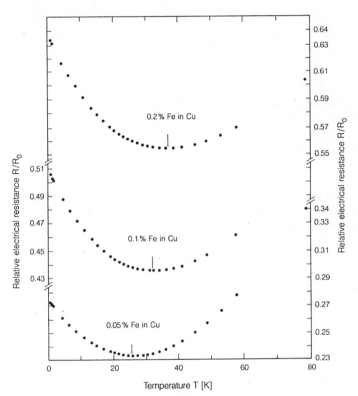

Fig.3.22. Resistance minima of various dilute alloys of Fe in Cu. R_0 is the resistivity at 0 °C. The position of the minimum depends on the concentration of iron [3.77]

decreasing T after passing through a minimum (Fig.3.22). It is then given by

$$\rho = \rho_0 - \rho_K \ln(T) \tag{3.43}$$

where ρ_K denotes the Kondo resistivity.

Because of the importance of copper and of other noble and platinum metals for making high-conductivity thermal joints (or for thermometry purposes; see Chap.12), I shall discuss a process by which magnetic impuri-

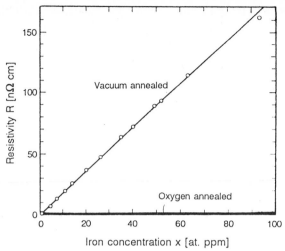

Fig.3.23. Resistivity of *Cu*-Fe at 4 K, as a function of Fe impurity concentration, annealed in vacuum and in an O_2 atmosphere (92 hours; about 10^{-6} bar air) [3.78]

ties can be "passivated" in Cu, Ag, Au, Pt, Pd, Rh and possibly some other metals as well, by oxidizing the less noble metal impurities, resulting in a dramatic increase of the low temperature conductivities. The following discussion applies to the "passivation" of the magnetic scattering of iron in copper [3.78-81] (for Ag, see [3.82]).

The typical residual resistivity ratio of a piece of copper which one can buy from a shop is in the range of 50 to 100. Heating the copper to a temperature of 400÷500°C anneals structural lattice defects, and the residual resistivity ratio usually increases to a value of 300 to 400. A further increase is only possible by passivation of magnetic impurities, in particular by oxidation of iron. The less noble impurities are oxidized by heat treatment of the Cu specimen at a temperature of 900÷1000°C in an atmosphere of oxygen or air at about 10^{-4} mbar (the time required for this treatment depends mainly on the thickness of the Cu sample). This oxidation and passivation is a two-step process. In the first step Fe is oxidized to FeO by oxygen diffusing through the Cu matrix. FeO is stable whereas copper oxide is unstable at these temperatures. The iron oxides attract more FeO and O and create small (0.1 μm) Fe_3O_4 clusters, reducing the number of magnetic scattering centres. These clusters are magnetically ordered; the conduction electrons do not suffer spin-flip scattering at the fixed iron moments any more. In this sense, the iron moments are magnetically inactive for the scattering of conduction electrons of the host lattice. Thus, although the Cu is not purer after oxygen annealing, the impurities are much less effective as scattering centres (Fig.3.23).

Another very effective purification of Cu from Fe reported in the literature is an electrolytic process starting from a Cu sulphate solution, followed by a wet-hydrogen treatment to remove non-magnetic impurities [3.83]. The residual hydrogen has then to be "pumped out" by heating the

62

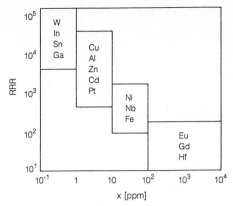

Fig.3.24. Typical values of the residual resistivity ratio (RRR) of various metals as a function of typical impurity concentrations with which they are available [3.85]

Cu in vacuum at around 1000° C. The resulting increased conductivity corresponds to a residual resistivity ratio of at least 1000 and in extreme cases up to several 10000, at which point dislocation scattering of the conduction electrons dominates.

Of course, it is an advantage if the starting copper already contains oxygen; oxygen-free high-conductivity (OFHC) Cu is often not well-suited for the production of high-conductivity copper needed for low-temperature experiments. – A survey on the transport properties of pure metals in the defect scattering limited range and a compilation of the smallest residual resistivities which have been reported in the literature for all metals except the rare earths can be found in [3.84]. Figure 3.24 gives typical values of the residual resistivity ratio which one can attain in pure metals as a function of the impurity concentration.

Comprehensive compilations of data on the thermal conductivity of solids can be found in [3.37, 38, 53-56].

4. Thermal Contact and Thermal Isolation

In any low-temperature apparatus it is necessary to couple some parts thermally very well whereas other parts have to be well isolated from each other and, in particular, from ambient temperature. The transfer of "heat" (or better "cold") and the thermal isolation are essential considerations when designing a low-temperature apparatus. These problems become progressively more acute at lower temperatures, and they will be discussed in this chapter. A general treatment of the thermal conductivity of materials is given in Sect.3.3. Besides learning how to take advantage of the very different thermal conductivities of various materials, we have to discuss how to design an apparatus to achieve the desired goals. For example, there are situations, as in low-temperature calorimetry, where two substances have to be in good thermal contact and then have to be very well thermally isolated from each other for the remainder of the experiment. For this purpose we need a thermal switch and I shall place special emphasis on the discussion of superconducting heat switches which dominate the temperature range below 1 K. One of the severest problems in low-temperature technology is the thermal boundary resistance between different materials. This is a particularly severe problem if good thermal contact between liquid helium and a solid is required as it will be discussed in the final sections of the present chapter.

The nuisance heat transfer by conduction and radiation will be considered at the beginning of the next chapter. The various heat sources will be treated in Sect.10.5, in connection with refrigeration to extremely low temperatures, where they can be particularly detrimental.

4.1 Selection of the Material with the Appropriate Cryogenic Thermal Conductivity

The low-temperature thermal conductivity of different materials can differ by many orders of magnitude and, fortunately, the thermal conductivity of the same material can even be varied by a great amount just by changing the number of defects or impurities in it (Fig.3.16). Hence one has to be careful in selecting the right material for a low-temperature apparatus. The low-temperature thermal conductivities of various materials commonly in use in low-temperature equipment are exhibited in Figs.3.16-21 and are listed in Table 3.2.

For *good thermal conductivity* the right choices are Cu (but: soft; nuclear specific heat at T < 0.1 K (Sect.3.1.6 and Fig.3.11), Ag (but: soft; expensive) or Al (but: soft, superconducting below 1K; soldering only possible in an elaborate process, see Sect.4.2.2). The highest practical conductivities of these metals are $\kappa \sim 10\,T$ [W/K·cm] if they are very pure; more typical is $\kappa \sim T$ [W/K·cm].

For *thermal isolation* the right choices are either plastics (Teflon, Nylon, Vespel, PMMA, etc.), graphite (careful, there exists a wide variety), Al_2O_3, or thin-walled tubing from stainless steel (but: soldering or silver brazing only with aggressive flux, which should be washed off very thoroughly; better is welding) or from $Cu_{0.7}Ni_{0.3}$ (easy to solder). However, the last two can be slightly magnetic at low temperatures and can interfere with sensitive magnetic experiments. In general, glasses or materials composed of small crystallites (for phonon scattering) and containing a lot of defects and impurities (for electron scattering) are good thermal insulators. For example, the thermal conductivity of quartz glass at 1 K is only about 1% of that of crystalline quartz at the same temperature. The lowest thermal conductivity, $\kappa \simeq 5 \cdot 10^{-6}\,T^{1.8}$ [W/Kcm] has been observed for AGOT nuclear graphite (Figs.3.18,20).

If other properties do not matter too much, aluminium alloys or brass should be used because of their relatively low prices and, above all, because they can be easily machined. If tubes are used which are filled with liquid ^{3}He, ^{4}He or an isotopic helium mixture, then the conductivity of the helium - which may be rather large (Sects.2.3.4,6 and Figs.2.11,16,17) - usually dominates. The effect can be reduced by using capillaries with a small diameter to reduce the mean free path of the liquid's atoms.

In each low-temperature apparatus one needs *wires* to carry signals from room temperature to the low-temperature part, and back. For low-current leads thin Constantan ($\rho_{300K} = 52.5\,\mu\Omega\cdot$cm, $\rho_{4K} = 44\,\mu\Omega\cdot$cm) or Manganin ($\rho_{300K} = 48\,\mu\Omega\cdot$cm, $\rho_{4K} = 43\,\mu\Omega\cdot$cm) wires should be used because of their low thermal conductivity and the small temperature dependence of their electrical resistivity. However, one has to take into account the increase of their electrical resistance and of their specific heat due to magnetic contributions at T < 1 K (Fig.3.9). This effect is smaller for PtW which has become a favorite heater wire for very-low-temperature applications; here the increase in specific heat due to a minute amount of magnetic impurities starts only below 0.1 K (Fig.3.9). If large electrical currents - for example, for superconducting magnets - have to be carried to the low-temperature part, the advantage gained by using a good conductor and a large wire diameter to reduce Joule heating, and the disadvantage of the then increased thermal conductivity have to be carefully considered. Often one may end up using Cu wires. Of course, then a proper heat sinking of the wires at various places on their way to low temperatures is of even greater importance. The optimum dimensions of leads carrying large currents into a cryostat were discussed in [4.1-6] (see also Sect.13.4). At T < 1 K the use of superconducting wires with their vanishing thermal conductivity for T → 0

(Sects. 3.3.4, 4.2.2) is the right choice. Often it is adequate just to cover a Manganin or Constantan wire with a thin layer of superconducting solder ($T_c \simeq 7K$, see below) to have a lead with low thermal conductivity but zero electrical resistance. At $T < 0.1$ K one can use mono-filamentary NbTi without Cu or even without a CuNi matrix if the lowest possible thermal conductivity is required. In extreme cases the fine filaments of multifilament superconducting wires can be used, but soft soldering to these wires is not possible, so spot-welding or squeeze contacts are necessary [4.6, 7]; these techniques require some practice before they can be applied reliably. If the joint does not have to be superconducting then one can remove the Cu coating with concentrated HNO_3 except at the ends of the wire where the solder joints have to be made. An even better method is to coat the superconducting wire electrolytically with a layer of Cu (use 1ℓ H_2O with at least 200g $CuSO_4$, 27cm^3 H_2SO_4, and a current density of about 40 mA/mm^2 between NbTi cathode and Cu anode). The same electrolytic process can be applied to cover stainless-steel tubing with a Cu layer to make the subsequent soldering easier.

Wires for mesurements of small signals have to be twisted pairwise on their way in the cryostat, rigidly fixed and well shielded to keep pick-up signals low (Sect. 12.5). The design of coaxial cryogenic cables and the proper heat-sinking of leads will be discussed in Sect. 13.3.

4.2 Heat Switches

4.2.1 Gaseous and Mechanical Heat Switches

The simplest way to thermally connect and disconnect various parts of a low-temperature apparatus is to use a gas (at such a pressure that it does not condense at the temperatures involved) for thermal coupling and then remove it by pumping. This method is usually employed in precooling the inner parts of a cryostat to LN_2 or LHe temperatures (Chap. 5). A gas pressure of 10^{-4} bar is sufficient for an adequate heat transfer. But usually many hours of pumping are then required to reduce the gas pressure for sufficient thermal isolation. The temperature at every place in the cryostat has to be above the condensation temperature of the gas so that efficient pumping is possible. If the exchange gas has not been pumped to a low enough pressure, time-dependent heat leaks due to a continuing desorption and condensation of the remaining gas at the coldest surfaces may result (Sect. 10.5.3).

For ^{4}He, the superfluid film contributes to the heat transfer, too. For thermal isolation, ^{4}He has to be pumped very well to make sure that there is not enough of it left to form an unsaturated superfluid film if $T \leq 2.2$ K (Sect. 2.3.5). The advantage of H_2 as an exchange gas is the fact that it can be totally condensed out ("cryo-pumping") when liquid helium is transferred into the cryostat, so that time consuming pumping can be avoided. However, one has to remember that the remaining H_2 molecules may undergo ortho-para conversion, giving rise to substantial heating (Sect.2.2). As a conclusion, [3]He with its high vapour pressure, absence of exothermic reaction, and absence of superfluidity in the Kelvin temperature range, is the safest exchance gas for thermal contact. A heat swith using liquid [3]He at T < 0.1 K and in magnetic fields up to 10 T has recently been described in [4.8].

For many purposes, for example for calorimetry at T > 1 K, a mechanical heat switch is adequate. Thermal contact is made by metallic contacts pressed together mechanically. Here the "open" state really is open, with no residual heat flow. Conductances of 1 mW/K in the Kelvin range are typical for the closed state (Sect.4.3.1). The main disadvantages of these switches are the large forces (typically 100 N) necessary to make adequate thermal contact and the heat generated when the contact is broken (typically $0.1 \div 1$ μJ/N). I will not discuss these switches in more detail here because they are being used less and less these days. Readers interested in mechanical thermal switches should consult the literature [4.1, 9-14].

4.2.2 Superconducting Heat Switches

In Sect.3.3.4 we concluded that the thermal conductivity κ_s of a metal in the superconducting state can become very small because the number of electrons decreases exponentially with temperature; it can be orders of magnitude smaller than the thermal conductivity κ_n of the same material in the normal state (Fig.4.1). Because some metals can easily be switched from the superconducting to the normal state by applying a magnetic field, we can build a "superconducting heat switch" as already mentioned in Sect. 3.3.4. Superconducting heat switches are the most common thermal switches at temperatures below about 1 K. Their advantages are that the heat flow in the open state is small, that they are very easy to switch, and that the switching ratio κ_n/κ_s can be very large; but for that we need $T \leq T_c/10$, which often means T << 1 K (Fig.4.2). Very little heat is generated in the switching process if the design ensures that eddy-current heating (Sect. 10.5.2) is small when the switching magnetic field is changing.

The quality of a superconducting heat switch is expressed by its switching ratio κ_n/κ_s. Here $\kappa_n \propto T$ whereas $\kappa_s \propto T\exp(-\Delta E/k_B T)$ for $T > 0.1 T_c$ (from the remaining unpaired electrons) and $\kappa_s \propto (T/\theta_D)^3$ at $T < 0.1 T_c$ (from the now dominating phonons), see Sect.3.3.4. Hence one has the switching ratio

$$\kappa_n/\kappa_s = aT^{-2} \quad \text{for} \quad T < 0.1 T_c , \tag{4.1}$$

with a constant a of 10^2 to 10^3 for a properly designed switch (but see the comment at the end of this section).

Various designs of superconducting heat switches made from a variety of metals have been described in the literature [4.9, 15-24]. High-purity metals are used for a superconducting heat switch in order to make κ_n large. One should use thin foils or wires (typically 0.1 mm) so that the mean free path of phonons - which is given by the sample dimensions for pure

67

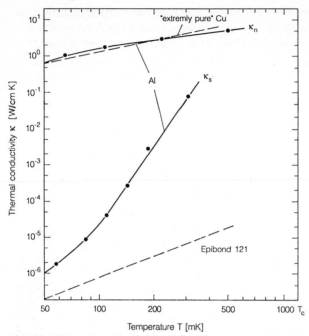

Fig.4.1. Thermal conductivity κ of Al in the normal-conducting state (compared to κ of Cu) and in the superconducting state (compared to κ of the dielectric Epibond 121) at $T > 50$ mK [4.15]

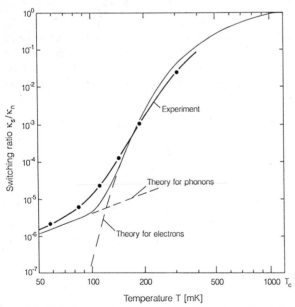

Fig.4.2. Switching ratio κ_s / κ_n of the thermal conductivity of Al compared to theoretical predictions [4.15]

materials - and therefore κ_{ph} as well as eddy current heating during the field change become small. If $T < T_c/10$ and if we have high purity thin foils of a superconductor (so that phonons are only scattered at boundaries), then ideally

$$\kappa_n/\kappa_s \simeq 0.05(\theta/T)^2 \, , \tag{4.2}$$

for Al as an example [4.15].

The temperature dependence of the phonon conductivity (3.25) of a metal in the superconducting state and of the switching ratio (4.1,2) should be used with caution. Recent measurements [4.24] of the thermal conductivity of massive pieces of superconducting Al (RRR $\geq$ 5000) have shown that $\kappa_{ph} \propto T^2$ at $10\,\mathrm{mK} \leq T \leq 80\,\mathrm{mK}$ (Fig.4.3). Deviation from $\kappa_{ph} \propto T^3$ were reported earlier for Al, Nb and Ta [4.25, 26]. These deviations may be attributed to a scattering of phonons at dislocations (3.26) [4.27, 28]. The results for Al are particularly disturbing because the known properties of Al ($T_c = 1.18\,\mathrm{K}$) indicate that for a superconducting heat switch it is superior to other candidates like Sn, In, Zn or Pb at $T \leq 0.1$ K. A switch from the latter materials in the form of wires or foils can be easily constructed because of their low melting temperatures and good soldering properties. However, Al usually has a higher switching ratio (Fig.4.2) because of its high κ_n and large Debye temperature ($\theta_D = 400\,\mathrm{K}$), which makes κ_{ph} small. Aluminium is also easily available in very high purity (5N or 6N; RRR > 1000), has a convenient critical field (10.5 mT), good durability and is easy to handle. Of course, there is a serious contact problem due to the tenacious surface oxide on aluminium; various ways of solving this problem have been described in the literature. For a successful but elaborate electroplating process see [4.6, 15], and procedures for welding Al to Cu or Ag have been described in [4.19-21]. In our laboratory recently contact resistances of $\leq$0.1 $\mu\Omega$ were achieved at 4.2 K by screwing well annealed Ag screws into Al threads. The thread diameter had to be at least 6 mm in order for the nec-

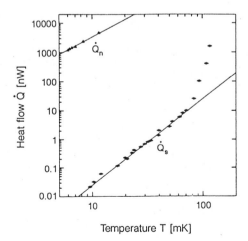

Fig.4.3. Heat flow $\dot{Q}$ across an Al heat switch in the normal (▲) and superconducting (•) states. The lines correspond to $\dot{Q}_n \propto T^{-2}$ and $\dot{Q}_s \propto T^{-3}$. The thermal conductivity is $\kappa \propto (\dot{Q}T)^{-1}$, resulting in $\kappa_n \propto T$ and $\kappa_s \propto T^2$ at $T < 80$ mK [4.24]

69

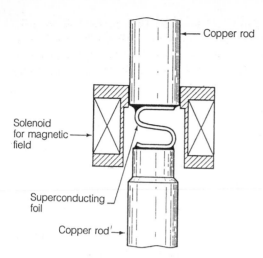

Fig.4.4. Typical assembly of a superconducting heat switch with the superconducting foil partly perpendicular to the magnetic field produced by the solenoid, thus avoiding magnetic flux lines being able to penetrate the switching foil along its entire length

essary forces to be applied to the soft, annealed metals. Because of its larger thermal expansion coefficient the Al will shrink onto the Ag in the cooldown process (Fig.3.14). Of course, for such a design high-temperature annealing does not help. The metals were chemically cleaned (HCl for Ag; $22g/\ell$ Na_3PO_4+$22g/\ell$ Na_2CO_3 at $T \geq 75°$ C, 60s), and annealed ($5 \cdot 10^{-5}$ mbar; 5h; 800° C for Ag, 500° C for Al). The best results for cold welding of Al to Cu are $\rho < 1$ $\mu\Omega$ and RRR ≥ 150 for a pressure of $P \geq 100$ N/mm^2 applied at 500° C.

Often the behavior of a superconducting heat switch is deteriorated by frozen-in magnetic flux from the switching field, which may cause parts of the metal to remain in the normal state when the field is removed. This problem can be avoided by orientation of at least part of the metal perpendicular to the field (Fig.4.4), so that the normal cores of trapped flux lines will not short-circuit the switch material, and/or by saw-tooth-like cycling of the field during its reduction. If a superconducting heat switch is used in a magnetic refrigerator (Chaps.9,10), then in many cases a superconducting Nb shield should be placed around it to shield the switch from the changing fringe field of the demagnetization solenoid. The shape of the switch should be such that eddy current heating (10.28) produced while the switching field is changing will not cause heating effects, and that closed superconducting rings trapping flux are avoided (put slits perpendicular to the field into bulk Al) [4.24].

4.3 Thermal Boundary Resistance

4.3.1 Boundary Resistance Between Metals

To achieve thermal equilibrium in a system becomes increasingly more difficult when the temperature is lowered, not only beause the thermal conductivity of materials decreases with decreasing temperature but also be-

70

cause the thermal boundary resistance at the interface between two materials becomes increasingly important. If we have two different materials in contact and heat $\dot{Q}$ has to flow from one material to the other, for example in a cooling process, there will be a temperature step at the boundary between them. This temperature step is given by

$$\Delta T = R_K \dot{Q} , \qquad (4.3)$$

where R_K is the thermal boundary resistance, or Kapitza resistance, named after the Russian physicist P. Kapitza who discovered this thermal boundary resistance in 1941 for the case of liquid helium in contact with solids. This is still a problem which is not fully understood, at least for very low temperatures (Sect.4.3.2). The boundary resistances between several materials are shown in Fig. 4.5.

Between the metals the actual contact area often is only about 10^{-6} of the nominal contact area due to the microscopic irregularities of the opposing surfaces. This actual area can be considerably increased by the application of pressure close to the yielding stress of the materials. The thermal conductance across the boundary between the two metals is proportional to the applied force used to press them together. The disadvantage of this procedure is a deformation of the lattice with a reduction in bulk conductivity. This problem is reduced by diffusion-welding joining surfaces because it uses high temperatures ($0.6T_{melting}$, for example) annealing lattice defects. The boundary resistance can be kept reasonably small, if the surfaces are clean, possibly gold-plated, and pressed together with a high force. We should then have an overlap of the electronic wave functions of the two metals, giving a good electric and thermal flow between them.

The heat transfer across the contact between two metals - similar or dissimilar - is a common problem in cryogenics. No unique solution can be found in the literature, even though it is full of recipes [4.1,9,29]. In Sect.3.2 I mentioned how important it is to correctly join two dissimilar materials, if good thermal contact is the goal. My own experience has shown that a well designed demountable press contact between two gold plated or well polished, clean metals can have a thermal resistance almost as small as a bulk, continuous part [4.15]. In order to achieve this, the surfaces have to be well prepared and strong enough bolts, made, for example, from hardened BeCu, have to be used. These are tightened in a controlled way until they almost yield, which supplies sufficient force for what is almost a cold weld to be produced between the two parts. This can rip up oxide layers and can then make an intimate metallic contact. Sometimes it helps if the joining surfaces are sprinkled with a fine Ag powder. As mentioned in Sect.3.2, a washer with a very small expansion coefficient (e.g., W or Mo) improves the contact after cool-down by taking advantage of the differential thermal contractions. Rather good results have also been obtained with a joint of two tapered metals. Recently, extremely small contact resistances of 10 nΩ at 4.2 K between gold-plated Cu discs bolted together with 4 mm stainless-steel screws with a tightening torque of at least 4 Nm have

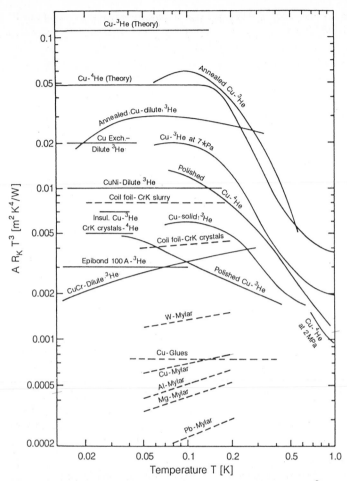

Fig.4.5. Thermal boundary resistance R_K multiplied by AT^3 between liquid helium and various solids, and also between various metals and various dielectrics [4.9]. (This book provides references to the original literature); for more recent helium data see Fig.4.9

been reported [4.29] (more typical, still good values are $0.1\,\mu\Omega$ at 4K). The measured contact resistance was inversely proportional to the tightening torque on the screw.

The mechanical and electrical contact between two metals often is made by soldering them together. Unfortunately, most solders, in particular soft solders, become superconducting at low temperature (Table 4.1) and eventually behave like a dielectric with regard to thermal conductivity [4.1, 30-35] (Fig.4.1); then one could just as well use a dielectric glue! Of course, this problem can be avoided if the solder joint can be exposed to a magnetic field high enough to suppress the superconducting state. In some cases the low superconducting thermal conductivity may not reappear even after removal of the field because magnetic flux may be trapped in the solder,

Table 4.1. Melting temperatures T_m and superconducting transition temperatures T_c of some solders [4.1, 30-35]

Solder	T_m [°C]	T_c [K]
12÷14%Sn, 25÷27%Pb, 50% Bi		
10÷13% Cd (Wood's metal)	70	8÷9
50÷52% In, 50÷48% Sn	120	7.1÷7.5
30÷60% Sn, 70÷40% Pb	257÷183	7.1÷7.8
97% Sn, 3% Ag	240	3.7
95.5% Sn, 3.5% Ag, 1% Cd	220	3.05
26% Sn, 54% Bi, 20% Cd	103	3.7
43% Sn, 57% Bi	140	2.25
82.5% Cd, 17.5% Zn	265	1÷1.6
60% Bi, 40% Cd		<0.8
40% Ag, 19% Cu, 20%Cd, 21% Zn	610	<0.064
56% Ag, 22% Cu, 17% Zn, 5% Sn	650	<0.064
60% Ag, 30% Cu, 10% Sn	(700)	<0.057
50% Ag, 15.5% Cu, 16.5% Sn, 18% Cd	630	<0.057
80% Au, 20% Sn	280	<0.01

keeping enough of it in the normal state to provide good thermal contact. The transition temperatures to the superconducting state and melting temperatures of various solder alloys are given in Table 4.1. In some cases solder joints with non-superconducting Bi may be appropriate [4.34]. These problems can be avoided by welding or using non-superconducting hard solders, but sometimes the alloy that is produced leads to a rather high thermal resistance at the interface between the two connected metals.

4.3.2 Boundary Resistance Between Liquid Helium and Solids

a) Acoustic Mismatch

Between dielectrics, for example a non-magnetic dielectric in contact with liquid or solid helium, the transfer of energy can only occur via phonon transmission. We then have to match the acoustic properties of the two materials to optimize the transmission of phonons from one material to the other. The temperature step ΔT at the interface arises from the acoustic mismatch [4.9, 36-38] of the two materials, which I will treat in analogy to optics. In the following I will consider the case of transferring heat from liquid helium to another body with which it is in contact, because this is the most important case in low-temperature physics. For helium/solid interfaces the situation is particularly grave because acoustic impedances are $\rho_s v_s \sim 10^6$ g/(cm$^2 \cdot$s) for solids but $\rho_h v_h \sim 10^3$ g/(cm$^2 \cdot$s) for liquid helium. The importance of this heat transfer for low-temperature physics arises first of all from the fact that, except for magnetic refrigeration (Chaps. 9, 10), all low-temperature refrigeration methods use helium as the working substance (Chaps. 5-8). Therefore the cold produced by changing the thermodynamic state of helium has to be transferred to solid bodies to be useful. Secondly, helium itself is a material of high scientific interest and in order to refrigerate it to the lowest possible temperatures by magnetic refrigeration, cold has to be transferred to it from a solid body, and its temperature has to be measured by a thermometer in intimate thermal contact with it. As a result, the thermal boundary resistance or energy transfer between liquid helium and solids is a matter of concern in the majority of low-temperature experiments, and it is a very interesting piece of physics in its own right.

If the velocity of phonons in helium is v_h and that in the solid is v_s, we have Snell's law

$$\sin\alpha_h / \sin\alpha_s = v_h/v_s \tag{4.4}$$

for the angles α at which the phonons cross the boundary. Because $v_h \sim 200$ m/s whereas $v_s \sim 5000$ m/s for metals, the critical angle of incidence at which phonons from helium may enter the solid is very small,

$$\alpha_{crit} = \arcsin(v_h/v_s) \sim 3° \ . \tag{4.5}$$

The fraction of phonons hitting the interface that fall into the critical cone is

$$f = \frac{1}{2}\left(\frac{v_h}{v_s}\right)^2 \approx 10^{-3} \ . \tag{4.6}$$

However, because of the difference in acoustic impedance $Z = \rho v$, not even all of these phonons are transmitted. The energy transmission coefficient is given by (with $Z_s \gg Z_h$)

$$t = \frac{4Z_h Z_s}{(Z_h + Z_s)^2} \simeq \frac{4\rho_h v_h}{\rho_s v_s} \simeq 2\cdot10^{-3} \ . \tag{4.7}$$

Therefore only a fraction

$$f\cdot t = 2\frac{\rho_h v_h^3}{\rho_s v_s^3} < 10^{-5} \tag{4.8}$$

of the phonons will enter the solid; hence the two bodies are rather well isolated from each other. The combination of acoustic mismatch and small critical angle severely limits the energy exchange between helium and other materials.

The transmitted energy flux of phonons hitting the contact area A per unit time is given by

74

$$\frac{\dot{Q}}{A} = \frac{\pi^2 k_B{}^4 T^4 \rho_h v_h}{30 \hbar^3 \rho_s v_s{}^3} . \qquad (4.9)$$

The boundary resistance is then (for $\Delta T \ll T$)

$$R_K = \Delta T / \dot{Q} = dT/d\dot{Q} = \frac{15 \hbar^3 \rho_s v_s{}^3}{2\pi^2 k_B{}^4 T^3 A \rho_h v_h} . \qquad (4.10)$$

In all the above equations, v_s is the transverse sound velocity.

A more rigorous consideration of the problem introduces corrections of order 2 depending on the materials properties. But the essential result is $R_K \propto (AT^3)^{-1}$; the boundary resistance increases strongly with decreasing temperature. This "acoustic mismatch prediction" is in reasonable agreement with most experimental data at $0.01\,K < T < 0.2\,K$ with typical values of $A R_K T^3 \simeq 10^{-2}\ m^2 K^4/W$ for liquid and solid helium in contact with metals, but deviates considerably both in the Kelvin temperature range (Figs. 4.5, 6) and at $T < 10$ mK (see next section). Another unexplained result is the observation that R_K seems to be about the same for ^{3}He and ^{4}He in the liquid as well as in the solid state at $T \sim 1$ K (Fig. 4.6). Without question, the physics of the anomalously good thermal coupling at $T \geq 1$ K is still not understood, even though very detailed frequency-, angle-, and surface-condition-dependent studies have been performed [4.38-42] employing even modern high-frequency spectroscopic techniques [4.43]. The above results apply to annealed, bulk, and clean metal surfaces. Of course, the experimental results depend strongly on the surface condition of the body in con-

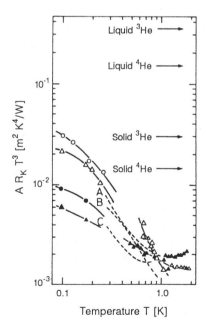

Fig. 4.6. Thermal boundary resistance R_K multiplied by AT^3 between ^{3}He or ^{4}He and copper as a function of temperature. (○): liquid ^{3}He; (●): solid ^{3}He; (△): liquid ^{4}He; (▲): solid ^{4}He. The dashed curves A, B and C are for liquid ^{3}He, liquid ^{4}He and solid ^{3}He, respectively. The arrows at the right indicate the prediction from the acoustic mismatch theory (4.10) for an ideal Cu surface [4.38], where references to the original work are given

tact with helium, in particular surface roughness or mechanical damage of the surface. It can easily be changed by an order of magnitude, for example, for ^{3}He-Cu interfaces from $AR_K T^3 = 4 \cdot 10^{-3}$ to $4 \cdot 10^{-2}$ m^{2}K^4/W at 10mK $\leq$ T $\leq$ 100mK for different surface treatments (sandblasting, machining) [4.38-42] (Figs.4.5,6). A rigorous treatment of the boundary resistance due to acoustic mismatch has to take into account the structure and properties of the solid and of helium near to the interface, and also the excitations there. Surface excitations as well as a deviation from crystalline structure and the compression of helium resulting from the van der Waals attraction of the solid may influence the transmission coefficent for phonons.

The thermal boundary resistance $R_K \propto 1/(AT^3)$ is the most severe obstacle for establishing thermal contact between helium and other substances at T < 1 K. The common approach to improving this contact is by increasing the contact area A . This is mostly done by using heat exchangers made from sintered metal powders; this will be discussed in Sect.13.6. In addition, experiments reveal that the boundary conductance is considerably improved at T < 20 mK, as compared to the predictions of the acoustic mismatch prediction; this will be discussed in the next subsections.

b) Acoustic Coupling Between Liquid Helium and Metal Sinters

In the preceding subsection we saw that the mechanism of energy transfer across a metal-to-liquid interface is not completely understood; it is even less so if the metal is a sinter. Neither the electrons nor the single-particle helium excitations can cross the interface. The transfer has to be mediated by phonons and - in the case of ^{3}He - possibly by a magnetic coupling (see next section). As shown in the preceding section, the phonon coupling varies as T^3 and becomes very weak at low temperatures. One can compensate for this weakening by increasing the contact area A, i.e., by using metal sinters. Those used have had surface areas of up to a few 100 m^2 (Sect.13.6). But this complicates the understanding even more because the vibrational modes of a sinter made of submicrometer particles will differ from the corresponding modes of the bulk metal. The lowest vibrational frequency ν for bulk phonons in a particle of diameter d is of order $(0.1 \div 1)v_s/d$, where v_s is the velocity of sound in the particle [4.38, 44-47]. This corresponds to several gigahertz or T $\sim$ hν/3k$_B$ $\sim$ 10 mK for a particle of d = 1 μm. At higher frequencies the particle and its Kapitza resistance will behave bulk-like, whereas at lower frequencies the latter would increase exponentially. However, when metal particles are sintered they are connected by narrow elastic bridges (Sect.13.6). This sponge with its elastic, open structure can have low-frequency continuum modes with a density of states which may be two orders of magnitude larger than the corresponding bulk density of phonon modes at T $\sim$ 10 mK [4.44-47]. These soft modes are assumed to couple well to the helium phonon modes with their small velocity of sound, as shown for a sinter of 1 μm Ag powder and liquid ^{3}He in Fig.4.7. As a further result, the boundary resistance will show a temperature dependence which is weaker than T^{-3} below a temperature where the

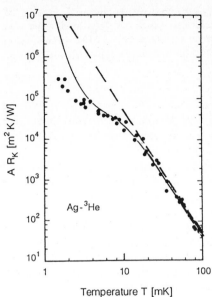

Fig.4.7. Thermal boundary resistance R_K multiplied by the surface area A between liquid ^{3}He and a sinter of Ag particles. Experimental data from [4.48]. The dashed line represents the prediction of the acoustic mismatch theory (4.10) for bulk Ag. The full curve shows the prediction for a coupling of (zero) sound modes of liquid ^{3}He to soft modes with a characteristic energy of $15\,\text{mK} \cdot k_B$ of the Ag sinter [4.38]

dominant phonon wavelength becomes comparable to the size of the sinter particles; in [4.44] this dependence was found to be $R_K \propto T^{-1}$. *Nakayama* [4.38], in particular, has reviewed the heat transfer due to (zero) sound in liquid ^{3}He from ^{3}He to a metal sinter, the most important contact medium in the problem of energy transfer to liquid helium. But the situation is now more complicated than one would expect just from the change of the vibrational modes. The mean free paths of the electrons (whose influence on R_K is not understood) and phonons are limited by the sinter grain size and the mean free paths of the ^{3}He particles and ^{3}He phonons are limited by the open dimensions of the sinter. The thermal resistance between excitations *in* the solid and/or *within* liquid helium can then become comparable to or even larger than the thermal boundary resistance at T < 10 mK, and it certainly has to be taken into account when the thermal resistances inside of the liquid helium and/or inside of the metal sinter are considered. These effects have not yet been fully investigated.

c) Magnetic Coupling Between Liquid ^{3}He and Solids Containing Magnetic Moments

If the thermal coupling between liquid helium and solids were limited to phonon transfer or if the T^{-3} dependence of R_K continued to low millikelvin temperatures, it would require extremely large surface areas to refrigerate liquid ^{3}He into its superfluid states. However, in the middle of the 1960s a completely unexpected behaviour of the thermal boundary resistance between liquid ^{3}He and the paramangetic salt CMN (Sect.9.3) was reported [4.49-53]. Whereas above about 20 mK the data were in reasonable agreement with the acoustic mismatch theory, at $2\,\text{mK} \leq T \leq 20\,\text{mK}$ the

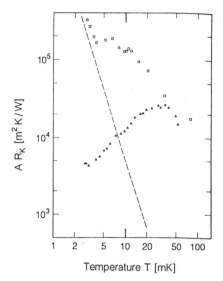

Fig.4.8. Thermal boundary resistance R_K multiplied by the surface area A between the paramagnetic salt CMN (Sect.9.3) and ^{3}He (▲) and a 6% ^{3}He-^{4}He mixture (□). The dashed line indicates the prediction of the acoustic mismatch theory, (4.10) [4.53]

thermal resistance between ^{3}He and powdered CMN was strongly reduced and *decreased* according to $R_K \propto T$ (Fig.4.8). This result has inspired much research and provided the means of coupling ^{3}He well and therefore cooling it into the low millikelvin temperature range. Even though details of this enhanced thermal coupling are still not quite understood theoretically there is no doubt that a surface magnetic interaction between the nuclear magnetic moments of ^{3}He and electronic moments in the solid in contact with ^{3}He plays an essential part and short-circuits the acoustic mismatch [4.38,54,55]. The most convincing support for this interpretation comes from the observation that the enhanced coupling dramatically decreases if the solid surface is "plated" by a layer of (non-magnetic) ^{4}He [4.50,52,53] (Fig.4.8). The ^{4}He atoms coat walls preferentially because - due to their smaller zero-point energy compared to ^{3}He - they sit deeper in the van der Walls potential exerted by the wall. This interpretation is also supported by theoretical treatment of the magnetic dipole-dipole coupling between ^{3}He nuclear spins in the liquid and electronic spins in CMN, leading to $R_K \propto T$ [4.38,54,55], but the theory contains a number of significant assumptions [4.37].

Later, qualitatively similar results - reasonable agreement with the acoustic mismatch theory in magnitude and temperature dependence at 20mK < T < 100mK, and an enhanced thermal coupling at lower temperatures - was found for liquid ^{3}He in contact with various metals, particularly ("dirty") sinters. However, now the temperature dependence is $R_K \propto T^{-1}$, with typical values of $AR_K T \sim$ several 10^2 to 10^3 m^2K^2/W for sintered Cu and Ag powders or metal foils containing magnetic impurities [4.48,56-61] (Figs.4.6,7,9). Strong support for the magnetic coupling explanation is the apparent absence of a contribution from the electron-phonon resistance in the metal and from the phonon-quasiparticle resistance

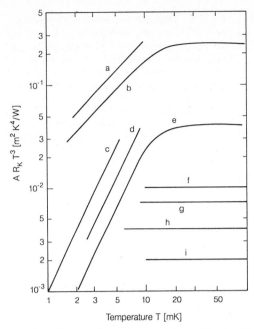

Fig.4.9. Thermal boundary resistance R_K (multiplied by AT^3) between liquid ^{3}He or a liquid 6.5% ^{3}He mixture and various solids as a function of temperature. The data are for (a) mixture to 400 Å Ag sinter ($25T^{-2}$); (b) mixture to 700 Å Ag sinter ($16T^{-2}$ at <10mK); (c) ^{3}He to 700 Å Ag sinter ($1000T^{-1}$); (d) ^{3}He to 400 Å Ag sinter ($470T^{-1}$); (e) ^{3}He to 1 μm Ag sinter ($200T^{-1}$ at <10mK); (f) mixture to CuNi ($10^{-2}T^{-3}$); (g) mixture to brass ($7 \cdot 10^{-3}T^{-3}$); (h) mixture to 7 μm thick Kapton foils ($4 \cdot 10^{-3}T^{-3}$); (i) mixture to Teflon tubing with 0.1 mm wall thickness ($2 \cdot 10^{-3}T^{-3}$); (the data in brackets are AR_K) [Ref.4.61b, this paper gives references to the original works]

in the liquid [4.38]; this indicates a direct ^{3}He spin-metal spin/electron coupling bypassing the phonons.

The possibility of changing the Fermi temperature T_F of liquid ^{3}He-^{4}He mixtures by changing their concentration (7.23a) offers an opportunity to gain more insight into the coupling between ^{3}He-^{4}He mixtures and solids. Indeed, for this combination, too, an enhanced coupling was found [4.60-65], but now with a dependence on T_F, with typical values $AR_K \sim 6T^{-2}T_F^{-1}$ m^{2}K/W at $T \le 20$ mK [4.38,64,65]. The dependence on the Fermi temperature T_F of the mixtures indicates the quantum and magnetic character of the coupling. For a saturated solution (Chap. 7) of a 6% ^{3}He-^{4}He mixture, values of $AR_K = (14\div35)T^{-2}$ m^{2}K/W have been reported [4.60-65].

These observations were far from understood when the first review article on the thermal boundary resistance at $T < 0.1$ K was written in 1979 [4.37]. Substantial experimental and theoretical effort in recent years enabled *Nakayama* to present a much more concise picture in his recent review article on the problem [4.38] (Fig.4.10). These two comprehensive reviews should be consulted for further details and, in particular, for ref-

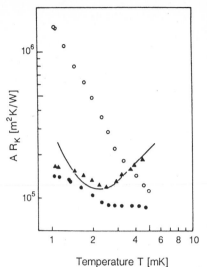

Fig.4.10. Thermal boundary resistance R_K multiplied by the surface area A between liquid ^{3}He and a sinter of Ag particles. The experimental data for zero magnetic field (•) and for a measurement in 0.385T (○) are from [4.66]. The field is assumed to suppress the magnetic contribution to R_K, leaving only the acoustic channel for heat transfer. Therefore the difference between the two sets of experimental data should give the magnetic contribution (▲) to R_K. The solid line represents the theoretical prediction for this magnetic contribution [4.38]

erences to other papers in the field. The situation still cannot be considered as understood and many more experiments on the thermal boundary resistance, particularly at T ≤ 20 mK, seem to be necessary. For example, there are conflicting results on the pressure and magnetic field dependence of R_K [4.66-68]. Furthermore, the influence of the changing structure of helium near to the substrate resulting from the van der Waals attraction (localization, compression, preferentially ^{4}He in the case of mixtures) is an interesting topic. Finally, the question of whether the magnetic coupling results from electronic magnetic moments in the metal or is due to absorbed impurity layers, particularly various paramagnetic oxides with localized moments [4.38], is of interest. The role of conduction electrons for R_K also remains to be more thoroughly investigated.

Even though much remains to be measured and understood, the Kapitza resistance problem can clearly be divided into three distinct temperature regimes:

a) Above 1 K: R_K is essentially the same for liquid and solid ^{3}He and ^{4}He; it is at least an order of magnitude smaller than predicted by the acoustic mismatch theory, and it is not understood.

b) At 20mK ≤ T ≤ 100mK: $R_K \propto T^{-3}$ and behaves as predicted by the acoustic mismatch theory if well characterized, clean, bulk metallic surfaces are used.

c) At T ≤ 10 mK: $R_K \propto T^{-2}$ or T^{-1} between liquid ^{3}He or helium mixtures and metals, and is again much smaller than predicted by the acoustic mismatch theory; here a magnetic dipole coupling between the ^{3}He nuclear moments and electronic moments in (or on) the solid together with a coupling of helium phonon modes to soft vibrational modes, if a sintered metal is used, seem to determine the energy flux. These effects have turned out to be extremely important for refrigeration in the low millikelvin and submillikelvin temperature ranges.

5. Helium-4 Cryostats

Here, and in the five chapters to follow, I will discuss the equipment needed for reaching and maintaining low temperatures, and start with cryostats for the Kelvin-temperature range in which the low temperatures are obtained by evaporating liquid helium [5.1-3]. An important aspect of our consideration will be keeping the evaporation rate of the cryoliquid as low as possible by optimizing the cool-down process and by minimizing the heat transferred from the warm surroundings to the cold parts of the equipment.

The main isolation of cold parts from warm parts is done by vacuum isolation. Therefore, cryotechnology always involves vacuum technology. A low-temperature physicist necessarily needs experience in vacuum physics: in the design of vacuum-tight equipment, in techniques of avoiding leaks, in the technologies of soldering, welding and gluing; or, if leaks occur, in ways of finding and fixing them. These technologies are very important because low-temperature equipment can experience extreme mechanical stresses due to the large temperature gradients and different thermal expansion coefficients of the various materials used in it.

Low-temperature experimentalists have to design and construct their equipment very carefully with a very high reliability because it is built and tested at room temperature, then closed, evacuated and cooled down. After having been cooled, defects may develop due to vacuum leaks resulting from thermal stresses, or because electrical leads may not have been properly connected and may open up or may short to ground after cool-down, etc. These defects cannot be removed at low temperature. Therefore the equipment has to be warmed up for repair. Even worse, there are defects which occur only at low temperatures and disappear again when the equipment has warmed up to room temperature. Often these defects cannot be easily located and time-consuming cross checks may be the only way to find out what went wrong and where. Therefore, careful design and careful construction is of utmost importance for low-temperature equipment.

In addition, we have to remember that cold surfaces adsorb gases. If the apparatus has a small leak to atmosphere, for example, air may leak in and will condense at helium-cooled surfaces. If the apparatus has been at low temperature for a long time, the cold surfaces may be covered by a large amount of air. During warm-up the condensed gases will desorb and a substantial pressure may build up in the "vacuum" space. Let me remind you that all containers which at some time will be filled with a cryogenic liquid either have to be able to withstand a rather high pressure or, better, must contain safety features so that following an accident, the pressure cannot rise to dangerous values. One should therefore have safety valves or bursting discs on the vacuum vessel as well as on the containers for the cryogenic liquids. For all these vessels certain safety regulations have to be followed, which in some countries are enforced by law.

5.1 Use of Liquid ^{4}He in Low-Temperature Equipment

Every refrigeration process to a temperature of 10 K or lower uses liquid helium in either the final or the pre-cooling stage. In the following I will stress some points that are important if the consumption of this expensive cryoliquid is to be minimized. For this optimization we have to distinguish between the cool-down and the running period of the experiment after cooling.

5.1.1 Cool-Down Period

The heat of evaporation for helium transforming from the liquid to the gaseous phase is about 2.6 kJ/ℓ at its normal boiling temperature of 4.2 K (Fig. 2.5). This is a rather small number compared to the enthalpy of helium gas between 4.2 K and 300 (77) K, which is about 200 (64) kJ/ℓ. When 1 W is applied, 1.4 ℓHe/h will evaporate if the heat of evaporation is used, but only 0.017 ℓHe/h if the enthalpy of the cold gas between 4.2 K and 300 K is used as well. As a result, it is very important to make use of the enthalpy of the cold helium gas after the liquid has undergone the transition to the gaseous state when cooling equipment, and the gas should leave the cryostat with a temperature as close as possible to room temperature. In addition, pre-cooling with liquid nitrogen from 300 to 77 K will save a large amount of liquid helium. Liquid N_2 has about 60 times the latent heat of evaporation of liquid helium, it is about an order of magnitude cheaper, and at 77 K most of the heat capacity of the materials to be refrigerated has been removed already. Table 5.1 lists how many litres of a cryoliquid we need to refrigerate 1 kg of aluminium, stainless steel or copper with liquid N_2 from

Table 5.1. Amount of cryoliquid [ℓ] necessary to refrigerate 1 kg of aluminium, stainless steel (SS) or copper if only the latent heat (latent heat plus enthalpy of the gas between its boiling point and room temperature) is used

Cryoliquid	Temperature change [K]	Al	SS	Cu
N_2	300 → 77	1.0 (0.63)	0.53 (0.33)	0.46 (0.28)
^{4}He	77 → 4.2	3.2 (0.20)	1.4 (0.10)	2.2 (0.16)
^{4}He	300 → 4.2	66 (1.6)	34 (0.8)	32 (0.8)

room temperature to 77 K, or with liquid He from room temperature to 4.2 K, or only from 77 to 4.2 K. In the table I distinguish between the two situations in which (a) only the heat of evaporation and (b) in addition the much larger enthalpies of the cold gases are used. The table demonstrates that it is clearly desirable to

- use liquid N_2 to first pre-cool the equipment from room temperature to 77 K, and only then use liquid helium for the lower temperatures, and/or
- make use of the enthalpy of the cold helium gas as much as possible to refrigerate the equipment.

Otherwise the experimentalist may waste more than two orders of magnitude of expensive liquid helium [5.2].

5.1.2 Running Phase of the Experiment

Now let us consider the situation where the experiment has reached a stationary state, which means that the equipment has reached the required low temperature and we can perform an experiment at this constant temperature. In this situation the heat transferred from external sources has to be compensated by the cooling power provided by the cryoliquid, which now mainly comes from the heat of evaporation. The cold gas can only be used for cooling, for example, the support structure of the experiment or the walls of the cryostat. Let us consider the main sources of heat for experiments in the Kelvin temperature range.

a) Heat Conduction

Heat conduction may be along leads used for performing measurements on the experiment or along the walls of the cryostat, for example. The transfer of heat by conduction is determined by the equations and the material properties considered in the discussion of thermal conductivity (Sects.3.3, 4.1). To minimize heat conduction we have to choose the right material and we have to give it the correct dimensions. In practice that means we should use strongly disordered or organic materials because of their low thermal conductivity, or, if we have to use metals, they should be low-conductivity stainless steel or Cu-Ni alloy tubes with thin walls.

b) Heat Radiation

The radiation of heat is determined by the Stefan-Boltzmann equation, which, in its simplest form, reads

$$\dot{Q}[W] = 5.67 \cdot 10^{-12} A[cm^2](T_1^4 - T_2^4) , \tag{5.1}$$

for the case that the radiating and the absorbing areas, A, are equal, and that the emissivities of these two areas are equal to 1 ("blackbody radiation"), which means we have dirty surfaces. In practice, of course, the situation can be improved by using polished metal surfaces. For this situation the emissivities ϵ can be reduced to the values given in Table 5.2. For $\epsilon \neq 1$, Eq.(5.1) has to be multipied by $\epsilon_1 \epsilon_2 / (\epsilon_1 + \epsilon_2 - \epsilon_1 \epsilon_2)$ [5.1]. If the emissivities of

Table 5.2. Typical emissivities of various solids [5.1]

Solid	Emissivity ϵ
Au	0.01÷0.03
Ag	0.02÷0.03
Cu	0.02÷0.6
Al	0.02÷0.3
Stainless Steel	0.05÷0.1
Glass/organic	0.1÷0.9

the radiating and absorbing surfaces are equal but much smaller than 1 this factor is $\epsilon/2$. If the heat due to radiation has to be reduced, surfaces should be gold-plated to avoid oxidation and to keep them clean and shiny. This is particularly important for apparatus used at T < 100 mK (Chaps. 7-10). We have to keep in mind that the dominant wavelength radiated by a body at T ≤ 300 K is in the infrared ($10\,\mu$m at 300K), therefore it is the emissivities at these wavelengths that matter rather than those in the visible. Highly polished metals are highly reflective in the infrared as well.

Equation (5.1) tells us that parts cooled to LHe temperatures should not be exposed to surfaces which are at room temperature, i.e. they should not be able to "see" surfaces at room temperature. If we calculate the heat radiated from a 10 cm² surface at 300 K we find 0.5 W, which means that this would evaporate 0.7 ℓHe/h. If we reduce the temperature of this 10 cm² area to the temperature of boiling nitrogen, 77 K, the radiated heat would be reduced to 2 mW and only 3 cm³ of liquid helium would be evaporated per hour. The inner part of a cryostat cooled by liquid helium should be surrounded by radiation shields or baffles at intermediate temperatures, to shield it from radiation from room temperature. These baffles should be either gas-cooled or, even better, directly thermally anchored to an intermediate temperature, for example to the LN_2 reservoir (see below).

c) Conduction by Gas Particles Remaining in the Vacuum Space

Because low-temperature surfaces act as cryopumps (Sect.2.3.2) the vacuum in a cryostat is usually good enough to make the conduction by remaining gases sufficiently small. For the possibly remaining helium gas the heat transferred by this process is [5.1,2]

$$\dot{Q}\,[W] \simeq 0.02a\,A\,[cm^2]\,P\,[mbar]\,\Delta T[K] \tag{5.2}$$

if the mean free path of the gas particles is large compared to the dimensions of the container, which is the usual low-pressure case. Here a is the accommodation coefficient for the gas particles on the walls; it is 1 as an extreme case but can become as small as 0.025 for a clean metallic surface exposed to helium gas. If we consider an apparatus with an area of 100 cm^2, take a = 1, and calculate how much heat is transported from room temperature to low temperatures if the remaining pressure is 10^{-6} mbar, then we arrive at about 1 mW, which is negligibly small for the Kelvin temperature range but may be detrimental at lower temperatures (Sect.10.5.3). To impove the cryopumping action, often a gettering material is attached to the cold wall of a cryostat, which can very effectively adsorb remaining gas (Fig.5.7).

For experiments in the low millikelvin or even microkelvin range, other heat sources become important; they will be discussed in Sect.10.5.

5.2 Helium-4 Cryostats

In London, at the end of the last century, the Scottish scientist J. Dewar presented public demonstration lectures on his low-temperature experiments. For these demonstrations [5.2], as well as for the experiments in his laboratory, he had to improve the storage vessels for cryogenic liquids. After various trials he eventually arrived at a double-walled vacuum isolation vessel, now commonly called a "dewar". The dewar in its simplest form is nothing but the double-walled flasks which are used to keep coffee warm on a camping trip.

5.2.1 Double-Walled Glass Dewars

The typical setup for experiments using liquid ^{4}He as the cryogenic liquid is a nested, double-walled glass dewar system [5.1,2], as shown in Fig.5.1. The advantages of such a system are its reasonably low price, the low thermal conductivity of glass, and the ease with which the level of the cryogenic liquid can be seen. A disadvantage, of course, is the ease with which glass can be broken. A particularly dangerous situation may arise if there is a small leak to the vacuum space between the two glass walls. Then air, for example, may enter this space and will condense onto the cold surfaces. A small leak may stay undetected. On warming the system, the condensed air will evaporate. If the air cannot escape fast enough through the tiny leak, pressure will build up in the vacuum space and the glass dewar may explode. To avoid serious consequences of such an explosion one has to follow two rules.

• Never take a cryogenic system apart before all of it has been warmed up to room temperature.
• A glass dewar system has to be surrounded by a protecting container, so that pieces of glass cannot fly through the laboratory.

One also has to keep in mind that at room temperature, helium diffuses through the glass walls (typically 10^{-12} - 10^{-10} cm^3/s through 1 cm^2 of glass of 1 mm thickness if ΔP = 1 bar, depending on the glass, with the smallest of the given numbers referring to Pyrex). The same is true for

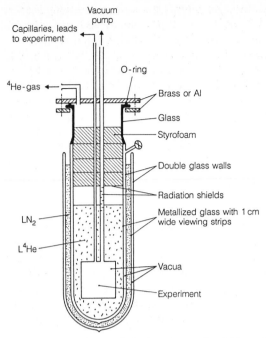

Vacuum pump

Capillaries, leads to experiment

O-ring

^{4}He-gas

Brass or Al

Glass

Styrofoam

Double glass walls

Radiation shields

Metallized glass with 1 cm wide viewing strips

LN$_2$

L^{4}He

Vacua

Experiment

Fig.5.1. A double-walled glass dewar for LN$_2$ and L^{4}He. The inner surfaces of the glass are covered with aluminium or silver to block thermal radiation (except for a vertical 1 cm wide viewing strip). Four or five radiation baffles reduce the thermal radiation; these baffles force the exiting cold gas to flow along the dewar walls, thus cooling it. The effectiveness of the baffles is increased by filling the spaces between them with Styrofoam

fibreglass often used in metal dewars (see below). To keep the vacuum one should therefore pump the helium gas from the inner volume immediately after warming to room temperature. In any case, the vacuum space of a glass dewar should be evacuated from time to time, at least every few weeks when operating with liquid helium, because some parts of the dewar may have been in contact with room-temperature helium gas even during the running period.

Such a dewar has to be equipped with radiation baffles to keep the radiation heat leak small and to force the cold gas to flow along the dewar walls, thereby cooling them. In a well-designed cryostat the helium gas is at 300 K when it reaches the top of the cryostat.

In Sect.5.1.1 we learnt that one should pre-cool everything with liquid nitrogen before taking the final cooling step with liquid ^{4}He. There are two methods of LN$_2$ pre-cooling in a system such as the one depicted in Fig. 5.1. One possibility is to let about a millibar of air into the vacuum space of the LHe dewar and also into the space which will later be filled with liquid helium. This pressure is enough for the gas to act as an exchange gas between the experiment and the liquid nitrogen in the outer container for pre-cooling. The air in the vacuum space does not have to be evacuated before liquid helium is allowed into the inner glass dewar; it simply freezes out. Another possibility is to fill the space for the liquid helium first with some liquid nitrogen to pre-cool the experimental setup. Of course, then the liquid nitrogen has to be blown out from this inner space through a tube which runs all the way down to the lowest point in the LHe dewar by increasing the pressure above the liquid nitrogen. One has to make sure that really *all* liquid nitrogen has been removed before liquid helium is transferred, because liquid nitrogen has a rather large specific heat and it would take a sizeable quantity of the liquid helium to cool nitrogen to the low Kelvin temperature range. A regulated and protected heater system to evaporate the remaining part of the liquid N_2 or to warm up a dewar system was described in [5.4].

5.2.2 Metal Dewars

Examples of metal ^{4}He dewars [5.2] are shown in Fig.5.2. A metal dewar has the advantage that such a setup is much more rugged and can withstand higher pressures or stresses than a glass dewar. In addition, it has a greater flexibility, so much more complex designs are possible and it does not have the helium diffusion problem. A disadvantage compared to the glass dewar system is the higher price of a metal cryostat, which is usually made from stainless steel or, more often now, from a combination of aluminium and fibreglass.

In such a system one does not usually have two vacuum spaces as in a double-walled glass dewar system. The vacuum space cannot be filled with air in order to provide thermal contact of the inner parts with the liquid nitrogen vessel since one would then also cool the outer room-temperature wall. Liquid nitrogen has to be put into the helium vessel for pre-cooling and then removed before transferring liquid helium into the cryostat.

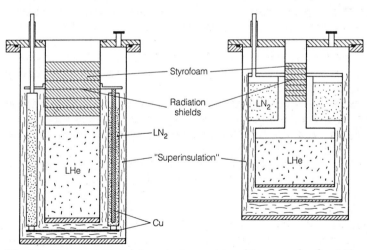

Fig.5.2. Two typical stainless steel cryostats with reservoirs for LN_2 and L^4He (see text)

Nowadays many of these metal ^{4}He cryostats do not use LN$_2$ vessels for pre-cooling and radiation shielding; this is particularly important when vibrations produced by the constantly boiling LN$_2$ may interfere with the experiment. In such a situation many layers of so-called "superinsulation" are wrapped around the LHe vessel and possibly around radiation shields. This superinsulation is a thin plastic foil onto which a reflective layer of aluminium has been evaporated. The sheets of superinsulation have decreasing temperature from the outermost to the inner ones, so they act as radiation shields at continuously decreasing temperatures. For further improvement there can be a metallic radiation shield between the room-temperature vessel and the LHe vessel, and to these radiation shields tubing may be soldered, through which the evaporating cold ^{4}He gas is vented before leaving the cryostat. This makes further use of the enthalpy of the cold gas by precooling the radiation shield. A good, simple helium dewar should have an evaporation rate of not more than 0.1 ℓ/h; but for large dewars, such as are necessary for a powerful nuclear magnetic refrigerator (Chap.10), this figure may go up to about 1 ℓ/h.

The design of ^{4}He dewars for various applications has been discussed in [5.1-3]. When possible, soft solder joints should be avoided on cryogenic equipment. They are less reliable, develop "cold leaks", fatigue sooner, and are weaker than silver solder joints. Of course, a welded design is superior to even silver soldering. Where flux has to be used in soldering, it has to be washed off very thoroughly to avoid later corrosion.

5.2.3 Cryostats for T > 5 K

For temperatures above the normal boiling point of liquid ^{4}He it is rather uneconomical to use the main ^{4}He bath at 4.2 K as a temperature reservoir and then to regulate the experiment at higher temperatures. It is much more efficient to use the cold gas evaporating from liquid helium and make use of its enthalpy for cooling the experiment in a continuous gas-flow cryostat. This allows the storage vessel containing the liquid helium to be separated from the cryostat with the experiment. Such an evaporation cryostat is shown in Fig.5.3. Here the cryogenic liquid is drawn from a reservoir (Sect.5.2.5) and is cooling an experiment via a heat exchanger in a separate cryostat. The rate and therefore cooling power and temperature can be controlled via the setting of a needle valve [5.1,2]. The system can easily be automated by using a solenoid valve in the pumping line which is controlled by a thermometer on the experiment and an appropriate bridge controller electronics. The advantages of such a design are a low consumption of the cryogenic liquid (in particular if T > 10K), that the temperature is variable in a rather wide range up to room temperature, and that the apparatus can be cooled down and warmed up in a very short time.

5.2.4 Cryostats with Variable Temperature at 1.3 K ≤ T ≤ 4.2 K

The temperature range 1.3K ≤ T ≤ 4.2K is determined by the normal boiling point of ^{4}He and the temperature at which its vapour pressure has be-

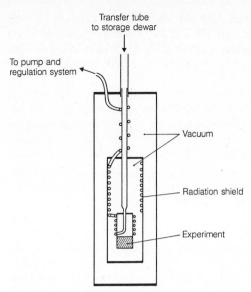

Transfer tube
to storage dewar

To pump and
regulation system

Vacuum

Radiation shield

Experiment

Fig.5.3. Evaporation cryostat for the temperature range T > 5 K. A mixture of liquid and gaseous ^{4}He is transferred via a transfer tube (Fig.5.8) from the storage dewar (Fig.5.7) to the cryostat. The mixture is pumped through a spiral tube which is first connected to a chamber on which the experiment is mounted and then soldered to a radiation shield before it leaves the cryostat. The temperature of the experiment can be regulated by a heater and/or a valve which regulates the helium flow

come very small (Fig.2.7). There are two ways to access this temperature range using pumped liquid ^{4}He.

a) Pumping on the Main ^{4}He Bath

Of course, one can just pump the vapour above the liquid ^{4}He bath away to decrease its temperature. This is very uneconomical because about 40% of the liquid ^{4}He has to be evaporated to cool it from 4.2 to 1.3 K, due to the large change of its specific heat in this temperature range. On the other hand, the specific heat of solids is rather small in this temperature range (see the figures in Sect.3.1); to cool them from 4.2 to 1.3 K we have to evaporate only a small fraction of liquid ^{4}He. It is therefore much more efficient to leave the main part of the liquid at its normal boiling point of 4.2 K and just pump on a small fraction of it in a separate container to reach the lower temperature for the experiment. This idea is realized in the design described in the following section.

b) Continuously Operating ^{4}He Evaporation Cryostat

The design of a continuously operating ^{4}He evaporation cryostat [5.5] is presented in Fig.5.4. In such a refrigerator a small fraction of the liquid from the main 4.2K bath flows through a suitable flow impedance (see below) into a small vessel of several cm^3 located in a vacuum can inside the

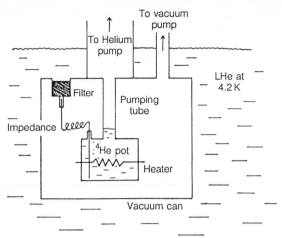

Fig.5.4. Schematic of a continuously operating ^{4}He refrigerator for the temperature range between 1.3 and 4.2 K (see text)

cryostat. Through the central tube we pump on the liquid arriving in this evaporation vessel. The liquid from the main bath at 1 bar is isenthalpically expanded through the impedance and will arrive at a lower temperature in the evaporation vessel. Again, almost half of the heat of evaporation is used for cooling the liquid; the other half can be used to fill up the inner vessel with liquid and to cool something else. This vessel will continue to fill until the level of the liquid in the pumping tube is at a height h at which the heat transferred from the main helium bath through this column of liquid, plus the heat from the experiment, just balance the cooling power of the refrigerator available from the latent heat L of evaporation. We then obtain the following equation for the steady-state operation of the refrigerator:

$$\dot{Q}_{He}(\simeq \tfrac{1}{2}\dot{n}L) = \dot{Q}_{tube}(h) + \dot{Q}_{ext} \ . \tag{5.3}$$

The refrigerator is self-regulating; if we increase the external load, the level of the liquid in the pumping tube will drop, so that its contribution to the heat transferred to the inner vessel is reduced. The temperature of the continuously evaporating ^{4}He refrigerator remains fairly constant at about 1.3 K when the heat load supplied to the vessel is varied (Fig.5.5). Of course, the externally supplied heat may be so large that all the liquid is evaporated from the vessel, resulting in a rapid temperature increase. The continuous ^{4}He evaporator today is a standard condensation or pre-cooling stage for ^{3}He cryostats and, above all, for ^{3}He-^{4}He dilution refrigerators, which will be discussed in the two chapters to follow. In this case one has to make sure that its refrigeration capability is sufficient to remove the heat of condensation of the circulating ^{3}He.

The equation for the required impedance is

$$Z = \Delta P/\dot{V}\eta \ , \tag{5.4}$$

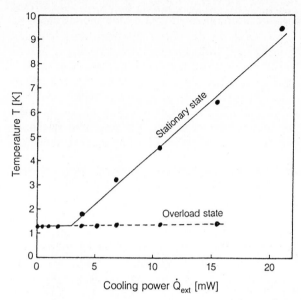

Fig.5.5. Temperature of a continuously operating ⁴He evaporation refrigerator. The refrigerator for which the data are shown can operate at a constant temperature up to a heat input of about 3 mW (this value can be changed by changing the impedance - see text and Fig.5.4). At higher heat inputs the refrigerator will work in the overload state for a short time until the pumped ⁴He pot (Fig.5.4) is empty. In the stationary state at T > 1.3 K, the refrigerator operates with an empty ⁴He pot at higher temperatures

where ΔP is the pressure drop (1 bar to about 1 mbar) required to cause a volume flow rate $\dot{V}$ of a medium with viscosity η, see also (7.47). The typical value required of several 10^{11} cm^{-3} can be obtained from a 1 m (several meter) long capillary with an inner diameter of about 0.05 mm (0.1 mm). Another possibility is to use a shorter piece (10÷20 cm) of a capillary and insert a tightly fitting wire into it [5.6]. With too large Z the ⁴He chamber will run dry and with too small Z the required temperature will not be reached. During cool-down the refrigerator should be connected to a volume with pressurized very pure ⁴He gas in order to prevent N$_2$ or air from entering and blocking the fill capillary. Sometimes problems arise because impurities in the main liquid helium bath (e.g., frozen air) block the fine capillary used for the impedance. One therefore has to put a filter (of Cu powder, for example) in front of the capillary and keep the main ⁴He bath clean. Using the heat of evaporation of liquid ⁴He (Fig.2.5) and a typical flow rate of $\dot{V} = 10^{-4}$ mol/s (obtainable with a mechanical pump of moderate size) one arrives at a cooling power of about 5 mW for such a ⁴He evaporation cryostat (Fig. 5.5).

The continuously operating ⁴He refrigerator substantially reduces the consumption of liquid ⁴He. And, as another advantage, the main ⁴He bath is kept at 4.2 K and 1 bar and can be refilled without interrupting the operation of the evaporation refrigerator and the experiment as long as the level of the main bath does not drop below the inlet to the evaporator.

Formerly, these evaporators were operated in a discontinuous mode by replacing the impedance by a valve. In this mode the vessel can be filled once with liquid from the main bath through the valve. The valve is then closed and pumping on the inner vessel can begin. Now, of course, the experiment has to be interrupted when the liquid in the vessel is used up, in order to refill it.

Recently, a continuously operating ^{4}He cryostat designed for insertion into storage dewars (32 or 50mm neck diameter, for example) has been described [5.7, 8]. A cryostat of this type used in our laboratory is shown in Fig.5.6. It can work from room temperature to $T \simeq 1.3$ K, and has extremely low helium consumption, fast cool-down and warm-up times, low price, easy construction and excellent temperature stability. The small diameter of the cryostat is made possible by using a tapered (7°) grease seal on the vacuum can (use non-aqueous silicon grease). The cryostat can even be equipped with a superconducting magnet of 2.5 (2) cm i.d., 4 cm o.d. for a 2 (4) T field, for example. These very useful cryostats are available commercially but can easily be constructed in the laboratory workshop according to the detailed description in [5.7, 8]. An alternative design has been described in [5.9]

5.2.5 Auxiliary Equipment

a) Storage Vessel

The storage vessels in which liquid helium is transported from the supplier or from one's own helium liquefier to the experiment are commercially available with a typical volume of 50 or 100 ℓ. The design of a modern commercial vacuum-isolated storage vessel containing superinsulation instead of LN_2 shielding is shown in Fig.5.7. Such vessels are made from aluminium to keep their weight low, or from stainless steel for more rugged applications. After drawing liquid helium from such a storage vessel, provided the periods between refilling are not too long, one should always leave a few litres of the cryoliquid in it to avoid recooling, which would consume a large amount of liquid helium. Such vessels have evaporation rates of about 1% per day. All commercial storage vessels are equipped with the appropriate safety features to avoid overpressure.

b) Transfer Tube

For transferring liquid helium from the storage vessel to the experimental cryostat we need a double-walled vacuum transfer tube [5.1, 2], which can be either bought or made in the laboratory workshop, if the necessary experience in welding and machining stainless steel is available. A typical design is presented in Fig.5.8. If bending of the two concentric tubes is necessary, then this should be done with ice as a filler between them to avoid collapse. Bending is usually necessary in order to take care of the differential contraction of the two tubes, which will be at different temperatures.

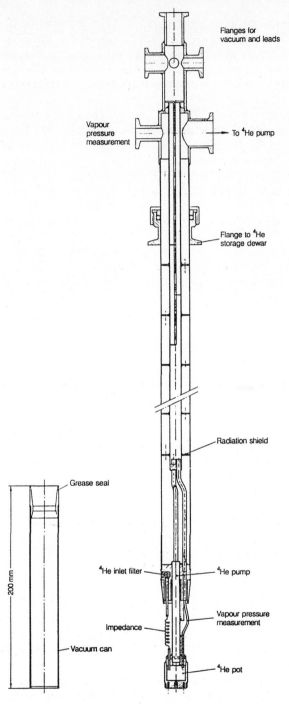

Flanges for
vacuum and leads

Vapour
pressure
measurement

To ^{4}He pump

Flange to ^{4}He
storage dewar

Radiation shield

Grease seal

^{4}He inlet filter

^{4}He pump

200 mm

Impedance

Vapour pressure
measurement

Vacuum can

^{4}He pot

Fig.5.6. Design of the low temperature part of a ^{4}He dipstick cryostat for the temperature range T > 1.3 K (see text). (Courtesy of P. Sekowski, Universität Bayreuth)

93

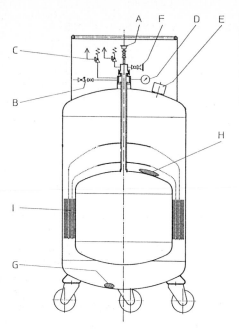

Fig.5.7. Commercial storage vessel for liquid ⁴He (*A*: connection for transfer tube, *B*: overflow valve, *C*: safety valve, *D*: manometer, *E*: vacuum and safety valves, *F*: gas valve, *G*: getter material, *H*: adsorbent material, *I*: superinsulation)

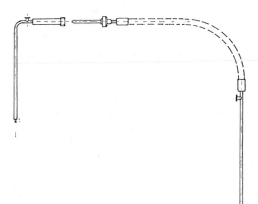

Fig.5.8. Double-walled vacuum-isolated transfer tube for liquid ⁴He. The dashed part is flexible. There should be a filter on the transfer tube. (Courtesy of P. Sekowski, Universität Bayreuth)

c) Level Detector

In containers for cryogenic liquids we need some means of determining the level of the liquid [5.1,2]. This is, of course, rather easy in a glass system where one can detect the level optically. However, a problem arises for metal containers, where we have to apply other means of determining the liquid level.

Acoustic Level Detection. A simple design for an acoustic level detector is shown in Fig.5.9. When the thin stainless steel tube of this device is lowered into the cold gas or into the cryogenic liquid, some of the liquid

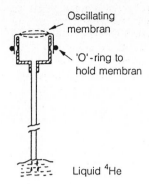

Oscillating membran

'O'-ring to hold membran

Fig.5.9. Acoustic level detector for liquid ^{4}He

Liquid ^{4}He

evaporates, the pressure in the vapour space suddenly increases, and the liquid level in the container oscillates. These oscillations have a different amplitude and frequence according to whether the tube has been lowered into the cold gas or into the liquid. The oscillations are transferred to a diaphragm (thin rubber or plastic sheet) on top of the tube and the high amplitude/high frequency oscillations when the tube is lowered just into the gas can easily be distinguished from the low amplitude/low frequency oscillations when the tube has been lowered all the way into the liquid.

Resistive Level Detection. Many conductors have a very distinct temperature dependence of their resistance; examples are discussed in Sect. 12.5. If one sends a current of about 0.1 mA through a semiconductor or a carbon resistor with a low-temperature resistance of some kΩ, this resistor stays at the temperature of its surroundings if it is in a cryogenic liquid. But the current can overheat the resistor if it is raised into the gas phase, because now the thermal contact with its surroundings is rather weak. The resistance and therefore the temperature of the element will change quite a bit as the resistor is lowered from the gas phase into the liquid, and this change can easily be detected with a Wheatstone bridge.

Another possible detecting element for the liquid level is a commercial superconducting wire of NbTi or a normal-conducting wire with a super-conducting coating (PbSn solder can be used) and a transition temperature between 5 and 10 K (Table 4.1) [5.10, 11]. If this wire is held vertically in the gas and liquid phases then the part which is in the liquid at 4.2 K will be superconducting and show zero resistance. The part of the wire in the gas phase will very rapidly attain a temperature above its transition temperature if an appropriate current is sent through it. It will become resistive and the total resistance of the wire is a direct measure of how much of its length is outside the liquid. Unlike the two level detection means discussed above, this detector is stationary and does not have to be moved up and down to detect the liquid level; it can give a continuous recording of the level height. Actually it is better to turn off these detectors except while taking a reading because the heat generated in the normal section of the wire can raise the helium consumption considerably. A recent discussion of capacitive level meters for cryogenic liquids with continuous readout can be found in [5.12].

6. Helium-3 Cryostats

The temperature range accessible with a liquid ^{4}He bath is typically 4.2÷1.3 K, but this temperature range can be extended to about 0.3 K if the rare isotope ^{3}He is used instead of the common isotope ^{4}He. The main reason is that ^{3}He has a substantially larger vapour pressure than ^{4}He at the same temperature; the ratio P_3/P_4 is 74 at 1 K but about 10^4 at 0.5 K (Figs. 2.6,7). A further advantage of using liquid ^{3}He instead of liquid ^{4}He at temperatures below their normal boiling point is due to the fact that the specific heat of liquid ^{3}He varies much less between, for example, 2 and 0.5 K than the specific heat of liquid ^{4}He does (Fig.2.8). One therefore has to evaporate only about 20% of ^{3}He to cool this liquid from 1.5 to 0.3 K by using its own heat of evaporation. Furthermore, the specific heat of liquid ^{3}He is larger than the specific heat of liquid ^{4}He below 1.5 K, resulting in a larger heat reservoir in this temperature range. Finally, liquid ^{3}He is not superfluid in the temperature range of concern in this chapter. One therefore does not have the heat transfer problems sometimes arising from the superfluid film flow of liquid ^{4}He (Sect.2.3.5).

There are two rather serious disadvantages of liquid ^{3}He. Firstly, its latent heat of evaporation is substantially smaller than that of liquid ^{4}He, see Fig.2.5. Secondly, and more importantly, ^{3}He is much more expensive than ^{4}He. A typical price is about 400 DM/litre gas or about 240 DM/cm^3 liquid (a litre of liquid ^{4}He, if bought commercially, can be obtained for about 20 DM). Due to this high price, which results from the expensive production method of ^{3}He (Sect.2.3.1), one can only use ^{3}He in a closed gas handling and cryogenic system, making sure that no gas is lost. As a second consequence, one never has enough ^{3}He gas to liquefy it on a technological scale in a liquefaction plant. The ^{3}He is transformed from the gaseous to the liquid state in the cryostat in which it will be used for doing experiments just by bringing it in contact with a ^{4}He bath at a temperature of, say, 1.3 K. This temperature can be obtained by the continuously evaporating ^{4}He refrigerator discussed in Sect.5.2.4. As the critical temperature of ^{3}He is 3.3 K, the ^{3}He gas will condense on surfaces which are below this temperature if the gas pressure is high enough.

Because the use of liquid ^{3}He as a refrigerant occurs in a ^{4}He cryostat anyway, all the parts refrigerated by the ^{3}He can be surrounded by shields kept at ^{4}He temperature. In addition, all the tubing and wiring going to the experiment can be thermally heat sunk at the ^{4}He bath. Therefore, the heat transferred from the outside world to parts below 1 K can be absorbed by the ^{4}He bath, which has a substantially larger volume and also a larger heat of evaporation than the ^{3}He bath. The ^{3}He bath is then only used for cooling from the temperature of the ^{4}He bath to the temperature obtained by the ^{3}He refrigerator. In any case, the use of an evaporating ^{3}He bath is the simplest way of reaching temperatures between 0.3 and 1 K, and several suppliers offer ^{3}He cryostats commercially. Earlier reports on ^{3}He cryostats can be found in [6.1-15].

6.1 Helium-3 Cryostats with External Pumps

Figure 6.1 schematically presents typical designs of ^{3}He cryostats in order of increasing sophistication. In each design a few cm^3 of ^{3}He are liquefied by bringing the ^{3}He in thermal contact with a ^{4}He bath, which is pumped to $T \leq 1.5$ K. Figure 6.1a shows a setup where the pre-cooling stage is the main ^{4}He bath pumped to a temperature of about 1.3 K and which absorbs the latent heat of condensation of the incoming ^{3}He. The ^{3}He gas condenses on the cold surfaces of the thin-walled pumping tube leading to and supporting the ^{3}He pot (surrounded by vacuum), which will slowly cool and eventually collect liquid ^{3}He. When all the ^{3}He has condensed we pump on this liquid to reduce its temperature from about 1.3 K to the desired temperature; the minimum is typically 0.3 K.

In the second setup the main ^{4}He bath is not pumped but is left at normal pressure and 4.2 K, and to condense the ^{3}He we use a continuously evaporating ^{4}He refrigerator, as discussed in Sect. 5.2.4. Both designs utilize the single-cycle discontinuous refrigeration method for the ^{3}He part because eventually all the ^{3}He is evaporated (and is hopefully recovered!) and we have to recondense it to start again.

Finally, in the third design the ^{3}He refrigerator, too, is run in a continuous mode by introducing a recondensing tube. The ^{3}He vapour that we pump away from the liquid ^{3}He bath at its vapour pressure will leave the room-temperature pump at a pressure of several 0.1 bar, it is pre-cooled by the ^{4}He pot and eventually recondensed into the ^{3}He pot. For this purpose the ^{3}He gas will run through a heat exchanger in the 4.2 K bath as well as a second heat exchanger in the 1.3 K ^{4}He bath where it will, of course, condense. The now liquid ^{3}He will then be isenthalpically (not isothermally) expanded through and over an impedance of order 10^{12}-10^{13} cm^{-3}, which maintains a pressure sufficient for condensation before the ^{3}He arrives as a low-pressure, low-temperature liquid at the pumped ^{3}He pot. In such a design we have introduced several features (like the heat exchanger and impedances) which will be discussed in more detail in the next chapter on ^{3}He-^{4}He dilution refrigerators. The narrow capillaries used as impedances can easily be blocked if there are impurities such as frozen air in the ^{4}He or ^{3}He entering them. One therefore has to be careful to avoid these impurities and, in particular, one may use a LN$_2$ cooled trap (Fig. 7.22) after the ^{3}He room-temperature pump to freeze out oil vapour or oil crack products possibly leaving the pump together with the ^{3}He gas, as well as any remaining air impurities. It is quite obvious that due to the high price of

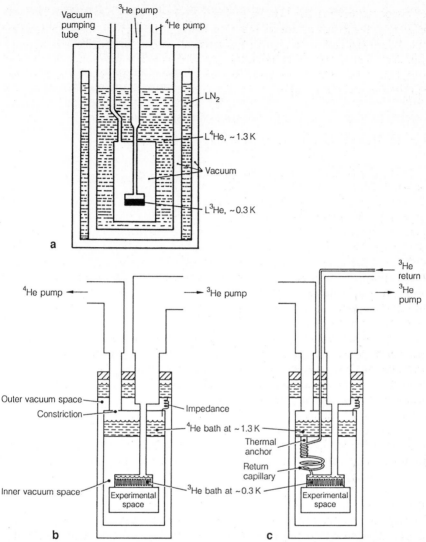

Fig.6.1a-c. ^{3}He cryostats of increasing sophistication. (a) Non-recirculating ^{3}He refrigerator with a pumped main ^{4}He bath. (b) Non-recirculating ^{3}He refrigerator with a continuously operating ^{4}He evaporator. (c) Recirculating ^{3}He refrigerator with a continuously operating ^{4}He evaporator [6.4]

^{3}He gas it is necessary to have a vacuum-tight closed ^{3}He system with a sealed pump avoiding any loss of this expensive gas. In addition, one has to be careful to design the room temperature part with the smallest possible volumes, so that not too much of the ^{3}He gas remains unused in these "dead" volumes.

Due to the low helium vapour pressure in the sub-kelvin temperature range, one has to use reasonably dimensioned pumps as well as pumping tubes to circulate the required amount of ^{3}He. Let us consider what we need to maintain temperatures of 0.5 or 0.3 K. At these temperatures the vapour pressure of ^{3}He is about 0.2 mbar and 2 μbar, respectively. The former pressure can be maintained by a mechanical pump, whereas for the latter one we need a combination of an oil-diffusion pump and a mechanical pump. We will see that very often the limitation is not the pump but rather the conductance of the pumping tubes. Let us assume that we need a cooling power of 1 mW. This requires an evaporation rate of

$$\dot{V} = \dot{Q}/L \simeq 7 \text{ cm}^3 \text{liq}^3\text{He/h} \simeq 3 \text{ }\ell\text{gas}^3\text{He/h} \quad \text{at} \quad P = 1 \text{ bar} . \tag{6.1}$$

At the pressures mentioned above, the volume flow rates have to be 15 m^3 gas/h and 1500 m$^3\cdot$gas/h, respectively. These volume rates are no problem for a mechanical pump and a diffusion pump, respectively. But what about the tubing? The conductance L [m^3/h] of a tube for a laminar flow is given by

$$L = 486\bar{P}d^4/\ell , \tag{6.2}$$

where d is the diameter [cm], ℓ is the length [cm], and $\bar{P}$ is the mean pressure [mbar]. We then find that we need pumping tubes with diameters of 3 and 10 cm, respectively, if the length is several m. A pumping tube with the latter diameter is bulky and one should rather try to reduce the heat input to the ^{3}He system to below 1 mW if temperatures below 0.5 K are required. Inside the cryostat, the diameter of the pumping tube can be reduced according to the temperature profile because the density of the evaporating gas increases with decreasing T and the circulation rate $\dot{n}$ is the same everywhere [6.4, 14].

6.2 Helium-3 Cryostats with Internal Adsorption Pumps

One can avoid the room temperature pump as well as the often bulky pumping tubes by using a cold adsorption pump inside the cryostat. Gases adsorb at cold surfaces if their temperature is low enough. If we keep a large surface at a low enough temperature above our ^{3}He bath, this surface will pump the helium vapour and keep the liquid ^{3}He at a low temperature. There are various suitable materials (e.g., charcoal, zeolites or fine metal powder) with surface areas of at least several m^2/g [6.10, 11, 16]. If we fill a volume of several cm^3 with such an adsorbent with large surface area at low temperature, it will very effectively pump the liquid ^{3}He bath. When all the ^{3}He has been pumped away, so that the ^{3}He pot is empty, we just have to lift the charcoal pumping system into a space at higher temperature in the cryostat to desorb the helium, which will then enter the gas phase, condense at the cold surfaces of the cryostat and eventually drip back down into the ^{3}He pot. Such a cryostat [6.7-15] with a hermetically sealed ^{3}He system reaching 0.25 K is shown in Fig.6.2. An alternative way of switch-

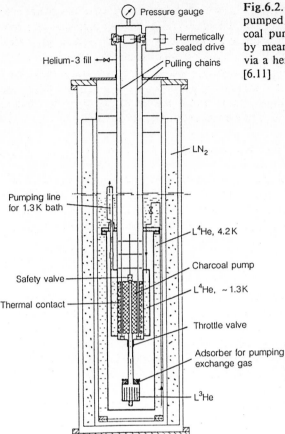

Pressure gauge

Hermetically
sealed drive

Helium-3 fill

Pulling chains

LN$_2$

Pumping line
for 1.3 K bath

L^{4}He, 4.2 K

Charcoal pump

Safety valve

L^{4}He, ~1.3 K

Thermal contact

Throttle valve

Adsorber for pumping
exchange gas

L^{3}He

Fig.6.2. Hermetically sealed, charcoal pumped ^{3}He refrigerator. The charcoal pump can be raised or lowered by means of a chain drive operated via a hermetically closed rotating seal [6.11]

ing between the pumping and the releasing state of the adsorbant (instead of lifting and lowering this part) is to switch the thermal contact of the adsorbent with the surrounding ^{4}He bath on and off. This can be done by using helium exchange gas in the space around the vessel containing the adsorbent and pumping this exchange gas away when the adsorbent has to be thermally isolated and heating it by a heater to a higher temperature to release the ^{3}He gas. We have to bear in mind that the heat of adsorption is rather large - of the order of the latent heat of evaporation - so the adsorbent has to be in good thermal contact with the ^{4}He bath to remove the heat of adsorption and avoid an unwanted high temperature of the adsorbent. The pumping speed of charcoal pumps is not only a function of its temperature but also, in practice, a complicated function of geometry, thermal coupling and pressure [6.10,11,16].

Cold charcoal pumping systems are also more efficient than room-temperature mechanical pumps because they are connected via a short, cold pumping tube to the ^{3}He pot, taking advantage of the very high pumping speed of the adsorbent (see below).

101

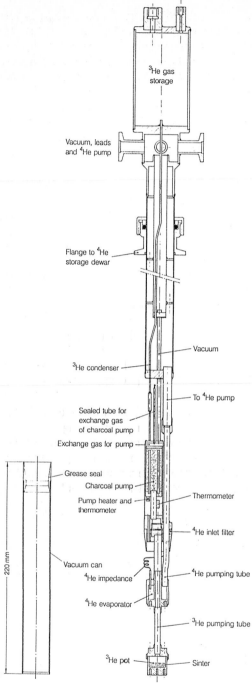

Fig.6.3. ^{3}He dipstick refrigerator with ^{3}He gas storage, charcoal pump, continuously operating ^{4}He refrigerator, and ^{3}He refrigerator; for details see text and [6.15] (Courtesy of P. Sekowski, Universität Bayreuth)

A very versatile ³He cryostat which can be inserted into a storage ⁴He dewar (50 mm neck diameter) has been designed by *Swartz* [6.14, 15], as well as in our laboratory (Fig. 6.3). It is an extension of the "⁴He dipper cryostat" mentioned in Sect. 5.2.4. The first stage of the cryostat is a continuously filling ⁴He pot at about 1.3 K, on which the ³He condenses out of its small room-temperature storage volume on top of the cryostat and then drips into the ³He pot. Cooling of the ³He to 0.3 K is achieved (within a few minutes!) by pumping with an activated charcoal pump which is located inside the cryostat close to the ³He pot. The charcoal pump is equiped with its own (charcoal pumped) vacuum/exchange gas space and heater so that its temperature can be regulated between about 5 and 25 K to adsorb or desorb the ³He. The small dead volumes allow the quantity of ³He to be restricted to just 1 STP liter of ³He (about 1.5 cm³ of liquid) in the permanently sealed ³He part of the cryostat. The pump and heaters can be computer controlled. The cold-time of the ³He charge in the pot depends, of course, on the heat load; typical times are from 3 h for $\dot{Q} \sim 0.1$ mW to about 20 h with no external load. Such a portable ³He cryostat requires no transfer of liquid ⁴He and no external gas handling or pumping system for the ³He part, it has a very fast turn-around time and low cost. The design and construction, as well as the operation and performance, are described in detail in [6.15]; it is available commercially.

The "pumping power" of activated charcoal is shown in Fig. 6.4, while Fig. 6.5 displays the refrigeration power of 20 g of activated charcoal as a function of the heating power. The figure shows that one can maintain temperatures as low as 0.25 K for heating rates below about 0.01 mW, and 0.4 K at 1 mW.

Of course, cold materials with a large surface area are not only useful as a pump for reducing the temperature above an evaporating cryogenic liquid. They are also quite useful in the vacuum space of cryogenic vessels, where they can substantially improve the vacuum by adsorbing remaining gas particles after cooling to low temperatures, or even make the gas entering the vacuum space through a tiny, not localized leak "harmless".

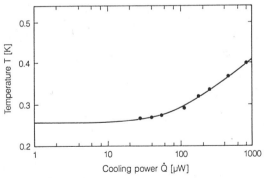

Fig. 6.4. Cooling power of a ³He refrigerator pumped by 20 g of charcoal [6.11]

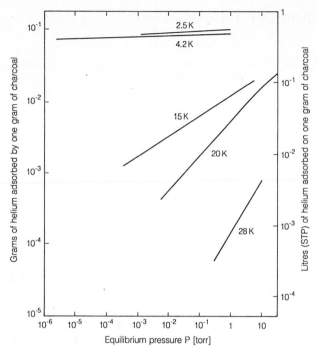

Fig.6.5. Adsorption isotherms of ^{3}He on activated charcoal as a function of the helium gas pressure [6.11]

With a ^{3}He cryostat we are taking the first step into the range of T < 1 K. At these temperatures the Kapitza thermal boundary resistance (Sect. 4.3.2) can be of importance. One should therefore increase the surface area of the ^{3}He pot to improve the thermal coupling between the cryoliquid and the wall of its container. This can be done by making grooves in the inside of the ^{3}He pot or, better, by sintering fine metal powder (Sect. 13.6) with a total surface area of about 1 m^2 to the bottom of the container.

Helium-3 cryostats were quite popular until about the end of the 1960s, when the ^{3}He-^{4}He dilution refrigerator (see the following chapter) was invented. This latter refrigerator reaches substantially lower temperatures. Today, ^{3}He refrigerators are mainly used if only a very simple setup is possible or necessary, or when one needs a very high cooling power at temperatures between about 0.4 and 1 K.

7. The ^{3}He-^{4}He Dilution Refrigerator

Until about the 1950s the only method of achieving temperatures below 1 K was magnetic refrigeration using demagnetization of a paramagnetic salt (Chap. 9). This method was then replaced for the temperature range down to 0.3 K by the ^{3}He refrigerator, as discussed in the preceding chapter. But in 1962 a new proposal for continuous refrigeration with liquid helium to even lower temperatures was published by H. London, G.R. Clarke, and E. Mendoza, based on an idea proposed by H. London about ten years earlier [7.1]. In contrast to the helium refrigerators discussed above, where the latent heat of evaporation is used for cooling, it was proposed to use the heat of mixing of the two helium isotopes to obtain low temperatures. A group at Leiden University built the first refrigerator based on this principle in 1965 and reached a temperature of 0.22 K [7.1], the lowest temperature obtained by the helium liquids up to that time. Only one year later, B.S. Neganov et al. in Dubna and H.E. Hall et al. in Manchester published their results with an improved design of a "^{3}He-^{4}He refrigerator" by which they could reduce this temperature by about a factor of three; the final version of the Dubna refrigerator soon reached 25 mK [7.1]. The ^{3}He-^{4}He dilution refrigeration method to be discussed in detail in this chapter is the only continuous refrigeration method for temperatures below 0.3 K. In addition, magnetic fields, often needed in low-temperature experiments, have negligible effects on its performance. Today it is the most important refrigeration technology for the temperature range between about 5 mK and 1 K, and it is the base from which lower temperatures can be reached.

The complexity of a ^{3}He-^{4}He refrigerator for the temperature range above 30 mK is comparable to the complexity of a ^{3}He cryostat. Actually, existing ^{3}He cryostats can easily be modified to ^{3}He-^{4}He refrigerators. If the temperature range has to be extended to about 15 mK, the system, of course, will become more involved, but it can still be built in the laboratory workshop. If the temperature has to be reduced to values even lower than 10 mK, substantial experience, time and manpower are necessary to achieve this goal, if you want to build the refrigerator yourself. Fortunately, these days commercial dilution refrigerators are available for temperatures down to about 4 mK, but they are expensive. The minimum temperature obtained by the method to be discussed below is about 2 mK, achieved by *Frossati* and co-workers, formerly at Grenoble and now at the University of Leiden [7.2, 3].

Today, ^{3}He-^{4}He dilution refrigerators are part of virtually all apparatus reaching T $\leq$ 0.3 K. Detailed discussions of the principle and methods of dilution refrigeration have been published by *Wheatley* et al. [7.4-6], by *Radebaugh* and *Siegwarth* [7.7], and more recently by *Frossati* [7.2,3] and are reviewed in [7.8-10]. I will start with a discussion of some relevant properties of ^{3}He-^{4}He mixtures.

7.1 Properties of Liquid ^{3}He-^{4}He Mixtures

In this section I will discuss the properties of isotopic liquid helium mixtures - the working fluid of the refrigerator - that are relevant for the design and operation of a ^{3}He-^{4}He dilution refrigerator. For more details the reader is referred to the specialized literature [7.2-17].

In the following, the respective concentrations of the two helium isotopes are expressed as

$$x = x_3 = n_3/(n_3 + n_4) \quad \text{and} \quad x_4 = n_4/(n_3 + n_4) \, , \tag{7.1}$$

where $n_3(n_4)$ is the number of ^{3}He (^{4}He) atoms or moles.

7.1.1 Phase Diagram and Solubility

The x-T phase diagram of liquid ^{3}He-^{4}He mixtures at saturated vapour pressure is depicted in Fig.7.1. This figure shows several of the remarkable features of these isotopic liquid mixtures. First we consider the pure liquids. We are reminded that liquid ^{4}He becomes superfluid at a temperature of 2.177 K. On the other hand, the Fermi liquid ^{3}He does not show any phase transition in the temperature range considered in this chapter (actually this liquid also becomes superfluid in the low millikelvin temperature range; see Sect.2.3.6). The temperature of the superfluid phase transition of liquid ^{4}He is depressed if we dilute the Bose liquid ^{4}He with the Fermi liquid ^{3}He. Eventually the ^{4}He superfluidity ceases to exist for ^{3}He concentrations above 67%. At this concentration and at a temperature of 0.87 K the λ-line meets the phase separation line; below this temperature the two isotopes are only miscible for certain limiting concentrations which depend on the temperature. The shaded phase separation region in the figure is a non-accessible range of temperatures and concentrations for helium mixtures. If we cool a helium mixture (with x > 6.5%) to temperatures below 0.87 K, the liquid will eventually separate into two phases, one rich in ^{4}He and the other rich in ^{3}He. Because of its lower density, the ^{3}He-rich liquid floats on top of the ^{4}He-rich liquid. If the temperature is decreased to close to absolute zero, we see that the ^{3}He-rich liquid becomes pure ^{3}He. But the great surprise occurs at the ^{4}He-rich side. Here the concentration of the dilute isotope, ^{3}He, does not approach zero for T approaching zero, but rather reaches a constant concentration of 6.5% ^{3}He in ^{4}He at saturated vapour pressure even for T = 0 K. This finite solubility is of utmost importance for ^{3}He-^{4}He dilution refrigeration technology. The limiting concentrations of the diluted isotopes on the phase separation line at T < 0.2 K and at saturated vapour pressure are given by [7.11]

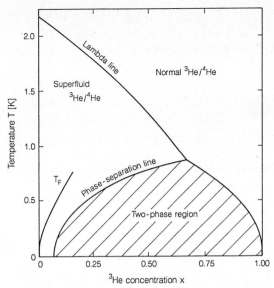

Fig.7.1. Phase diagram of liquid ^{3}He-^{4}He mixtures at saturated vapour pressure. The diagram shows the lambda line for the superfluid transition of ^{4}He, the phase separation line of the mixtures below which they separate into a ^{4}He-rich and a ^{3}He-rich phase, and the line of the Fermi temperatures T_F of the ^{3}He component. (From [7.10, 16] which give references to the original work from which data were taken to construct this phase diagram)

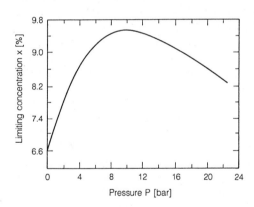

Fig.7.2. Limiting concentration of ^{3}He in ^{4}He at T = 50 mK as a function of pressure (after data from [7.18])

$$x_4 = 0.85\,T^{3/2}e^{-0.56/T} , \qquad (7.2)$$

$$x = x_3 = 0.065(1 + 10T^2) . \qquad (7.3)$$

The solubility of ^{3}He in ^{4}He can be increased to almost 9.5% by raising the pressure to 10 bar (Fig.7.2) [7.18].

As we will see below, cooling in a ^{3}He-^{4}He dilution refrigerator is achieved by transferring ^{3}He atoms from the ^{3}He phase to the diluted, mostly ^{4}He containing phase. The cooling capacity in this cooling process is the heat of mixing of the two isotopes. But why is the finite solubility of ^{3}He in ^{4}He so important for this method? In Sect.2.3.2 we had the equation for the cooling power of an evaporating cryogenic liquid:

$$\dot{Q} = \dot{n}\Delta H = \dot{n}L . \tag{7.4}$$

If we make use of the latent heat L of evaporation as we did in the previous chapters on refrigerators, for example by pumping with a pump of constant volume rate $\dot{V}$ on a ^{3}He or ^{4}He bath with vapour pressure P, we obtain

$$\dot{Q} = \dot{V}P(T)L(T) . \tag{7.5}$$

Because the latent heat of evaporation changes only weakly with temperature (Fig.2.5), the temperature dependence of the cooling power is essentially given by

$$\dot{Q} \propto P(T) \propto e^{-1/T} . \tag{7.6}$$

For ^{3}He-^{4}He dilution refrigeration the corresponding quantities are the entropy ΔH of mixing, which is given by the integral of the differences of the specific heats of the two phases,

$$\Delta H \propto \int \Delta C dT , \tag{7.7}$$

and the concentration x of the dilute ^{3}He phase, which is almost constant at $T \leq 0.1$ K, 6.5% ^{3}He, see (7.3), in contrast to the vapour density in the refrigerator discussed above, where the number of atoms decreases exponentially with temperature. The high ^{3}He particle density in the dilute phase is essential for ^{3}He-^{4}He dilution refrigeration because it permits a high ^{3}He

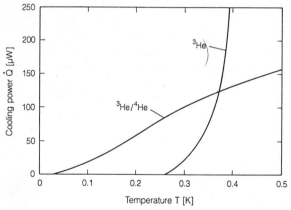

Fig.7.3. Cooling power of a ^{3}He evaporation cryostat and of a ^{3}He-^{4}He dilution refrigerator, assuming that the same pump with a helium gas circulation rate of 5 ℓ/s is used [7.8]

molar flow rate. Because the specific heats of concentrated and diluted ^{3}He are proportional to T at low enough temperatures (Figs.2.14,7.5), we end up with the following temperature dependence of the cooling power of this dilution process:

$$\dot{Q} \propto x\Delta H \propto T^2 \; ; \tag{7.8}$$

this result is shown in Fig.7.3.

This substantial advantage of the ^{3}He-^{4}He dilution process, that the temperature dependence of the cooling power is weaker than that of the evaporation process, was only realized after scientists detected the finite solubility of ^{3}He in ^{4}He even for T approaching absolute zero. Before this experimental discovery it was believed that the liquid helium isotopes - like other two-component liquids - have to fully separate into the two pure liquids when the temperature is low enough to fulfil the third law of thermodynamics, so that the entropy of mixing is zero for T = 0. Of course, the helium liquids have to fulfil this law as well, and they can do so even if they do not separate completely for T→0 because they are quantum liquids. For T = 0 the ^{3}He-^{4}He mixtures are in their fully degenerate Fermi momentum ground state ("one ^{3}He particle/state") with S = 0, whereas for a classical system, a finite solubility means S > 0.

7.1.2 ^{3}He-^{4}He Mixtures as Fermi Liquids

The isotope ^{4}He has a nuclear spin I = 0 and therefore in its liquid state it obeys Bose statistics. Such a Bose liquid will undergo a so-called Bose condensation in momentum space, and for liquid ^{4}He this corresponds to its transition to the superfluid state. At T < 0.5 K liquid ^{4}He is almost totally condensed into this quantum mechanical ground state; there are essentially no excitations (phonons, rotons) left. Its viscosity, entropy and specific heat go to zero. In a helium mixture at these temperatures the component ^{4}He acts as an "inert superfluid background", which contributes to the volume of the liquid and to the effective mass of the dissolved isotope ^{3}He (see below) but has negligible heat capacity, for example (Fig.2.8).

The rare and lighter isotope ^{3}He with its nuclear spin I = 1/2 is a Fermi particle, and it has to obey Fermi statistics and the Pauli principle like the conduction electrons in a metal. However, unlike the Fermi temperature of conduction electrons, which is of order 10^4 K, the Fermi temperature of liquid ^{3}He is of order 1 K only. In analogy to the conduction electrons, the specific heat of liquid ^{3}He behaves as

Fermi-degenerate: $C_3 = (\pi^2/2)(T/T_F)R$ at $T \ll T_F$ (7.9)

or

       classical: $C_3 = (5/2)R$ at $T > T_F$ and   P = const. (7.10)

This means the behaviour is classic-gas-like at T > 1 K but Fermi-gas-like at T ≪ 0.1 K.

Of course, if ^{3}He is diluted by ^{4}He in a liquid helium mixture, it still has to obey Fermi statistics, but now it is diluted. Therefore, its Fermi temperature and its effective mass (which is a measure of its interactions with the surroundings) are altered. Many experiments confirm that the properties of liquid ^{3}He-^{4}He mixtures can be described by the laws for an interacting Fermi gas [7.4, 5, 11–17, 19–21]; because of the dilution by ^{4}He, this description is much better for dilute ^{3}He-^{4}He mixtures than for concentrated ^{3}He. That the liquid helium mixtures are not a *dilute non-interacting* gas is taken into account by replacing the bare ^{3}He mass m_3 in the equations by the effective mass m^*. The effective mass is slightly dependent on ^{3}He concentration, with $m^*/m_3 = 2.34$ for $x \rightarrow 0$ and $m^*/m_3 = 2.5$ for $x = 6.5\%$ at $P = 0$ [7.22–25] ($m^*/m_3 = 2.80$ for pure ^{3}He at SVP [7.26]), and more strongly dependent on pressure; these values are calculated with (7.22) from the measured specific-heat data. In this description ^{3}He is treated as an interacting quasi-particle Fermi gas with a pressure equal to the osmotic pressure of ^{3}He in ^{4}He (Sect. 7.1.5).

7.1.3 Finite Solubility of ^{3}He in ^{4}He

Let us consider whether a ^{3}He atom would prefer to be in a vessel filled with liquid ^{3}He or in a vessel filled with liquid ^{4}He. Each atom that hits the phase separation line of a phase-separated ^{3}He-^{4}He mixture is asked this question and has to decide whether to stay in the upper ^{3}He phase or go into the lower ^{4}He rich phase. The ^{3}He atom will go into the phase where it has the larger binding energy.

In the following I shall discuss the situation for T = 0. An extension to finite temperatures does not change the essentials of the results. A discussion for finite temperatures can be found in the books of *Lounasmaa* and *Betts* [7.8, 9], for example.

a) ^{3}He in Pure ^{3}He (x = 1)

The chemical potential[1] of pure liquid ^{3}He is given by the latent heat of evaporation

$$\mu_{3,c} = - L_3 , \qquad (7.11)$$

corresponding to the binding energy of ^{3}He in liquid ^{3}He. So L_3/N_0 is the energy one has to supply to remove one ^{3}He atom from liquid ^{3}He into vacuum.

b) One ^{3}He Atom in Liquid ^{4}He (x ≃ 0)

For the dilute phase, the binding energy of a ^{3}He atom in liquid ^{4}He (x → 0) is given by

$$\mu_{3,d}(0)/N_0 = \epsilon_{3,d}(0) . \qquad (7.12)$$

---

[1] From now on I shall use the subscripts 'c' for the upper, concentrated ^{3}He phase and 'd' for the lower, dilute ^{3}He phase.

We have already discussed in Sect. 2.3 that due to the identical chemical structure of the helium isotopes the van der Waals forces between them are identical. But due to its smaller mass the ^{3}He atom has a larger zero-point motion than the ^{4}He atom. Therefore, in the liquid phase ^{4}He atoms occupy a smaller volume than ^{3}He atoms. The ^{3}He atom will be closer to the ^{4}He than it would be to ^{3}He atoms or, in other words, its binding - due to the smaller distance or larger density - is stronger if it is in ^{4}He than it would be in ^{3}He. Because the ^{3}He atom will be more strongly bound in ^{4}He it will prefer to stay in liquid ^{4}He. We have the inequalities

$$\mu_{3,d}(0) \ < \mu_{3,c}(0) \ ,$$
$$|\epsilon_{3,d}(0)| > |L_3|/N_0 \ , \qquad\qquad (7.13)$$
$$-\epsilon_{3,d}(0) < -L_3/N_0 \ .$$

Of course, the finite solubility of ^{3}He in ^{4}He at T = 0 is itself an indication that a ^{3}He atom is more strongly bound in ^{4}He than in ^{3}He. This stronger binding is shown in Fig. 7.4.

c) Many ^{3}He Atoms in Liquid ^{4}He (x > 0)

When we put more and more ^{3}He atoms into liquid ^{4}He the situation will change due to two effects. Firstly, there is an attractive interaction between the ^{3}He atoms in liquid ^{4}He. This attraction arises from a magnetic interaction due to the nuclear magnetic moments of ^{3}He as in pure ^{3}He, and, in addition, in the mixtures only from a density effect. Remember that the ^{3}He, due to its larger zero-point motion, needs more space than a ^{4}He atom. Therefore, the liquid near to a ^{3}He atom is more dilute than the

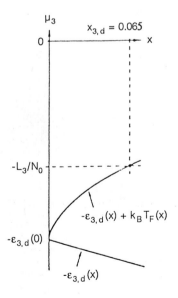

Fig. 7.4. Chemical potential of a ^{3}He atom in pure ^{3}He (L_3/N_0) and in ^{3}He-^{4}He mixtures as a function of the ^{3}He concentration x. In the latter case due chemical potential is enhanced by $k_B T_F(x)$ due to the Pauli principle (see text). At the limiting concentration $x_{3,d}$ = 6.5% the chemical potential of ^{3}He in ^{4}He reaches the chemical potential of pure ^{3}He.

liquid near to a ^{4}He atom. This low-density region around a ^{3}He atom is felt by another ^{3}He atom in the liquid; it would like to be combined with the first ^{3}He atom, because then it does not have to push so hard against the ^{4}He atoms to make enough space for itself. Due to this attractive interaction between ^{3}He atoms the binding energy of a ^{3}He atom in ^{4}He should increase with increasing ^{3}He concentration x (Fig.7.4),

$$|\epsilon_{3,d}(x)| > |\epsilon_{3,d}(0)| \ ,$$

$$- \epsilon_{3,d}(x) < - \epsilon_{3,d}(0) \ . \tag{7.14}$$

But now we have to remember that the ^{3}He atoms have to obey the Pauli principle: If we put additional ^{3}He atoms in the liquid they have to go into successively higher energy states so that eventually all the energy states up to the Fermi energy $E_F = k_B T_F$ are filled with two ^{3}He atoms of opposite nuclear spin. Therefore, the binding energy of the ^{3}He atoms has to decrease, due to their Fermi character, if their number is increased. Eventually we arrive at the following equation for the chemical potential of a ^{3}He atom in dilute ^{3}He-^{4}He liquid mixtures (at T = 0):

$$\mu_{3,d}(x)/N_0 = - \epsilon_{3,d}(x) + k_B T_F(x) \ , \tag{7.15}$$

where $k_B T_F = (\hbar^2/2m^*)(3\pi^2 x N_0/V_m)^{2/3}$ is the Fermi energy of a Fermi gas with effective mass m^* of the particles. We have $T_F \propto x^{2/3}$ because V_m and m^* depend only weakly on the ^{3}He concentration x. The result (7.15) is illustrated in Fig.7.4. If we continue to increase the ^{3}He concentration, the binding energy of a ^{3}He atom in a liquid isotopic mixture will eventually reach the binding energy of a ^{3}He atom in pure liquid ^{3}He. The chemical potentials of the two liquids become equal and we arrive at the limiting concentration of ^{3}He in liquid ^{3}He-^{4}He mixtures. The limiting concentration is 6.5% for the liquids under their saturated vapour pressure at T = 0, but depends on pressure (Fig.7.2). Thus, we have for the equilibrium concentration

$$- \epsilon_{3,d}(6.5\%) + k_B T_F(6.5\%) = - L_3/N_0 \ . \tag{7.16}$$

We could ask the ^{4}He atoms, too, whether they would rather stay in a ^{4}He environment or whether they prefer to be in a ^{3}He environment. Of course, they prefer to stay in ^{4}He for the same reasons as the dilute ^{3}He atoms: they feel a stronger binding when surrounded by ^{4}He, and because they do not have to obey the Pauli principle there is no reason to decrease their binding energy if we increase their concentration. As a result, the concentration of ^{4}He will approach zero rapidly in the upper ^{3}He-rich phase if the temperature is lowered to zero, (7.2). The reason for the finite (zero) solubility of ^{3}He (^{4}He) in liquid ^{4}He (^{3}He) even at absolute zero is that a single ^{3}He (^{4}He) atom is more strongly bound to liquid ^{4}He than to liquid ^{3}He.

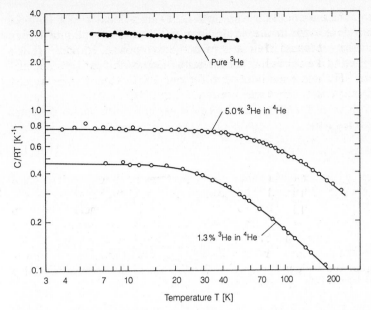

Fig.7.5. Specific heat C/RT of ^{3}He and of two dilute solutions of ^{3}He in ^{4}He at saturated vapour pressure [7.4, 22]. In this figure C is the specific heat per *total* number of helium moles (not: per ^{3}He moles!). (For more recent data for pure ^{3}He see Fig.2.14)

7.1.4 Cooling Power of the Dilution Process

From measurements of specific heats (Fig.7.5), we know that the enthalpy of ^{3}He in the dilute phase is larger than the enthalpy of ^{3}He in the concentrated phase; we have a *heat of mixing*,

$$\dot{Q} = \dot{n}_3[H_d(T) - H_c(T)] . \tag{7.17}$$

If we transfer ^{3}He atoms at a molar flow rate $\dot{n}_3$ from the concentrated phase into the dilute phase of a phase-separated mixture, cooling will result according to the enthalpy difference of the two phases. Because the enthalpy is given by

$$H(T) - H(0) = \int_0^T C(T')dT' \tag{7.18}$$

(neglecting PV terms which do not matter here or in the following), we must have

$$C_{3,d}(T) > C_{3,c}(T) \tag{7.19}$$

for the molar heat capacities of ^{3}He in the two phases to obtain cooling by the dilution process.

113

In both phases, of course, the specific heat varies linearly with temperature at low enough temperatures because both are Fermi liquids (Figs. 2.14,7.5). But the prefactor is different for the two phases. Liquid ^{3}He is a strongly interacting Fermi liquid and present theories do not allow calculation of the specific heat reliably enough for our purpose. We therefore have to take the specific heat from the recent very accurate experimental data of *Greywall* [7.26], who, for temperatures below about 40 mK and at saturated vapour pressure, gives

$$C_3 = 2.7RT = 22T \quad [\text{J/mol·K}] . \tag{7.20}$$

C_3/T is temperature independent at $T < 40$ mK to within about 4%.[2] Remember that this is a very large specific heat due to the small Fermi temperature of ^{3}He. For example, the molar heat capacity of copper is about a factor of 3×10^4 smaller, due to its correspondingly larger Fermi temperature (Fig.2.8; Sect.3.1.2). We then have for the enthalpy of liquid ^{3}He

$$H_3(T) = H_3(0) + 11T^2 \quad [\text{J/mol}] . \tag{7.21}$$

If we need the specific heat and enthalpy at temperatures above about 50 mK we cannot use such simple equations because $C_3/T \neq$ constant;[2] we have to integrate the experimental data for C_3 to obtain $H_3(T)$ [7.26].

To calculate the enthalpy of the mixtures we can in principle follow the same procedure. But in our dilution refrigerator we have mixtures at various concentrations (Sect.7.2), and the specific heat has only been measured at a few low concentrations of ^{3}He [7.22-25]. Calculated thermodynamic data for liquid ^{3}He-^{4}He mixtures at $x \leq 8\%$ and $T < 250$ mK have been published in [7.27]. However, very little is known about mixtures at high ^{3}He concentrations which are circulating in a dilution refrigerator (see below). Of course, most important is the mixture in the chamber where the cooling occurs (see below) and there we have 6.5% ^{3}He. Fortunately, in the mixtures where the ^{3}He is diluted by ^{4}He we have a weakly interacting Fermi liquid, for which it is a good approximation to take the equations for a Fermi gas and replace the bare ^{3}He mass m_3 by the effective mass m^*. This substitution reflects the influence of the neighboring ^{3}He and ^{4}He atoms with which the ^{3}He interacts. We then have at $T < T_F/10$ the following relation for the specific heat of the mixture per mole of ^{3}He:

$$C_{3,d} = N_0 k_B \frac{\pi^2}{2} \frac{T}{T_F} = 0.745 \frac{m^*}{m_3} \left(\frac{V_m}{x} \right)^{2/3} T , \tag{7.22}$$

with the equation for the Fermi temperature

---

[2] From [7.26], $C_3/RT = 2.78$ at $T < 6$ mK, which is reduced by about 4% at $T = 40$ mK and by about 8% at $T = 60$ mK.

$$T_F = \frac{\hbar^2}{2m^* k_B} \left[\frac{3\pi^2 N_0 x}{V_m} \right]^{2/3} = 55.2 \frac{m_3}{m^*} \left[\frac{x}{V_m} \right]^{2/3} , \tag{7.23a}$$

and for the molar volume of the mixtures

$$V_m = V_{m,4}(1 + 0.284x) , \tag{7.23b}$$

where $V_{m,4}$ is the molar volume of pure ^{4}He [7.18].

This means that the specific heat *per ^{3}He atom* in the mixture increases with decreasing concentration! For one mole of *mixture* of ^{3}He concentration x we have

$$C'_{3,d} = xC_{3,d} \propto \frac{x^{1/3} T}{m^*} \quad (\text{at } T < T_F/10) , \tag{7.24}$$

which indicates that the specific heat $C'_{3,d}$ of ^{3}He-^{4}He mixtures increases not proportional to the ^{3}He concentration x but proportional to $x^{1/3}$ only. The effective mass m^* is weakly dependent on the ^{3}He concentration, and for a mixture of 6.5% at saturated vapour pressure $m^* \simeq 2.5m_3$. This then gives for the Fermi temperature $T_F(6.5\%) = 0.38$ K, and we find for the specific heat of a 6.5% mixture below 40 mK [7.22-25]

$$C_{3,d}(6.5\%) \simeq 106T \quad [\text{J/mol}^3\text{He·K}] . \tag{7.25}$$

When the two phases are in thermodynamic equilibrium we must have for the chemical potentials

$$\mu_{3,c}(x_c,T) = \mu_{3,d}(x_d,T) . \tag{7.26}$$

With

$$\mu = H - TS \tag{7.27}$$

we find

$$H_3 - T S_3 = H_{3,d} - T S_{3,d} . \tag{7.28}$$

This then gives with (7.20,21,25)

$$H_{3,d}(T) = H_3(0) + 11T^2 + T \int_0^T (C_{3,d}/T' - C_3/T')dT'$$

$$= H_3(0) + 95T^2 \quad [\text{J/mol } ^3\text{He}] . \tag{7.29}$$

Combining this with (7.21) for the enthalpy of pure ^{3}He we find for the cooling power occurring at the phase separation line when n_3 moles of ^{3}He per unit time are transferred from the concentrated to the dilute phase

$$\dot{Q}(T) = \dot{n}_3[H_{3,d}(T) - H_3(T)] = 84\dot{n}_3 T^2 \quad [W] . \tag{7.30}$$

With a value of $\dot{n}_3$ = 100 μmol/s and T = 10(30) mK we find

$$\dot{Q} \simeq 1 \ (10) \ \mu W . \tag{7.31}$$

For the above calculation I have used the recent, very accurate specific heat data of *Greywall* [7.26] for the properties of pure ^{3}He. The older data on the specific heat of mixtures [7.22-25] are much less reliable. Therefore the figures given above may have to be revised slightly when more accurate specific heat data for the mixtures become available.

7.1.5 Osmotic Pressure

Before describing the design of a ^{3}He-^{4}He dilution refrigerator we have to discuss one more property of liquid helium mixtures: their osmotic pressure [7.11, 28, 29]. As we shall see later, we have isotopic helium mixtures at varying concentrations and temperatures in our refrigerator. In such a situation an osmotic pressure develops in a two-fluid mixture.

A set-up for determining the osmotic pressure in helium mixtures is shown schematically in Fig.7.6. It consists of two thermally isolated containers separated by a membrane which can only be crossed by superfluid ^{4}He. A semipermeable membrane or "superleak" for the helium mixtures can easily be made from tightly compressed powders. Such a superleak with very small pores ($\leq$ 1000Å) is permeable for superfluid ^{4}He but not for the Fermi liquid ^{3}He with its rather large viscosity (Fig.2.18). For that reason, an osmotic pressure develops across the superleak, so that the liquid height is higher on the mixture side than on the pure ^{4}He side. The osmotic pressure results from the "desire" of the liquids to exist at equal concentrations on either side of the semipermeable wall.

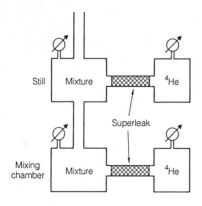

Fig.7.6. Schematic set-up for a *Gedankenexperiment* to measure the osmotic pressure of ^{3}He-^{4}He solutions in the still and in the mixing chamber of a ^{3}He-^{4}He dilution refrigerator

We can approximately calculate the osmotic pressure π in ^{3}He-^{4}He mixtures by considering them as ideal solutions (which is valid for liquid helium mixtures in the classical regime at $T > T_F$, e.g., at $T \gtrsim 0.15$ K, $x \lesssim 0.03$). In this situation we have van't Hoff's law

$$\pi \, V_{m,4} \simeq xRT \, , \tag{7.32}$$

where $V_{m,4}$ is the molar volume of ^{4}He. In a dilution refrigerator a tube connects the mixture in the mixing chamber (where we have the phase separation line) with the mixture in the still (where ^{3}He is evaporated), see Fig.7.9. Let us assume that both the mixture in the mixing chamber and the mixture in the still are connected via a superleak to separate second vessels, which in each case contain pure ^{4}He (Fig.7.6). Then an osmotic pressure will develop in both the mixing chamber and the still. The difference of the osmotic pressures due to the different concentrations and temperatures in the mixing chamber and the still is given by

$$\pi_{mc} - \pi_{st} \simeq (x_{mc} T_{mc} - x_{st} T_{st}) R / V_{m,4} \, , \tag{7.33}$$

where st stands for still and mc for mixing chamber. If no ^{3}He is pumped from the still, then there is no difference in osmotic pressure between the still and the mixing chamber. Assuming the mixing chamber with 6.5% mixture to be at 10 mK and the still to be at 0.65 K, we then have

$$x_{st} = x_{mc} \frac{T_{mc}}{T_{st}} \sim 0.1\% \, . \tag{7.34}$$

If we pump ^{3}He from the still, the concentration of ^{3}He will decrease there, and an osmotic pressure will develop that will drive ^{3}He from the mixing chamber into the still and therefore "suck" ^{3}He from the concentrated into the dilute phase in the mixing chamber. The maximum osmotic pressure will be obtained when the concentration of ^{3}He in the still goes to zero. We then have (Fig.7.7)

$$\Delta\pi_{max} = \frac{x_{mc} RT}{V_{m,4}} \simeq 20 \text{ mbar} \tag{7.35}$$

for $T \lesssim 0.1$ K, below which π becomes T-independent for $x = 6.5\%$ (see below and Fig.7.7). This pressure corresponds to the hydrostatic pressure of about 1 m of liquid helium. In other words, the osmotic pressure will be large enough to drive the ^{3}He from the mixing chamber into the still even if they are separated by a vertical distance of about 1 m.

A more correct treatment takes into account that, at the temperature of the mixing chamber, the ^{3}He in both phases is in the Fermi degenerate state and at $T < T_F/3$ we have to use

$$\pi V_{m,4} = 0.4xRT_F \, . \tag{7.36}$$

117

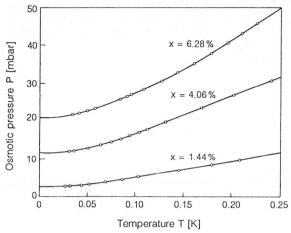

Fig.7.7. Osmotic pressures of some dilute ^{3}He-^{4}He mixtures at a pressure of 0.26 bar (from [7.10] who used the data of [7.28])

This results in a temperature-independent osmotic pressure $\pi \propto x^{5/3}$ at $T \lesssim$ 50 mK; its value is about 20 mbar for a 6.5% mixture (Fig.7.7).

In the above discussion fountain pressure effects $\Delta P = \rho S \Delta T$, which result from the superfluidity of ^{4}He [7.14-17], have been neglected because they are small in comparison to the osmotic pressure.

7.2 Realization of a ^{3}He-^{4}He Dilution Refrigerator

The realization of a dilution refrigerator can be understood if we compare the cooling process with cooling which occurs when liquid is evaporated; this comparison is shown in Fig.7.8. But we have to keep in mind that the *physics* of these cooling processes is quite different. In evaporation we rely on the classical heat of evaporation for cooling. In dilution refrigeration we rely on the enthalpy of mixing of two quantum liquids. Here the cooling results from quantum mechanical effects: the different zero-point motions of the two helium isotopes and the different statistics which we have to apply to understand their properties at low temperatures.

In the closed ^{3}He circulation cycle of a dilution refrigerator shown in Fig.7.8, the cooling occurs when ^{3}He atoms are transferred from the ^{3}He-rich to the ^{3}He-poor side. The ^{3}He is then driven up along the liquid mixture column by the osmotic pressure. It eventually reaches the "^{3}He pump", which in this scheme is our still. From the still we can pump and evaporate the ^{3}He, if it is operated at an appropriately high temperature, e.g. 0.7 K, where the vapour pressure of ^{3}He is much larger than the vapour pressure of ^{4}He (Fig.2.6). For example, at $T = 0.7$ (0.6) K for an $x = 1.0\%$ (1.2%) mixture, we have $P_3 + P_4 = 88$ (46) μbar and $P_3/(P_3 + P_4) = 97\%$ (99%), which are rather convenient conditions. The vapour pressure of ^{3}He-^{4}He

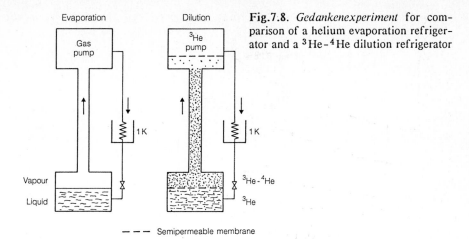

Evaporation

Dilution

Fig.7.8. *Gedankenexperiment* for comparison of a helium evaporation refrigerator and a ³He-⁴He dilution refrigerator

Gas pump

³He pump

1 K

1 K

Vapour

Liquid

³He-⁴He

³He

— — — Semipermeable membrane

mixtures at various T and x can be found in [7.9, 30]. The still operates like a destillation chamber, evaporating almost pure ³He. As a result, ³He will flow from the dilute phase in the mixing chamber to the still driven by the osmotic pressure difference. This flow of cold ³He from the mixing chamber to the evaporation chamber is utilized to precool the incoming ³He in a heat exchanging process. The ³He concentration in the dilute phase of the mixing chamber will stay constant because ³He atoms are continuously crossing the phase separation line from the concentrated to the dilute phase, producing cooling due to the latent heat of mixing. Of course, the circuit cannot operate in the way shown, because we would have the heavier mixture on top of the lighter liquid ³He. In reality we have to design the refrigerator slightly differently.

The main components of a working dilution refrigerator and a flow diagram for its liquids are shown in Fig.7.9. The ³He gas coming from the exit of a pump at room temperature will first be precooled by a liquid ⁴He bath at 4.2 K. It will then be condensed in a second ⁴He bath at about 1.5 K, which we can obtain by using a continuously operating ⁴He refrigerator (Sect.5.2.4). The heat transfer surface area may have to be increased by using a sintered metal (Sect.13.6) to absorb the heat of condensation of ³He. This ⁴He evaporator is also used as a heat sink at which all tubes and leads going to colder parts of the refrigerator should be thermally anchored. Below the ⁴He refrigerator we need the so-called main flow impedance (Z~10¹² cm⁻³, see Sect.5.2.4 for its design [7.31]), to establish sufficient pressure (30÷200 mbar) for the incoming ³He so that it will indeed condense at 1.5 K. The now liquid ³He will flow through a heat exchanger which is in thermal contact with (or even inside) the still at a temperature of about 0.7 K. Below the still we have a secondary flow impedance (Z ~ 10¹¹cm⁻³) to prevent reevaporation of ³He. After leaving this secondary flow impedance the liquid ³He will flow through one or several heat exchangers (Sect.7.3.3) to precool it to a low enough temperature before it enters the upper, concentrated phase in the mixing chamber.

Fig.7.9. Schematic ^{3}He-^{4}He dilution refrigerator

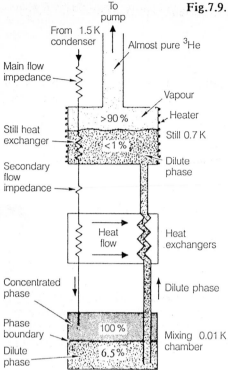

A wider tube for the dilute phase in the refrigerator leaves the lower, dilute mixture phase of the mixing chamber, and then goes through the heat exchanger to precool the incoming ^{3}He. It enters the dilute liquid phase in the still, where we have a liquid ^{3}He concentration of less than 1%. The vapour above the dilute liquid phase in the still has a concentration of typically 90% ^{3}He due to the high vapour pressure of ^{3}He at the temperature of the still. If we then pump on the still and resupply the condensation line continuously with ^{3}He gas we have a closed ^{3}He circuit in which ^{3}He is forced down the condensation line. Then, again after liquefaction and precooling, it enters the concentrated phase in the mixing chamber. It will cross the phase boundary, giving rise to cooling, and will eventually leave the mixing chamber and be pushed up by the osmotic pressure into the still, where it will evaporate. Circulation of the ^{3}He is maintained by a pumping system at room temperature.

Each component of a dilution refrigerator has to be carefully designed to achieve the required properties, but the quality of its heat exchangers is particularly critical, as will become obvious in the next section.

7.3 Properties of the Main Components of a ^{3}He-^{4}He Dilution Refrigerator

7.3.1 Mixing Chamber

We will now perform an enthalpy balance for the mixing chamber where cooling is produced by the transfer of $\dot{n}_3$ ^{3}He moles from the concentrated (assumed pure ^{3}He) to the dilute phase of $x = 6.5\%$. The cooling power will be used to precool the warmer liquid ^{3}He coming from the heat exchangers as well as to cool an experiment or to balance other external heat inflow. This enthalpy balance can be easily established by considering Fig.7.10. We then have

$$\dot{n}_3[H_{3,d}(T_{mc}) - H_3(T_{mc})] = \dot{n}_3[H_3(T_{ex}) - H_3(T_{mc})] + \dot{Q} , \qquad (7.37)$$

resulting in a cooling power, using (7.21,29), of

$$\dot{Q} = \dot{n}_3(95\,T_{mc}^2 - 11\,T_{ex}^2) \quad [W] . \qquad (7.38)$$

If the liquid leaving the last heat exchanger already has a temperature equal to the temperature of the mixing chamber or if we operate the refrigerator in a discontinuous mode, which means we do not supply any more incoming ^{3}He which has to be precooled, then we obtain the maximum cooling power

$$\dot{Q}_{max} = 84\,\dot{n}_3\,T_{mc}^2 , \qquad (7.39)$$

or the minimum achievable temperature [but see (7.48, 52, 54)]

$$T_{mc,min} = (\dot{Q}/84\,\dot{n}_3)^{1/2} . \qquad (7.40)$$

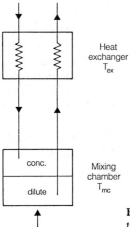

Fig.7.10. Schematic for calculating the enthalpy balance in the mixing chamber of a ^{3}He-^{4}He dilution refrigerator (see text)

On the other hand, we can calculate the maximum temperature allowed for the liquid leaving the last heat exchanger and entering the mixing chamber, which we obtain for the case that there is no cooling power from the dilution refrigerator available, $\dot{Q} = 0$, resulting in

$$T_{ex} \leq 3T_{mc} . \tag{7.41}$$

This gives a rather severe requirement for the efficiency of the heat exchangers, telling us that the liquid has to leave the last heat exchanger at a temperature which is *at the most* a factor of three higher than the temperature which we want to obtain in the mixing chamber. This is a very important result and immediately demonstrates the importance of the efficiency of the heat exchangers in a dilution refrigerator.

Assume that we are circulating 100 μmol ^{3}He/s and we would like to have a cooling power of 1 μW at the mixing chamber. We then obtain

$$T_{mc} = 12 \ (15) \ \text{mK}$$
for
$$T_{ex} = 18 \ (30) \ \text{mK} ,$$

demonstrating again the importance of adequately precooling the incoming ^{3}He in the heat exchangers, particularly the last one (Sect. 7.3.3).

Let me emphasize the important result $\dot{Q} \propto \dot{n}_3$, with $\dot{n}_3$ independent of T below about 0.1 K. This demonstrates the advantage of dilution refrigeration in comparison to evaporation refrigeration, where we have $\dot{n} \propto P_{vap} \propto \exp(-1/k_B T)$ (Fig. 7.3).

7.3.2 Still

One of the main requirements on the design of the still is that the ratio of ^{3}He to ^{4}He in the vapour phase of the still should be as large as possible. In Sect. 7.2 we argued that a value of $0.6 \div 0.7$ K is reasonable for the temperature of the still. In this range the ^{3}He vapour pressure (about 1 mbar) is still large enough to keep the circulation rate reasonably large with a typical pump, and the concentration of ^{4}He in the vapour phase is only some percent.

We now perform an enthalpy balance for the still, where ^{3}He will arrive with the temperature of the condenser (Fig. 7.9) and will leave with the temperature of the still. Cooling is produced by the heat of evaporation of ^{3}He at the temperature of the still,

$$\dot{n}_3 L_3(T_{st}, x_{d,st}) = \dot{n}_3 [H_3(T_{cond}) - H_3(T_{st})] + \dot{Q}_{st} . \tag{7.42}$$

If we again assume a circulation rate of 100 μmol/s, a condenser temperature of 1.2 K and a still temperature of 0.7 K, we find that the required rate of heat supply $\dot{Q}_{st}$ to the still is several milliwatts; more generally, a good rule is $\dot{Q}_{st}[W] \sim 40\dot{n}_3[\text{mols}]$. This heat will be partly supplied by a conventional heater. In addition, we can thermally anchor to the still a radiation shield surrounding all the lower, colder parts of the dilution refrigerator to reduce the heat of radiation; this is done in most modern dilution refrigerators. Of course other parts, like electrical leads and capillaries, could and should be heat sunk at the still as well.

Unfortunately, in many dilution refrigerators the circulating gas contains $10 \div 20\%$ ^{4}He if no special precautions are taken; it is then not pure ^{3}He which circulates but a mixture. This results in a deterioration of the ^{3}He circulation rate $\dot{n}_3$ because it loads the pumping system, which has a constant *total volume* flow rate. It puts also a heat load on the heat exchangers because the specific heat/^{3}He in mixtures can be substantially higher than for pure ^{3}He (Fig.7.5). In addition, separation of ^{3}He from ^{4}He will result in heating effects, so that the temperature of the heat exchangers will increase. An increased ^{4}He circulation rate has a negligible effect on the behaviour of the liquids in the mixing chamber because at these low temperatures dx/dT is essentially independent of T (Fig.7.1). Of course, the mixing chamber temperature and the cooling power of our refrigerator will deteriorate. To keep the amount of ^{4}He pumped from the still reasonably low, one has to suppress, in particular, the superfluid ^{4}He film flow (Sect.2.3.5) up the still pumping tube to a point warm enough to evaporate there. The film flow can result from a combination of siphoning (typically $0.25\,\mu$mol/s per mm of inner circumference of the pumping tube) and of evaporation at the upper, warmer parts of the tube. The introduction of a small orifice (≤ 1 mm diameter) in the pumping tube or, for more powerful refrigerators, a so-called ^{4}He film burner [7.2-10, 32, 34] in the tube is necessary to keep the film flow and hence the amount of ^{4}He in the circulating gas low enough (Fig.7.11).

7.3.3 Heat Exchangers

The purpose of the heat exchangers [7.2-10, 33-37] is to bring the temperature of the incoming ^{3}He as close to the temperature of the mixing chamber as possible by using the cold mixture leaving the mixing chamber to precool the incoming warmer ^{3}He. For this purpose, in general, one

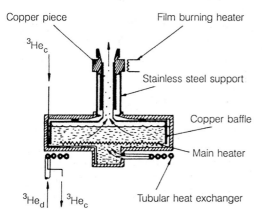

Copper piece

Film burning heater

^{3}He$_c$

Stainless steel support

Copper baffle

Main heater

^{3}He$_d$ ^{3}He$_c$

Tubular heat exchanger

Fig.7.11. A film-flow inhibiting still of a ^{3}He-^{4}He refrigerator [7.2]

needs several heat exchangers between the still and the mixing chamber to achieve the best performance of the refrigerator. An enthalpy balance for the heat exchangers similar to the one performed above for the still and for the mixing chamber is much more involved. Firstly, because we need to know the enthalpy of the concentrated phase (assuming that it is pure [3]He) as a function of temperature and of the dilute phase as a function of temperature and concentration. Secondly, a heat exchanger is a very complicated system with temperature gradients in the viscous fluid streams as well as in the heat exchanger body, both in the direction of the flow and perpendicular to it. We can take the available data on the specific heat of [3]He (Fig.2.14) and on helium mixtures (Fig.7.5) to construct an enthalpy diagram [7.7,8]. But, of course, the values for the mixtures are only an approximation, because the concentration changes along the heat exchangers from a value of 6.5% in the mixing chamber to a value of about 1% in the still.

For the heat exchangers we assume ideal behaviour, in the sense that the exit temperatures of both fluid streams are the same, and neglect viscosity and axial conduction effects. The enthalpy balance for the N-th heat exchanger is then given by

$$\dot{Q}_N + \dot{n}_3[H_3(T_{N-1}) - H_3(T_N)] = \dot{n}_3[H_{3,d}(T_N) - H_{3,d}(T_{N+1})] \,. \qquad (7.43)$$

Fortunately, $H_{3,d} > H_3$, so that the incoming [3]He can in principle always be effectively precooled by the outgoing mixture if the exchangers are designed properly. To compute the temperatures of the various heat exchangers with the mentioned assumptions, one first starts by setting T_{N+1} equal to T_{mc}, the temperature of the mixing chamber. Then the temperature of the N-th heat exchanger is calculated and so on, until one arrives eventually at a temperature equal to the temperature of the still. This procedure determines the number of heat exchangers for a certain desired temperature of the mixing chamber. The result of such a procedure with the additional assumption that the external heat flow to mixing chamber and to each heat exchanger is negligible can be found in [7.7,8]. It shows that three ideal heat exchangers are needed to arrive at $T_{mc} = 10$ mK. In reality, due to the non-ideality of the heat exchangers, the finite conductivities and viscosities of the flowing liquids, and the heat load from some circulating [4]He, one or two additional heat exchangers are needed.

The requirements on the heat exchangers can be quite severe for a powerful dilution refrigerator. Besides coming close to the mentioned ideal behaviour they should have small volumes, so that the liquids attain temperature equilibrium quickly, small impedances, so that the viscous heating due to flow is small, and there should be a small thermal resistance between the streams to obtain good temperature equilibrium between them. This last requirement is of particular importance and leads us back to the thermal boundary resistance between different materials already discussed in Sect. 4.3.2.

The thermal boundary resistance between helium and other materials is given by

$$R_K = \frac{a}{A} T^{-3} \quad [K/W] , \qquad (7.44)$$

at T > 20 mK, where A [m^2] is the contact area. Typical values for the constant a obtained from experiments are $a_c \simeq 0.05$ (^{3}He) and $a_d \simeq 0.02$ (helium mixtures), see Sect.4.3.2; but, of course, they depend on the properties of the body in contact with liquid helium. In a heat exchanger of a dilution refrigerator the two resistances are in series, and because $a_c > a_d$, we should have $A_c > A_d$.

As an example, for $\dot{Q}$ = 0.1 mW, A = 0.1 m^2 and T = 100 mK, we would have $\Delta T \sim$ 50 mK for ^{3}He. Or, at lower T, with $\dot{Q}$ = 0.01 mW, A = 10 m^2 and T = 20 mK, we would have $\Delta T \sim$ 6 mK. Both temperature steps are unacceptably large, so that we either have to decrease the heat flow $\dot{Q}$ or increase the surface area A. Usually one requires many square meters of surface area to overcome the Kapitza boundary resistance in the heat exchangers at T < 0.1 K. Because the thermal boundary resistance increases with decreasing temperature, it is particularly serious in the mixing chamber, where one needs surface areas between several 10 m^2 and several 100 m^2, depending on $\dot{n}_3$ and T_{mc} [7.2-10, 33-37].

Heat exchangers are the most important and most critical part of a dilution refrigerator; they determine its minimum temperature, for example. For the design of heat exchangers we have to take into account the problems and considerations discussed above. In particular, we have to take into account that the thermal boundary resistance as well as the liquids' viscosities and conductivities increase with decreasing temperature. When designing dilution refrigerators, former practical experience with a successful refrigerator [7.2-10, 33-39] is sometimes more important than a recalculation of various parameters.

For a rather simple dilution refrigerator with a minimum temperature of about 40 mK, one continuous counterflow tube-in-tube heat exchanger consisting of two concentric capillaries (with diameters of order 0.5mm and 1mm, and with 0.1mm or 0.2mm wall thickness) several meters long is sufficient [7.2-10, 33-37]. These concentric capillaries should be of low thermal conductivity (CuNi, stainless steel or brass) and are usually coiled into a spiral so they do not take up too much space. In such a heat exchanger the temperatures change continuously along the exchanger. Heat is transferred across the body of the wall, and conduction along the capillary and along the liquid streams should be negligible. The dilute phase moves in the space between the tubes and the concentrated liquid moves in the inner tube. - In a more elaborate design, the inner capillary is not straight but spiralled, to increase the surface area, and then put into the outer, somewhat larger capillary (Fig.7.12) [7.2,3,34]. In spite of their simple design and small inner volumes, continuous heat exchangers can be quite effective. If one uses the appropriate dimensions, a refrigerator with a well-designed continuous heat

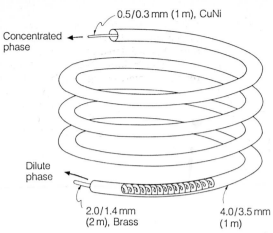

0.5/0.3 mm (1 m), CuNi

Concentrated phase

Dilute phase

2.0/1.4 mm (2 m), Brass

4.0/3.5 mm (1 m)

Fig.7.12. Schematic of a concentric heat exchanger. The design used in [7.34] had for the dilute phase: $Z \sim 10^7$ cm^{-3}, $A_{brass} = 126$ cm^2, $A_{CuNi} = 16$ cm^2, $V_{liq} = 6$ cm^3; and for the concentrated phase: $Z_{brass} \sim 5 \cdot 10^8$ cm^{-3}, $Z_{CuNi} \sim 8 \cdot 10^9$ cm^{-3}, $A_{brass} = 88$ cm^2, $A_{CuNi} = 9$ cm^2, $V_{liq,brass} = 2$ cm^3, $V_{liq,CuNi} \sim 0.07$ cm^3

exchanger can reach minimum temperatures of $15 \div 20$ mK. The warmer end of a continuous heat exchanger can also be designed as a secondary flow impedance by reducing its diameter or by inserting a wire into it to prevent reevaporation of the ^{3}He.

For a more powerful dilution refrigerator with a larger cooling power and lower minimum temperature we need more than one heat exchanger. These are, first a continuous heat exchanger below the still, as described above, and then several step heat exchangers in series [7.2–10, 33–38]. At lower temperatures the above-discussed continuous heat exchanger can no longer be used because it does not provide enough surface area to defeat the increasing thermal boundary resistance. This can only be provided by step exchangers, which in their simplest design can be machined from Cu blocks into which two holes have been drilled (Fig.7.13). To reduce the thermal boundary resistance, each channel has to be filled with pressed and/or sintered metal powder to provide the required surface area for adequate heat exchange (Sect.13.6). Other design criteria are a low flow impedance (to reduce $\dot{Q}_{visc}$, see below) and a small size (to economize on the amount of ^{3}He needed and to give a short thermal time constant). For example, the flow channel diameter in the heat exchangers has to be increased with decreasing T. To produce a large surface area but small flow impedance, the metal powder can first be sintered, then broken up, and the sinter blocks are then sintered together to leave large open flow areas. Another possibility is to drill an open flow channel through the sintered powder (Fig.7.13). This large flow area is important not only in order to keep viscous heating low but also to take advantage of the high thermal conductivity of ^{3}He (Sect.2.3.6), which is then always in good thermal contact with the almost stationary liquid in the sinter. Table 7.1 lists the

126

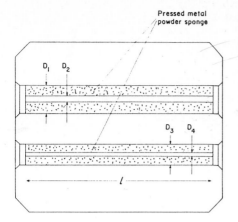

Pressed metal powder sponge

D_1 D_2

D_3 D_4

l

Fig.7.13. Schematic of a step heat exchanger made from Cu with compressed and sintered metal powder in the two channels into which flow channels for the counterflowing liquids have been drilled. The dilution refrigerator of [7.34] with T_{min} = 3 mK and $\dot{n}_3$ = 700 μmol/s used six such step exchangers with the parameters given in Table 7.1

Table 7.1. Data for the Cu-sinter heat exchangers used in the ^{3}He-^{4}He dilution refrigerator of [7.34], which has reached T_{min} = 3 mK. For the symbols, see Fig.7.13. (The filling factor f is for sinter made from powder of grain size d)

T_N [mK]	83	48	32	19	13	10
l [mm]	62	94	94	94	94	88
D_1 [mm]	8	13	13	18	18	22
D_2 [mm]	2.7	2.7	3.2	4.8	6.5	8.0
D_3 [mm]	6	10	10	14	14	17
D_4 [mm]	2.0	2.0	2.4	3.2	4.8	6.5
Sintered	Cu	Cu	Cu	0.2Cu	0.4Cu	0.4Cu
metal powder				0.8Ag	0.6Ag	0.6Ag
d [μm]	100	50	30	44 Cu	44Cu	44Cu
				2.5Ag	0.07Ag	0.07Ag
f		0.55	0.65	0.65	0.75	0.70	0.70
A_c [m^2]		0.05	0.27	0.45	6.5	100	135
A_d [m^2]		0.09	0.46	0.76	10.6	164	230
V_c [cm^3]		1.6	7.1	7.0	13.7	12.8	17.1
V_d [cm^3]		2.8	11.9	11.7	22.2	20.8	29.0

dimensions used for the six step heat exchangers of a rather successful dilution refrigerator with a minimum temperature of about 3 mK inside the mixing chamber at $\dot{n}_3$ = 300 μmol/s. The simple step exchangers were filled with compressed Cu and Ag powders [7.34]. The art of designing heat exchangers [7.7] has been greatly advanced by *Frossati* [7.2,3]. His welded, rectangular heat exchangers filled with submicrometer sintered silver powder (Fig.7.14) are now also used in powerful commercial dilution refrigerators. In [7.2,3,10] the two important steps in designing the step heat exchangers are discussed:

127

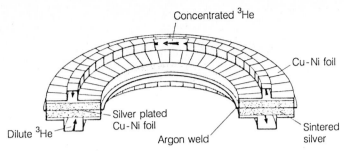

Fig.7.14. Schematic of a semicontinuous heat exchanger developed by *Frossati* et al. [7.2,3] of welded Cu-Ni foil filled with submicrometer silver powder sintered to a silver plated Cu-Ni foil

a) Determination of the required total surface area for the heat exchangers for a given minimum temperature at optimum flow rate and at a given heat leak;

b) optimization of the size of the flow channels for a given exchanger length to minimize the heat generated by viscosity and axial heat flow.

Calculations of the required surface areas in the heat exchangers can be found in [7.2-10,33,34,37]. Assuming for the Kapitza resistance $R_K \propto T^{-i}$ (Sect.4.3.2) we have for the heat flow $\dot{Q}$ between the two streams in an exchanger with contact area A

$$\dot{Q} = \lambda_{i+1} A (T_1^{i+1} - T_2^{i+1}) . \tag{7.45}$$

Frossati [7.2,10] gave evidence for the following values:

$$\lambda_4 = 63 \ \mathrm{W \cdot m^{-2} \cdot K^{-4}} ,$$

$$\lambda_3 = 6.7 \cdot 10^{-3} \ \mathrm{W \cdot m^{-2} \cdot K^{-3}} , \tag{7.46}$$

$$\lambda_2 = 2.1 \cdot 10^{-4} \ \mathrm{W \cdot m^{-2} \cdot K^{-2}} .$$

Typical required surface areas in the last heat exchanger for the following mixing chamber temperatures are then

T_{mc} [mK]	4	8	15	25
A [m²]	71	34	18	10

assuming i = 2, $\dot{n}_3 = 2 \cdot 10^{-4}$ mol/s, $\dot{Q} = 30$ nW [7.10].

As mentioned, the large surface areas necessary in the heat exchangers as well as in the mixing chamber are provided by sintered metal powders. Various recipes for their fabrication and characterization have been described in the literature (Sect.13.6).

Another point to be considered is the low thermal conductivity of the sintered metal powders themselves, which can be orders of magnitude lower than the bulk metal conductivity (Table 13.1). Obviously, a mathematical analysis of the performance of real heat exchangers is very involved. One

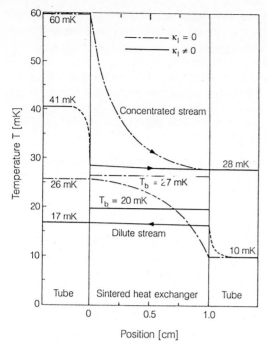

Fig.7.15. Calculated liquid and body temperature profiles within and near a discrete heat exchanger of length 1 cm for a mixing chamber temperature of 10 mK. One set of curves is calculated neglecting the finite thermal conductivity of the liquids ($\kappa_l = 0$), and the other set is calculated using the correct liquid thermal conductivities ($\kappa_l \neq 0$). The liquid volume on the concentrated side is 0.85 cm³, and the dilute liquid volume is 2.1 times larger. The surface area per unit liquid volume is 400 cm⁻¹. The ³He flow rate is 20 μmol/s. External heat flow to the heat exchanger and to the mixing chamber is neglected. Obviously a design where the influence of the liquid conductivity is minimized is more favorable [7.7, 8]

has to solve coupled differential equations for the concentrated and diluted helium streams, where properties like the thermal conductivity of the liquids, of the exchanger body and of the sinter, thermal boundary resistances between them, viscous heating and osmotic pressure are taken into account to calculate the temperature profile in the exchanger. Figure 7.15 shows as an example the effect of the finite thermal conductivities of the liquids in the heat exchangers on the temperatures of the liquids inside the exchanger and of the body of the heat exchanger itself. If the finite thermal conductivity of the liquids is taken into account, most of the temperature changes in the two liquid streams occur in the inlet tubes just before the heat exchanger. Even the inclusion of just this one property results in substantial changes in the temperature profiles [7.7, 8, 36, 37].

The selection of the diameters of the tubes connecting mixing chamber, heat exchangers and still is important. Here we have to make a compromise. We would like to have a large diameter for the tubes to ensure that the circulation of the rather viscous ³He is large and viscous heating effects are negligible. Yet the diameter of the tubes must be small enough for an osmotic pressure to develop between the mixing chamber and the still, and we also want to have the diameter small so that the refrigerator will not suffer from hydrodynamic instabilities and convection. We have to bear in mind that the ^{3}He concentration decreases towards the still and therefore the density of the mixture in the dilute phase increases when going from the mixing chamber to the still. Typical diameters of the connecting tubes are about 1 mm just below the still up to 10 mm before the mixing chamber of a powerful dilution refrigerator [7.2, 3, 33-35].

Viscous heating is given by

$$\dot{Q}_{visc} = \dot{V}\Delta P = Z\eta V^2 \dot{n}^2 \tag{7.47}$$

for a laminar flow with $Z = 128\ell/\pi d^4$ in case of a circular-cross-section tube of length ℓ and diameter d [cm] and $Z = 12\ell/ab^3$ in case of a square with width b and height a; $\dot{Q}_{visc}$ may eventually limit the performance of a dilution refrigerator. Viscous heating is more serious in the dilute than in the concentrated stream, and it increases with decreasing temperature ($\eta \propto T^{-2}$ for a degenerate Fermi liquid, Fig.2.18). To keep viscous heating of the two streams in a heat exchanger equal, one needs $D_d \sim 1.7 D_c$ [7.8].

Wheatley et al. [7.4-6] have given arguments that the practical lower limit for T_{mc} is due to viscous heating and conduction of heat in the flowing dilute phase at the outlet of the mixing chamber; they arrived at

$$T_{mc,min} = 4d^{-1/3} \quad [mK], \tag{7.48}$$

where d is the diameter of the exit tube measured in millimeters. *Frossati* [7.2, 3] has discussed these problems by considering viscous heating and heat conduction contributions for the concentrated and dilute streams. With $\dot{Q}_{visc} \propto d^{-4}$ (assuming Poiseuille flow) and $\dot{Q}_{cond} \propto d^2$, the sum of the two is

$$\dot{Q}_{visc} + \dot{Q}_{cond} = ad^{-4} + bd^2, \tag{7.49}$$

yielding an optimal channel size

$$d_{opt} = (2a/b)^{1/6}. \tag{7.50}$$

He gave the resulting d_{opt} for the various heat exchangers of a powerful dilution refrigerator which has reached $T_{mc} \simeq 2$ mK. Since viscosity and thermal conductivity in both Fermi liquid streams increase with decreasing temperature, their limiting influence becomes more and more severe as lower temperatures are required.

Let me come back to the influence of the thermal boundary resistance. Taking the temperature step due to the Kapitza resistance R_K between the helium liquid and the solid with a surface area A into account [7.2] modifies (7.40) for the minimum temperature of a dilution refrigerator to

$$T_{mc}^2 = 0.012\dot{Q}/\dot{n}_3 + 6.4R_K\dot{n}_3 T^3 \quad \text{if} \quad R_K \propto T^{-3} , \tag{7.51}$$

and

$$T_{mc} = 0.11(\dot{Q}/\dot{n}_3)^{1/2} + 27R_K\dot{n}_3 T^2 \quad \text{if} \quad R_K \propto T^{-2} . \tag{7.52}$$

Taking the value $AR_K T^2 = 28 \text{ m}^2 \cdot \text{K}^3/\text{W}$ (Sect.4.3.2) for (7.52) we arrive at the optimum circulation rate

$$\dot{n}_{3,opt} \simeq 1.8 \cdot 10^{-3} \dot{Q}^{1/3} A^{2/3} \text{ [mol/s]} , \tag{7.53}$$

and the minimum temperature

$$T_{mc,min} = 4.0(\dot{Q}/A)^{1/3} \quad [\text{K}] . \tag{7.54}$$

7.4 Examples of ^{3}He-^{4}He Dilution Refrigerators

Figures 7.16 and 17 are schematic diagrams of some rather successful "home-made" dilution refrigerators. Figure 7.18 shows the low-temperature part of a commercial dilution refrigerator with a minimum temperature of about 4 mK. The cooling power as a function of temperature of a dilution refrigerator with a dilution unit very similar to the one shown in Fig.7.18 is depicted in Fig.7.19. The most powerful ^{3}He-^{4}He dilution refrigerators have been built by *Frossati* et al. [7.2,3] (Fig.10.21). Their latest design has a maximum circulation rate of $\dot{n}_3 = 10$ mmol/s, a minimum temperature of 1.9 mK at $\dot{n}_3 = 0.85$ mmol/s and a cooling power of 20 μW at 10 mK. It contains the enormous quantity of 1.6 kg Ag, and $A_c = 1000 \text{ m}^2$, $A_d = 1300$ m^2 in total in the heat exchangers!

Recently, a small ^{3}He-^{4}He dilution refrigerator which can be inserted into a ^{4}He storage dewar (50mm neck diameter) has been described [7.38]. A similar design is shown in Fig.7.20; it is based on the same principles as the ^{4}He and ^{3}He dipper cryostats discussed in Sects.5.2.4 and 6.2. It can be cooled from room temperature to the final temperature of about 15 mK within a few hours; a typical circulation rate is 30 μmol/s. Such units are available commercially. A small all-plastic dilution refrigerator with a minimum temperature of 10 mK at $\dot{n}_3 = 0.27$ mmol/s especially designed to be used in high magnetic fields is described in [7.39].

A dilution refrigerator is a rather complicated apparatus with many parts joined together by welding, hard soldering, soft soldering, or even gluing. To avoid later problems, it therefore should be carefully leak checked at room temperature, at LN_2 temperature, and possibly at LHe temperature in each run. Localizing a leak may be quite time consuming and the refrigerator may have to be separated into various sections to find it, in particular if it is a "cold leak". A procedure of localizing a leak which is only penetrated by superfluid helium is described in [7.40]. In addition, the flow rates through the continuous ^{4}He refrigerator and through the dilution unit should be tested at room temperature and at LN_2 temperature.

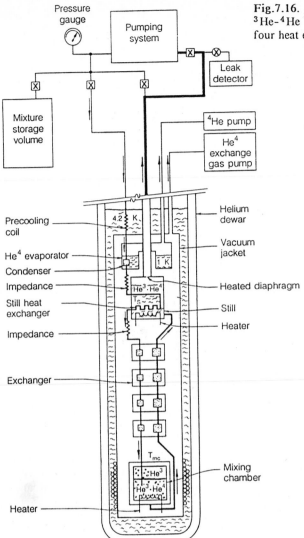

Pressure gauge

Pumping system

Leak detector

Mixture storage volume

^{4}He pump

He^4 exchange gas pump

Precooling coil

He^4 evaporator

Condenser

Impedance

Still heat exchanger

Impedance

Exchanger

Heater

Helium dewar

Vacuum jacket

Heated diaphragm

Still

Heater

Mixing chamber

4.2 K

1 K

He^3·He^4

T_s

He^3

He^3·He^4

T_{mc}

Fig.7.16. Schematic of a typical ^{3}He-^{4}He dilution refrigerator with four heat exchangers [7.5]

General considerations in designing a dilution refrigerator are, of course, the space available for experiments and leads, access to experiments and to thermal heat sinks for the leads, mechanical stability, etc.

In addition to the low-temperature part of a dilution refrigerator, one needs substantial room-temperature equipment for the pumping and gas handling circuits [7.5,8]. A self-explanatory example of such a system is shown in Fig.7.21. Of course, such a system should not have and should not develop leaks, in order to avoid loss of the expensive ^{3}He gas. This is particularly important for equipment containing moving parts like pumps and valves. One should therefore only use valves sealed by bellows and sealed

132

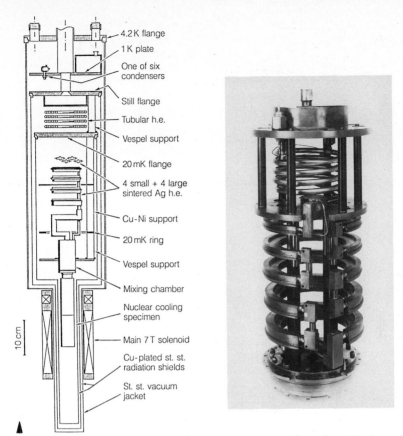

Labels on schematic (Fig. 7.17):
- 4.2 K flange
- 1 K plate
- One of six condensers
- Still flange
- Tubular h.e.
- Vespel support
- 20 mK flange
- 4 small + 4 large sintered Ag h.e.
- Cu-Ni support
- 20 mK ring
- Vespel support
- Mixing chamber
- Nuclear cooling specimen
- Main 7 T solenoid
- Cu-plated st. st. radiation shields
- St. st. vacuum jacket
- 10 cm

Fig.7.17. Schematic of the low temperature part of a ^{3}He-^{4}He dilution refrigerator with a nuclear refrigeration stage below it [7.35]

Fig.7.18. Low temperature part of a commercial ^{3}He-^{4}He dilution refrigerator with the still, a continuous heat exchanger, five step heat exchangers and mixing chamber

mechanical pumps modified for use with ^{3}He as backing pumps for the usual Roots or Booster pumps. The system must also contain safety features for the event of cooling water failure or blockages in the refrigerator.

A gas handling system for a dilution refrigerator will always be operated at sub-atmospheric pressure. If there is a tiny undetected leak, air will get into the circulating gas. In addition, there will be products from cracking of pumping oil. Both the air and the organic gases would condense in the refrigerator and would very soon plug the condenser, capillaries, impedances or heat exchangers of such refrigerators, which are sometimes intended to run for months. To avoid this problem, a "cold trap" at LN$_2$ temperature (and sometimes possibly a second one at LHe temperature [7.41]) has to be inserted after the pumps to freeze out these gases (Fig.7.22). With proper precautions, dilution refrigerators have been continuously operated for about a year.

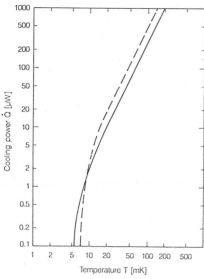

Fig.7.19. Cooling power as a function of temperature of a commercial ^{3}He-^{4}He dilution refrigerator with a dilution unit very similar to the one shown in Fig.7.18. Data are for two still heating powers: 8 mW (full line) and 22 mW (dashed line)

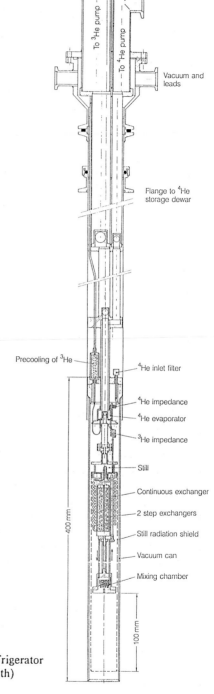

Fig.7.20. A dipstick ^{3}He-^{4}He dilution refrigerator (Courtesy of P. Sekowski, Universität Bayreuth)

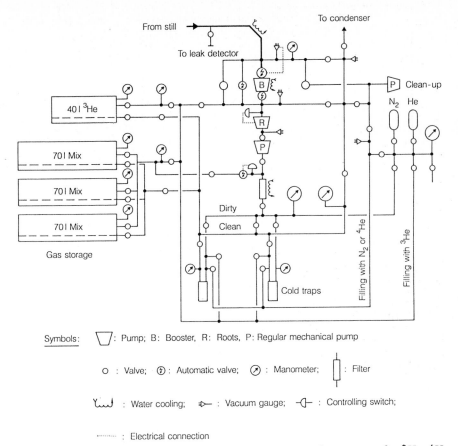

Symbols: $\bigtriangledown$: Pump; B: Booster, R: Roots, P: Regular mechanical pump

○ : Valve; ⊘ : Automatic valve; ⊘ : Manometer; ▯ : Filter

ᨦᨦ : Water cooling; ▷▬ : Vacuum gauge; ─◁─ : Controlling switch;

········ : Electrical connection

Fig.7.21. Schematic diagram of the gas handling and pumping system of a ^{3}He-^{4}He dilution refrigerator (Courtesy of P. Sekowski, Universität Bayreuth)

Before starting up a dilution refrigerator one has to know the volumes of its various components, to determine the necessary total molar quantity of helium (n_3+n_4), and the isotopic ratio $n_3/(n_3+n_4)$ - typically 25% - to position the free surface in the still and the phase separation line in the mixing chamber. Later corrections of n_3 and/or n_4 after the first low temperature trials may be necessary. A cylindrical capacitance gauge in the mixing chamber to monitor the phase separation line is very helpful when adjusting the amount of ^{3}He for maximum performance of the refrigerator [7.3].

^{3}He-^{4}He dilution refrigerators are among the most important equipment for condensed-matter physics nowadays because many properties of matter have to be investigated at temperatures below 1 K to understand their behaviour. To build such a system needs substantial experience and time; to buy it needs appropriate funds. There are probably several hundred of these refrigerators in operation in research institutes today, and without doubt their number will increase in the future. Their thermodynamics is

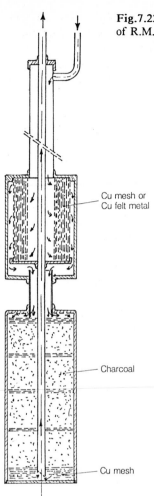

Fig.7.22. LN$_2$ cooled activated charcoal/Cu mesh trap (Courtesy of R.M. Mueller and P. Sekowski)

Cu mesh or
Cu felt metal

Charcoal

Cu mesh

well established and problems usually result from design errors rather than from unknown phenomena. A description of how to start up a dilution refrigerator and how to troubleshoot it is given in [7.42].

Most dilution refrigerators operate according to the principles and designs discussed above. There are a few alternative designs of dilution refrigerators which have actually been built and used. Their main purpose is to avoid the expensive room-temperature gas handling and pumping system or to reduce the problem of the thermal boundary resistance between helium and solids. They have not yet found widespread use and the reader is referred to the relevant literature [7.8,9,43-46]. Of particular interest are the "Leiden Superleak Refrigerator", where ^{4}He is circulated instead of ^{3}He [7.44], and a refrigerator in which the circulation of the helium gas is achieved with an internal regenerating charcoal pump [7.45]. They may become more widespread in the future. A ^{3}He-^{4}He dilution refrigerator where the entering ^{3}He is not precooled and liquified by a pumped ^{4}He bath but in a counterflow heat exchanger which makes use of the enthalpy of the ^{3}He gas pumped out of the still was described in [7.46].

Let me close this chapter by summarizing the five facts which are the basis for the successful operation of this only known continuous cooling technology for temperatures below 0.3 K.

- ^{3}He-^{4}He mixtures undergo phase separation when cooled below 0.87 K, resulting in two phases between which the ^{3}He atoms can be moved.
- The specific heat of a ^{3}He atom is larger in the dilute phase than in the concentrated phase, which results in the "production of cold" if this atom passes from the concentrated phase to the dilute phase.
- There is a finite solubility of ^{3}He in ^{4}He even for temperatures approaching absolute zero, resulting in a cooling power which decreases only with T^2 and not exponentially as in the evaporation cooling process.
- There is a substantial difference in the vapour pressures of ^{3}He and ^{4}He at the same temperature, which allows the circulation of almost pure ^{3}He.
- If the helium mixtures are at different temperatures in a cryogenic apparatus, there is an osmotic pressure driving the ^{3}He from the mixing chamber up into the still.

8. Refrigeration by Solidification of Liquid ^{3}He: Pomeranchuck Cooling

Solidification of matter at a rate $\dot{n}$ usually results in the production of heat according to

$$\dot{Q} = \dot{n}T(S_{sol} - S_{liq}) < 0 , \qquad (8.1)$$

because the liquid's entropy is usually larger than the solid's entropy, as the liquid state is a state of lower order than the solid state.

In 1950 the Russian physicist I. Pomeranchuk predicted that for ^{3}He on the melting curve below about 0.3 K the entropy of the liquid phase is smaller than the entropy of the solid phase (which means the liquid phase is more ordered), and that therefore adiabatic solidification of ^{3}He along the melting line should result in cooling. For quite some time this attractive proposal was not put into practice. Physicists were afraid of the experimental problems which might arise from the required low starting temperature and the possibility of frictional heating during solidification of ^{3}He. However, in 1965 the Russian physicist *Anufriev* picked up Pomeranchuk's proposal and indeed succeeded in reducing the temperature in his experiment from 50 mK (which he produced by paramagnetic cooling; see Chap.9) to a final temperature of about 18 mK [8.1]. It is possible that the temperature in his experiment was somewhat lower, but the thermometry was not appropriate for determining lower temperatures conclusively. At the end of the 1960's several American groups, in particular *Johnson, Wheatley* and their co-workers, started experiments on "Pomeranchuk cooling" and arrived at final temperatures of $2 \div 3$ mK (see Fig.8.6 below) [8.2, 3].

This cooling method was of great importance in the 1970's. Today it is no longer quite as important because above a few millikelvin this "one-shot" method offers no advantage over continuously operating dilution refrigerators, and at lower temperatures nuclear demagnetization (Chap.10) is much more powerful. I shall discuss the method here anyway for the following reasons:

a) The method was - as just mentioned - of importance in the 1970's, because it provided the necessary experimental conditions for the detection of the superfluid phase transitions of liquid ^{3}He below 2.5 mK [8.4, 5] and for the detection of the nuclear antiferromagnetic phase transition of solid ^{3}He at 1 mK [8.6], both at Cornell University.

b) This cooling method offers interesting insight into some important properties of matter, in particular liquid and solid ^{3}He, to be discussed in the following.

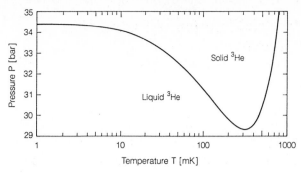

Fig.8.1 Melting curve of ^{3}He, based on the data of [8.6-9]

8.1 Phase and Entropy Diagrams of ^{3}He

The unusual behaviour of the melting curve of ^{3}He below 1 K is shown in Fig.8.1. Down to about 0.3 K the melting curve shows the usual positive slope, $dP_m/dT > 0$, but below this temperature the slope reverses sign and the pressure increases along the melting line if the temperature is decreased. The melting curve of ^{3}He shows a pronounced minimum at 29.32 bar and 316 mK [8.6-10]. Obviously, if we move along the melting curve below this minimum by increasing the pressure and so solidifying more and more ^{3}He, the temperature has to decrease (*Pomeranchuk cooling*).

According to the Clausius-Clapeyron equation

$$\frac{dP_m}{dT} = \frac{(S_{liq} - S_{sol})_m}{(V_{liq} - V_{sol})_m} \tag{8.2}$$

(where the differences are taken at melting) and because the molar volume of the liquid phase is always larger (by a constant value of 1.31 cm^3/mol at T < 40 mK [8.6, 7]) than the molar volume of the solid phase, we have

$$\frac{dP_m}{dT} < 0 \quad \text{if} \quad S_{liq} < S_{sol} . \tag{8.3}$$

This negative slope of the melting curve means that we have the unusual situation of a liquid phase with a smaller entropy than the solid phase (Fig. 8.2). The fact that there is more order in the liquid state results in solidification cooling if we perform an isentropic compression. The resulting cooling power is

$$\dot{Q} = \dot{n}_{sol} T(S_{sol} - S_{liq})_m , \tag{8.4}$$

where $\dot{n}_{sol}$ is the rate of solidification of ^{3}He. The right-hand side of (8.4) is the latent heat of freezing.

139

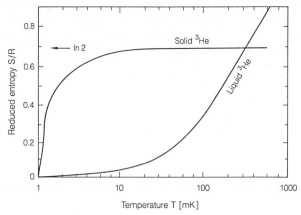

Fig.8.2 Entropies (divided by the gas constant R) of solid and liquid ^{3}He along the melting curve. The full disorder nuclear spin entropy of solid ^{3}He, $S_s/R = (2I+1) = \ell n(2)$, is marked. The entropy curves cross at the minimum of the melting curve at 316 mK, 29.32 bar

8.2 Entropies of Liquid and Solid ^{3}He

Due to its nuclear spin I = 1/2 we have a spin disorder entropy of ^{3}He, which in the fully disordered state is given by

$$S = R\ln(2) . \tag{8.5}$$

At low enough temperatures, i.e., below the minimum of the melting curve at 316 mK, this disorder entropy is far larger than other entropy contributions of the liquid or solid phases of ^{3}He, which will therefore be neglected in the following. In both states the entropy has to decrease as the temperature decreases because eventually it has to vanish at absolute zero. The decrease results from interactions between the nuclear spins or nuclear moments. The interactions are different in the two states of ^{3}He and the decrease of the spin disorder entropy starts at different temperatures (Fig.8.2).

Helium-3 atoms are indistinguishable in the liquid state and we have to apply Fermi-Dirac statistics as for conduction electrons in a metal. In liquid ^{3}He the atoms move rather freely and they approach each other quite closely (Fig.8.3). Therefore, a strong interaction results. Most importantly, the Pauli principle has to be applied to this Fermi liquid. That means that at low enough temperatures we have two particles with opposite spins in each translational energy state. This reduces the volume of the Fermi sphere by a factor of two compared to the situation with parallel spins. This "ordering in momentum space" results in a corresponding reduction of the entropy. Increasing the temperature results in excitation of particles near the Fermi energy, as for conduction electrons, and an increase of the entropy according to

140

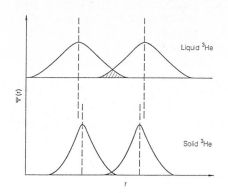

Fig.8.3 Schematic representation of the wavefunctions $\psi(r)$ of ^{3}He in the liquid and solid phases, demonstrating the larger overlap in the liquid phase in spite of the larger average separation of the atoms

Liquid ^{3}He

Solid ^{3}He

$$S_{liq} = \frac{\pi^2 R}{2} \frac{T}{T_F} = 4.56 RT \tag{8.6}$$

(below about 10 mK, along the melting line [8.10]), giving a Fermi temperature of about 1 K at melting pressure.

In the solid phase the ^{3}He atoms are constrained to vibrate about their lattice sites. Again, the thermal kinetic energy and the excitation of phonons, for example, are negligible at millikelvin temperatures; only the nuclear spin contribution matters. Solid ^{3}He is a nuclear paramagnet with spin 1/2 and bcc structure. In the solid state the overlap of the wave functions is much smaller than in the liquid state, even at T = 0, due to the zero point energy (Fig.8.3). The Pauli principle does not apply to the occupation of energy states because the particles in the solid phase are already distinguished by their spatial parameters. Because of their very weak magnetic and exchange interactions these particles can be described as independent particles for temperatures T > 10 mK, resulting in the full spin disorder entropy of S = Rln(2) for 10 mK < T < 1K (Fig.8.2). Here $C_{sol} \propto dS_{sol}/dT \simeq 0$. The interactions between the nuclear moments in solid ^{3}He become noticeable only at temperatures below about 10 mK, so the entropy then starts to decrease in this phase as well. One type of interaction is the direct nuclear dipole-dipole interaction, which was originally believed by I. Pomeranchuk to be the only important one; this is a very weak interaction of order 0.1 μK. But solid ^{3}He is a very remarkable material, because here - due to the large zero-point motion - the overlap of the wave functions is still so strong that there is direct particle exchange, resulting in an exchange interaction of order 1 mK. Solid ^{3}He is the only system where the term "exchange" is meant in the literal sense of the word: the particles exchange sites.

The nuclear magnetic properties of solid ^{3}He were originally described in terms of a spin I = 1/2 Heisenberg magnet with an exchange Hamiltonian [8.11]

$$H = -2J \sum_{i<j} I_i I_j , \tag{8.7}$$

where J is the exchange coupling constant, which is 0.88 [mK] k_B at melting pressure, resulting in a nuclear antiferromagnetic ordering transition temperature of 0.97 mK [8.6, 10]. With the general formulae

$$Z = \text{Tr}\{\exp(-H/k_B T)\}, \quad \text{and} \quad S = k_B \frac{\partial(T \ln Z)}{\partial T}, \tag{8.8}$$

we obtain for temperatures T > 3 mK

$$\frac{S_{sol}}{R} \simeq \ln(2) - 1.5 \left(\frac{J}{k_B T}\right)^2 + \left(\frac{J}{k_B T}\right)^3 + \text{higher-order terms}, \tag{8.9}$$

for a bcc lattice [8.11, 12], so that at T > 10 mK we have $S_{sol}/R = \ln(2)$ to within 1%.

The details are rather complicated because the particles cannot move "through" each other. Instead, they perform a cyclic motion, leading to a three-particle or four-particle exchange, to keep out of each other's way and this becomes the dominant part in the exchange. In more elaborate theories these processes have been taken into account [8.11]. Anyway, the exchange interaction results in a pronounced decrease of the entropy of solid ^{3}He below about 1 mK due to the antiferromangetic nuclear magnetic ordering [8.6], see Fig.8.2.

8.3 Pomeranchuk Cooling

As is obvious from Fig.8.1, for Pomeranchuk cooling we have to start with liquid ^{3}He at T < 0.32 K and perform a continuous adiabatic solidification of part of it, meaning that the sum of the entropies should be kept constant as we compress along the melting curve. If the process is isentropic we can calculate the relative amount of solid phase and liquid phase in our experimental chamber from

$$n_{total} S_{liq}(T_i) = n_{sol} S_{sol}(T_f) + (n_{total} - n_{sol}) S_{liq}(T_f) \tag{8.10}$$

and therefore

$$\frac{n_{sol}}{n_{total}} = \frac{S_{liq}(T_i) - S_{liq}(T_f)}{S_{sol}(T_f) - S_{liq}(T_f)}. \tag{8.11}$$

We see that the lower the starting temperature T_i, the smaller the proportion of ^{3}He which we have to solidify to obtain a desired final temperature T_f. For example, for T_i = 25 mK and T_f = 3 mK, only 20% of the liquid has to be solidified. It is always advantageous to have a large amount of liquid in the experimental chamber in order to obtain fast thermal equilibrium and to avoid the possibility of crushing solid crystals.

The temperature dependence of the cooling power of this refrigeration process at $5\,mK \leq T \leq 30\,mK$ is given by

$$\dot{Q} = \dot{n}_{sol}\,T(S_{sol} - S_{liq}) = \dot{n}_{sol}\,T(R\ln 2 - 36T) \propto T \qquad (8.12)$$

when n_{sol} moles are solidified per unit time. $\dot{Q}$ decreases proportional to temperature rather than proportional to temperature squared as it did for the dilution refrigerator (Fig.8.4) because $S_{liq} \ll S_{sol} =$ constant at these temperatures.

Two experimental problems had to be solved before Pomeranchuk's idea could be converted into a refrigeration device. Firstly, when ^{3}He is compressed we perform mechanical work according to

$$\dot{W} = - \dot{n}_{sol}\,P_m(V_{sol} - V_{liq}) \ . \qquad (8.13)$$

This has to be compared to the temperature-dependent cooling power (8.12). The ratio of the two is given by

$$\frac{\dot{W}}{\dot{Q}} = - \frac{P_m}{T}\frac{\Delta V}{\Delta S} = - \frac{P_m}{T}\frac{dP_m}{dT} \ . \qquad (8.14)$$

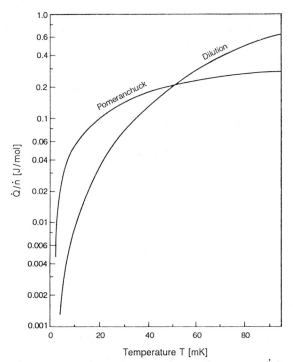

Fig.8.4 Comparison of the relative cooling powers $\dot{Q}/\dot{n}$ of a Pomeranchuk refrigerator and of ^{3}He-^{4}He dilution refrigerator. In the former case liquid is converted into solid at a rate of 10 μmol/s; in the latter case ^{3}He is being removed from the mixing chamber at the same rate [8.13]

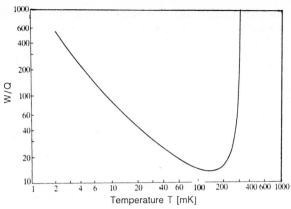

Fig.8.5 Ratio W/Q of compressional work to heat extraction as a function of temperature [8.13]

This ratio - which is shown in Fig.8.5 - is always larger than 10 and can reach values above 100 at temperatures below about 8 mK. Work itself would do no harm if performed reversibly, but obviously the system will not cool if even only a small fraction of this mechanical work is irreversibly transformed into heat, for example, by rubbing or crushing of the ^{3}He crystals or by exceeding the elastic limit of the cell wall. Fortunately, only a small fraction of liquid ^{3}He has to be solidified in practice (see above). It was a happy surprise that Pomeranchuk cooling worked, an indication that physicists were indeed able to build setups for this refrigeration method where these problems could be avoided (see below).

In the above discussions I have assumed thermodynamic equilibrium, $\mu_{liq} = \mu_{sol}$, which is justified by the hydrostatic and thermal equilibria established by the liquid phase as long as there is not too much solid ^{3}He in the cell, and if the solid crystals are small enough that thermal conduction and nuclear spin diffusion keep the crystals in equilibrium.

Secondly, the shape of the melting curve of ^{3}He has a substantial impact on how Pomeranchuk cooling can be realized. The precooled sample cell is connected to a room temperature compressor via a capillary. If we increase the pressure of ^{3}He in this capillary, the minimum of the melting curve at T = 0.32 K is hit first at some intermediate point along the capillary, and a solid plug will be formed there. This plug will isolate the cell at $T < T_{min}$ from the room temperature set-up and we cannot increase the pressure in it by increasing the gas pressure at room temperature. One therefore has to resort to an indirect pressure increase by "squeezing" the cold cell. How this squeezing is accomplished distinguishes the various Pomeranchuk refrigerators. An indirect hydraulic pressure increase can be achieved by surrounding the sample cell containing the ^{3}He by a second cell containing ^{4}He. The ^{3}He is then first compressed until a solid plug has been formed in the filling capillary. At that moment everything is at the pressure of the minimum of the melting curve, 29.3 bar. Any further pressure increase can only be achieved by increasing the pressure in the sur-

144

rounding ^{4}He chamber, which will compress the walls separating it from the ^{3}He sample cell. The pressure in the ^{3}He sample cell is then given by

$$P(^3He) = P_{wall} + P(^4He). \qquad (8.15)$$

Of course, it is now also not possible to measure the pressure in the ^{3}He sample cell by connecting it to a room temperature manometer. We have to measure the pressure in situ at low temperatures, which can be done capacitively (Sect. 13.1). The ^{4}He is not a heat load on the device because its specific heat and that of the cell walls are very small at these temperatures compared to the specific heat of liquid ^{3}He (Fig. 2.8).

Experimental advances in Pomeranchuk cooling were obtained in three steps. As mentioned at the beginning of this chapter, in 1965, in his original experiment, *Anufriev* [8.1] reached a temperature of 18 mK (or lower) starting from 50 mK. About four years later, *Wheatley, Johnson* and co-workers [8.2, 3] using a more elaborate design, demonstrated the full power of Pomeranchuk cooling by achieving a minimum temperature of about 2 mK (Fig. 8.6). Very successful Pomeranchuk cells were built at Cornell University [8.4-6, 14, 15] making use of convoluting flexible BeCu bellows as shown in Fig. 8.7. In such a design bellows with different diameters can be combined to work as hydraulic pressure amplifier and to allow for the fact that ^{4}He has a lower freezing pressure than ^{3}He (Fig. 2.3). The Cornell device enabled the scientists there to detect the superfluid transitions of liquid ^{3}He [8.4, 5] and the nuclear antiferromagnetic transition of solid ^{3}He

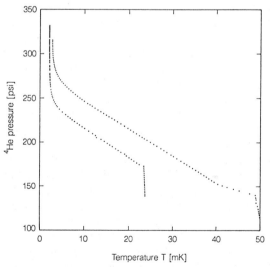

Fig. 8.6 Results of Pomeranchuk cooling experiments [8.2, 3]. The starting temperatures were 24 and 50 mK, respectively. The final temperatures were between 2 mK and 3 mK, respectively. The ^{4}He pressure (in pounds per square inch) is not of any particular quantitative significance but is simply the experimental parameter which was varied to change the volume of the ^{4}He and ^{3}He cells (see text)

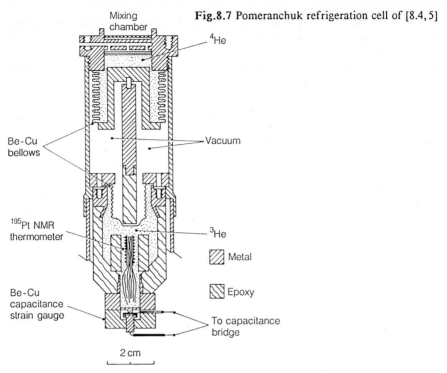

Mixing chamber

Fig.8.7 Pomeranchuk refrigeration cell of [8.4, 5]

⁴He

Be-Cu bellows

Vacuum

¹⁹⁵Pt NMR thermometer

³He

▨ Metal

Be-Cu capacitance strain gauge

▨ Epoxy

To capacitance bridge

2 cm

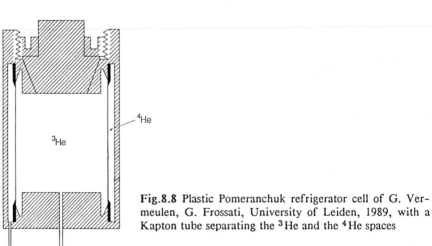

⁴He

³He

Fig.8.8 Plastic Pomeranchuk refrigerator cell of G. Vermeulen, G. Frossati, University of Leiden, 1989, with a Kapton tube separating the ³He and the ⁴He spaces

[8.6], (Fig.2.3). More recent applications of Pomeranchuk cooling are investigations of the influence of nuclear polarization on the properties of liquid ³He [8.16-18]. Here the advantage is that this cooling method is only weakly influenced by moderate magnetic fields. The cells to be used in changing high magnetic fields are then made almost entirely of plastic with a stretched Kapton tube as the pressure transmitter (Fig.8.8).

In all recent applications of Pomeranchuk cooling, the cell is precooled by a ^{3}He-^{4}He dilution refrigerator to about 25 mK, and the pressures and volumes in the ^{3}He and ^{4}He cells are monitored by low-temperature capacitive manometers (Sect.13.1). The experiments have clearly demonstrated that Pomeranchuk cooling is rather powerful if ^{3}He at melting pressure is itself the subject of the investigation. If one wants to apply Pomeranchuk cooling to refrigerate other materials indirectly, one has the problem of the Kapitza thermal boundary resistance between the ^{3}He inside the Pomeranchuk cell and the sample, which is connected to the outside of the cell or floating in the ^{3}He. Thermal contact problems are even more severe because, due to the slope of the melting curve, solid ^{3}He with its low thermal conductivity forms at the warmest places of the device, i.e., at the places where heat has to be absorbed [8.19]. In principle, Pomeranchuk cooling is more powerful than dilution refrigeration below about 50 mK, where it has a higher cooling power at the same $\dot{n}$ (Fig.8.4), but a disadvantage - in addition to the experimental problems already mentioned - compared to the latter is its discontinuous nature. Pomeranchuk cooling is basically a "one shot" method. It can be carried out in a semicontinuous mode by continuously compressing at a controlled rate to keep the temperature constant [8.20]. However, it seems to be easier to continuously circulate ^{3}He in a dilution refrigerator. In addition, Pomeranchuck cooling is limited to $T \geq 2$ mK. For the first reasons given above, continuous dilution refrigeration is most widely used for $T \geq 5$ mK, and for the last reason nuclear refrigeration is the method of choice for lower temperatures.

9. Refrigeration by Adiabatic Demagnetization of a Paramagnetic Salt

The year 1926 was a remarkable year for low-temperature physics and technology. H. Kamerlingh Onnes reached 0.7 K by pumping on his liquid ^{4}He bath with an enormous battery of pumps. Realizing that there would be no element with a lower boiling point than helium, he predicted that the temperature of 0.7 K would remain the minimum temperature achievable by mankind in the laboratory unless somebody discovered a completely new refrigeration technology that did not depend on the latent heat of evaporation. (Of course, he was not aware that there exists a lighter helium isotope, ^{3}He, which pushes this limit down by about a factor of three). In the same year this completely new refrigeration technology was proposed. P. Debye and W.F. Giauque independently made the proposal that lower temperatures could be reached by using the magnetic disorder entropy of electronic magnetic moments in paramagnetic salts, a method later called *adiabatic demagnetization of paramagnetic salts*. Not until seven years later, in 1933, was this proposal converted into a practical realization, when W.F. Giauque and D.P. MacDougall (Berkeley) reached 0.53 K, and a little later W.J. de Haas, E.C. Wiersma and H.A. Kramers (Leiden) reached 0.27 K. In fact, this was the first important low-temperature experiment since the end of the 19th century in which the University in Leiden was not the first to achieve success (for this early work see the relevant references in [9.1-3]).

Adiabatic demagnetization of paramagnetic salts was the first method of refrigeration to reach temperatures significantly below 1 K. Today this method can be applied to experiments at $2\,\mathrm{mK} \leq T \leq 1\,\mathrm{K}$. For about the last 15 years it has not been used much, because it has been replaced by the ^{3}He-^{4}He dilution refrigerator, which has the substantial advantage of being a continuous refrigeration method. I will discuss adiabatic demagnetization of paramagnetic salts for historical reasons and because it is the basis for understanding the presently much more important nuclear adiabatic demagnetization to be discussed in Chap. 10.

9.1 The Principle of Magnetic Refrigeration

Let us consider paramagnetic ions with an electronic magnetic moment μ in a solid. We assume the energy ϵ_m of interaction between the moments themselves as well as with an externally applied magnetic field to be small compared to the thermal energy $k_B T$. This means that we are considering free paramagnetic ions with magnetic moment μ and total angular momentum J with entropy contribution

$$S = R\ln(2J + 1) \qquad\qquad (9.1)$$

if they are completely disordered in their $2J+1$ possible orientations with respect to a magnetic field.

As in the case of Pomeranchuk cooling, it is this magnetic disorder entropy which we want to use for refrigeration. At the temperatures of interest in this chapter, this magnetic disorder entropy, which is of the order of joules per mole of refrigerant, is always large compared to all other entropies of the system, for example the lattice and conduction electron entropies, which we will therefore neglect.

If the temperature is decreased, eventually the interactions between the magnetic moments will become comparable to the thermal energy. This will then lead to spontaneous magnetic order, e.g., ferromagnetic or antiferromagnetic orientation of the electronic magnetic moments. As a result the entropy will decrease and approach zero, as required by the third law of thermodynamics. An externally applied magnetic field will interact with the magnetic moments, at least partially orienting them along its axis to create a magnetized state of higher order. Therefore, in the presence of a field the entropy will decrease at a higher temperature than without a field (Fig.9.1).

The entropy diagram of Fig.9.1 makes it very easy to understand magnetic refrigeration. We bring the paramagnetic salt in contact with a precooling bath to precool it to a starting temperature T_i. Then a magnetic field B_i is applied to perform an isothermal magnetization at T_i from $B = 0$

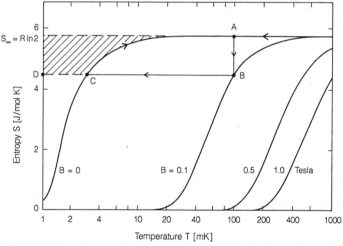

Fig.9.1 Molar entropy of a single crystal of the paramagnetic salt CMN (Sect.9.4) as a function of temperature for magnetic fields applied along the cystallographic a axis. For the refrigeration process the salt is first isothermally magnetized (AB), and then after thermal isolation adabatically demagnetized (BC). Eventually it warms up along the entropy curve at the final demagnetization field, which is zero in the example shown. The heat of magnetization during magnetization is given by the rectangle $ABDS_\infty$. The cooling power of the salt after demagnetization is given by the shaded area [9.4]

to $B = B_i$. During this process the heat of magnetization has to be absorbed by the precooling bath. The next step is thermal isolation of the paramagnetic salt from the surrounding bath which then allows the adiabatic demagnetization to be carried out by reducing the external field from its starting value B_i to a final field B_f, which may be in the millitesla region. The temperature has to decrease accordingly (Fig.9.1). Finally the cooling agent, the paramagnetic salt, will warm up along the entropy curve at $B_f =$ const. due to an external heat leak until its cooling power has been used up. It is obvious from Fig.9.1 that a spontaneous magnetic ordering process of the magnetic moments represents the lower limit for magnetic refrigeration. Magnetic refrigeration is a "one-shot" technique, where the demagnetization ends at a low field and then sample and refrigerant warm up.

9.2 Thermodynamics of Magnetic Refrigeration

In this section I present some simple thermodynamic calculations relevant for the three steps of a magnetic refrigeration process.

a) Heat of Isothermal Magnetization

The heat of magnetization released when the applied field is increased from zero to B_i and which has to be absorbed by the precooling bath at constant temperature T_i is given by

$$Q(T_i) = nT_i[S(0,T_i) - S(B_i,T_i)] \tag{9.2}$$

or more exactly

$$Q(T_i) = nT_i \int_0^{B_i} (\partial S/\partial B)_{T_i} \, dB = nT_i \int_0^{B_i} (\partial M/\partial T)_B \, dB \,, \tag{9.3}$$

where M is the magnetization (magnetic moment/unit volume). The resulting $Q(T_i)$ is indicated in Fig.9.1; it is typically several joules per mole of refrigerant, so it can easily be absorbed by an evaporating helium bath, with its latent heat of several of joules per mole, or by a ^{3}He-^{4}He dilution refrigerator if lower starting temperatures are required.

b) Adiabatic Demagnetization

For free magnetic moments the entropy is a function of just the ratio of magnetic energy to thermal energy (see below). We therefore have for the adiabatic process

$$S(B_i/T_i) = S(B_f/T_f) \,, \tag{9.4}$$

which results in

$$T_f/B_f = T_i/B_i .$$ (9.5)

We arrive at the same result by remembering that the magnetization does not change during adiabatic changes of the magnetic field. Of course, we cannot reach $T_f \to 0$ by letting $B_f \to 0$ because eventually the condition $k_B T \gg \epsilon_m$ is violated and the internal interactions will align the moments and the entropy vanishes (Fig.9.1).

c) Warming up due to External Heating

The cooling power of the salt after demagnetization to B_f, or the heat it can absorb, is given by

$$Q(B_f) = n \int_{T_f}^{\infty} T(\partial S/\partial T)_{B_f} dT .$$ (9.6)

This, too, is indicated in Fig.9.1. It is, of course, substantially smaller than the heat of magnetization due to the fact that the energy is absorbed at a temperature $T < T_i$. Hence the external heat leak should be kept as small as possible.

These results demonstrate that one has to make a compromise between a low final temperature T_f [which would require a low final field B_f; see (9.5)], and a large cooling power (which requires a large final field; see Fig.9.1).

For the above analysis we have to know the entropy $S(B, T)$, which can be calculated from data for the specific heat as a function of temperature and field according to

$$S(B, T_1) - S(B, T_2) = \int_{T_2}^{T_1} (C_B/T) dT .$$ (9.7)

Another possibility is to use the magnetization

$$M = \chi B/\mu_0$$ (9.8)

to calculate the magnetic entropy via the Maxwell relation $(\partial S/\partial B)_T = (\partial M/\partial T)_B$.

9.3 Non-Interacting Magnetic Dipoles in a Magnetic Field

If we have paramagnetic ions carrying a magnetic moment μ and a total angular momentum J, then at temperature T the (2J+1) energy levels with energies ϵ_m will be populated according to

$$P(m) = N_0 e^{-\epsilon_m/k_B T} / \sum_{m=1}^{2J+1} e^{-\epsilon_m/k_B T} ,$$
(9.9)

and the partition function is given by

$$Z = N_0 \left(\sum_{m=1}^{2J+1} e^{-\epsilon_m/k_B T} \right) .$$
(9.10)

Once we have calculated the partition function, we can calculate all the required thermodynamic properties, for example

$$S = k_B \partial(T \ln Z)/\partial T ,$$
$$C_B = T(\partial S/\partial T)_B ,$$
$$M = k_B T(\partial \ln Z/\partial B)_T ,$$
(9.11)

and hence the susceptibility $\chi = (\partial M/\partial B)_T$ is known as well. In other words, once we know the energeis ϵ_m, everything else can be calculated. Fortunately, if we assume non-interacting magnetic dipoles in an external magnetic field, where $\epsilon_m \ll k_B T$, we have

$$\epsilon_m = - \boldsymbol{\mu} \cdot \mathbf{B} = \mu_B g m B ,$$
(9.12)

with the electronic Landé factor

$$g = 1 + \frac{J(J+1) + S(S+1) - L(L+1)}{2J(J+1)} .$$
(9.13)

In (9.12), $\mu_B = e\hbar/2m_e = 9.27 \cdot 10^{-24}$ J/T is the Bohr magneton and m = -J, ..., 0, ..., + J are the magnetic quantum numbers.

Accordingly, the partition function for independent magnetic dipoles is given by

$$Z = \sum_{m=-J}^{+J} N_0 e^{-mx} = N_0 \frac{\sinh[(J + \frac{1}{2})x]}{\sinh(x/2)}$$
(9.14)

with $x = \mu_B g B/k_B T$. After some manipulation we find

$$S/R = (x/2)\{\coth(x/2) - (2J+1)\coth[x(2J+1)/2]\}$$

$$+ \ln\left[\frac{\sinh[x(2J+1)/2]}{\sinh(x/2)}\right], \tag{9.15a}$$

$$C_B/R = (x/2)^2 \sinh^{-2}(x/2) - [x(2J+1)/2]^2 \sinh^{-2}[x(2J+1)/2], \tag{9.15b}$$

$$M/M_s = [(2J+1)/2J]\coth[x(2J+1)/2] - (1/2J)\coth(x/2), \tag{9.15c}$$

where $M_s = N_0\mu_B gJ$ is the saturation magnetization, and the right-hand side of (9.15c) is the Brillouin function $B_J(x)$. This function is tabulated for various J in [9.2, 3]. The Brillouin function $B_J(x) = M/M_s$ for various J is shown in Fig. 10.5 as a function of x^{-1} and the dependence of the specific heat C_B on x for various J is depicted in Figs. 3.8, 10 and 10.4. These results demonstrate a previously mentioned fact, namely that with the above assumptions the entropy is a function of B/T only. Therefore, in Fig. 9.1 the entropy curves are simply translated if we change the field. In addition, the above results give (9.5), valid for an ideal adiabatic process: S = const. and therefore B/T = const., which means that the starting conditions determine the final state.

The above equations can not, of course, be used in the limit $B_f \to 0$, because then the assumption of negligible interactions between the moments breaks down. For very small B_f we have to replace B_f in the above equations by an effective field

$$B_{eff} = \sqrt{B_f^2 + b^2} \tag{9.16}$$

acting on the moments, where b is an internal field resulting from the neighbouring moments in the paramagnet. This then leads to

$$T_f = \frac{T_i}{B_i}\sqrt{B_f^2 + b^2}. \tag{9.17}$$

The internal field b determines the minimum temperature $T_{f,min}$ that can be reached by demagnetizing to $B_f = 0$. Finally, we find that the magnetization is kept constant during the demagnetization process or, in other words, that the populations of the various energy levels do not change during the demagnetization (Fig. 10.2). Only their energy difference changes when we decrease the field. Figure 9.1 also demonstrates that the cooling power Q is proportional to the final field B_f. When the demagnetized salt absorbs heat it has to change the population of its energy levels, which means that the spins of the paramagnetic ions have to flip. The ions can absorb more heat if the energy change per spin flip is larger, i.e., if their energy separation, which is proportional to the field B_f, is larger.

Very often the magnetic energy $\mu\mu_B B$ is substantially smaller than the thermal energy $k_B T$, or $x \ll 1$. In this approximation one does not have to use the full (9.15) but can use the so-called high-temperature approximations. I will give these approximations in the next chapter, on nuclear demagnetization, where usually $x \ll 1$, because the nuclear moments are rather small.

9.4 Paramagnetic Salts and Magnetic Refrigerators

The behaviour of a magnetic refrigerator is mainly determined by the experimental starting conditions (B_i, T_i), the heat leaks (Sect.10.5), and the properties of the selected paramagnetic salt. Typical starting conditions for paramagnetic refrigeration, $B_i = 0.1 \div 1$ T, $T_i = 0.1 \div 1$ K, are fairly easy to achieve nowadays. With these starting conditions large entropy reductions are possible (Fig.9.1).

I shall not discuss here the magnetic and electric interactions of paramagnetic ions in salts; they are covered in [9.3, 5]. In general, the paramagnetic refrigerant, the salt, should have a low magnetic ordering temperature T_c and a large magnetic specific heat in order to achieve a large cooling power, which means a large angular momentum J (Fig.3.10). The ordering temperature T_c is determined by the interactions between the magnetic moments.

Paramagnetic salts suitable for magnetic cooling must contain ions with only partly filled electronic shells, i.e. either 3d transition elements or 4f rare earth elements. The following four paramagnetic substances have often been used for magnetic refrigeration in the so-called "high-temperature range" as well as in the "low-temperature range" (where T_c is the approximate magnetic ordering temperature).

"High"-temperature salts:

MAS: $Mn^{2+}SO_4 \cdot (NH_4)_2 SO_4 \cdot 6H_2 O$; $T_c \simeq 0.17$ K
FAA: $Fe_2^{3+}(SO_4)_3 \cdot (NH_4)_2 SO_4 \cdot 24H_2 O$; $T_c \simeq 0.03$ K

"Low"-temperature salts:

CPA: $Cr_2^{3+}(SO_4)_3 \cdot K_2 SO_4 \cdot 24H_2 O$; $T_c \simeq 0.01$ K
CMN: $2Ce^{3+}(NO_3)_3 \cdot 3Mg(NO_3)_2 \cdot 24H_2 O$; $Tc \simeq 0.002$ K.

Their entropy curves are shown in Fig.9.2.

All these salts contain a lot of water of crystallization, which assures a large distance (about $10\,\text{Å}$ in CMN) between the magnetic ions and therefore leads to a low magnetic ordering temperature. Details on the properties of these and other suitable salts can be found in [9.1-3, 5-7].

Due to the weak interactions between the rather remote and well-sheltered Ce^{3+} ions in CMN [9.6], which result in a small internal field b and a low ordering temperature T_c (Fig.9.1), this salt has been quite en vogue as a

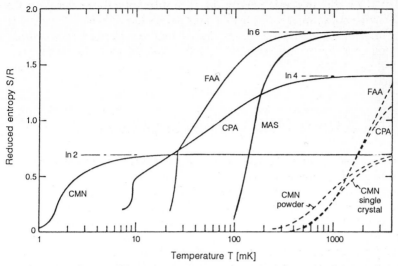

Fig.9.2 Entropies S (divided by the gas constant R) of four salts suitable for paramagnetic demagnetization as a function of temperature in zero field (full lines) and in 2 T (dashed lines). (For the chemical formula of the salts see the text)

refrigerant as well as for thermometry (Sect. 12.8) in the last two or three decades. Its electronic ground state is a doublet with an effective spin of one-half at T < 1 K. CMN has been extensively used by *Wheatley* and co-workers [9.7, 8] to refrigerate liquid ^{3}He to about 2 mK. This low final temperature is possible due to a magnetic coupling between ^{3}He nuclear moments and Ce electronic moments which strongly reduces the thermal boundary resistance (Sect. 4.3.2). Even lower temperatures can be achieved by using LCMN, a salt where the magnetic Ce ions are partly replaced by non-magnetic La ions [9.9-11]. This dilution, of course, reduces the cooling power/volume as well. CMN and LCMN are the salts with the lowest known electronic magnetic ordering temperature. A combination of a moderate dilution refrigerator and a magnetic refrigeration stage of CMN or LCMN at a starting field of about 1 T is a very suitable and reasonably cheap setup for ^{3}He research. For the use of CMN and LCMN in magnetic thermometry, see Sect. 12.8.

Figure 9.3 shows some typical setups for paramagnetic refrigeration used mainly in the 1960s and 1970s before the advent of the dilution refrigerator; they are described in [9.1-3, 7-14] and references therein.

The advantages of paramagnetic refrigeration are that the required starting conditions can nowadays be fairly easily achieved with simple dilution refrigerators and superconducting magnets. In addition, the refrigerant can also be used as a thermometer by applying the Curie law $\chi = \lambda/T$ to determine the temperature T by measurements of the susceptibility χ of the salt (Sect. 12.8). However, paramagnetic refrigeration also has some severe drawbacks. The thermal conductivity of dielectric salts is rather poor; a typical value is 10^{-4} W/K·cm at 0.1 K. It is therefore difficult to achieve

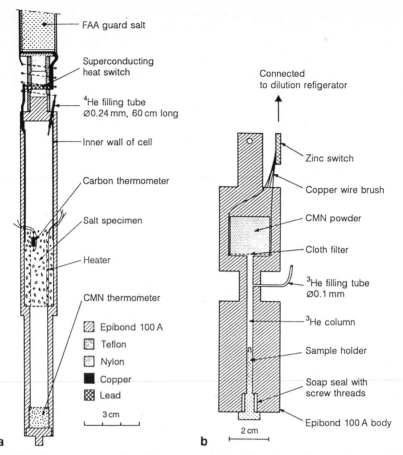

FAA guard salt

Superconducting
heat switch

^{4}He filling tube
⌀0.24 mm, 60 cm long

Inner wall of cell

Carbon thermometer

Salt specimen

Heater

CMN thermometer

Epibond 100 A
Teflon
Nylon
Copper
Lead

3 cm

Connected
to dilution refrigerator

Zinc switch

Copper wire brush

CMN powder

Cloth filter

^{3}He filling tube
⌀0.1 mm

^{3}He column

Sample holder

Soap seal with
screw threads

Epibond 100 A body

2 cm

a   b

Fig.9.3 Two paramagnetic refrigerators used by Wheatley and co-workers (a: [9.7]; b: [9.12]). These original references and [9.1] should be consulted for details

thermal equilibrium within the salt, leading to temperature gradients and long thermal relaxation times in the millikelvin temperature range. Similarly it is rather difficult to achieve thermal contact to the salt and special con-struction methods have been developed for paramagnetic refrigeration stages. Probably, the mostly applied one is to compress the powdered salt (typically at 100 bar pressure) together with some "glue" (Apiezon grease or oil or epoxy) and the ends of some fine Cu or Ag wires spread out uni-formly in the pill. The other end of the wires should already have been welded to the places where the thermal contact is desired (to a heat switch connecting to the precooling stage and to a metal plate for mounting exper-iments and thermometers), see Sect. 12.8. In some cases it may be necessary to seal the salt pill to prevent chemical changes (dehydration) leading to de-terioration. Consideration of the thermal path from the spins to the lattice of the salt, to the metal wires, and to the sample/thermometer is advised to avoid unnecessary, unpleasant surprises [9.2]; these problems, of course,

156

become more and more serious the lower the temperature range of operation. Finally, the minimum temperature is determined by interactions of the electronic magnetic moments with their surroundings and eventually by spontaneous magnetic ordering, leading to a minimum temperature of about 2 mK for paramagnetic refrigeration (reached in 1953 with CMN). Because these temperatures can nowadays also be achieved by dilution refrigerators, this latter continuous refrigeration method has replaced magnetic refrigeration with paramagnetic salts. For lower temperatures, where dilution refrigerators become inefficient, magnetic refrigeration using nuclear magnetic moments in metals is the only known refrigeration technique and will be discussed in detail in the following chapter.

10. Refrigeration by Adiabatic Nuclear Demagnetization

There are many elements and compounds that contain no electronic magnetic moment but whose nuclei carry nuclear magnetic moments. These nuclear magnetic moments can be used for magnetic refrigeration in a similar way as the electronic magnetic moments. Nuclear magnetic refrigeration was proposed, and nowadays is applied in several specialised laboratories, to avoid the main disadvantages of electronic paramagnetic refrigeration - the low thermal conductivities and the "high" magnetic ordering temperatures of paramagnetic salts - and to refrigerate into the microkelvin temperature range.

The minimum temperature for magnetic refrigeration is given by spontaneous magnetic ordering. The interaction energy between magnetic moments in the simplest case, for dipole-dipole interaction only, is given by

$$\epsilon_d = \boldsymbol{\mu} \cdot \mathbf{b} = \frac{\mu_0 \mu}{4\pi} \cdot \sum_i \left[\frac{\mu_i}{r_i^3} - 3r_i \frac{\mu_i \cdot r_i}{r_i^5} \right] , \tag{10.1}$$

where b is the internal dipole field created by neighbors, r_i is the distance between the dipoles with magnetic moments μ_i, and $\mu_0 = 4\pi \cdot 10^{-7}$ V·s/A·m. This means that the ordering temperature is

$$T_c \propto \mu^2 / r^3 . \tag{10.2}$$

Because the nuclear magnetic moments are of the order of the nuclear magneton $\mu_n = 5.05 \cdot 10^{-27}$ J/T rather than of the Bohr magneton $\mu_B = 9.27 \cdot 10^{-24}$ J/T, which we had for the electronic magnetic moments, the ordering temperature due to nuclear dipole–nuclear dipole interaction is much lower, typically of order 0.1 μK or less. Therefore, nuclear magnetic refrigeration can be used to much lower temperatures than electronic magnetic refrigeration; it has opened up the microkelvin temperature range to condensed-matter physics.

For electronic magnetic refrigeration we could not use pure metals with their high thermal conductivity because the magnetic ordering temperature of magnetically ordering metals with their polarized conduction electrons is usually substantially higher than the magnetic ordering temperature of electronic moments in paramagnetic salts. But now for nuclear magnetic refrigeration, where we have the weak nuclear magnetic moments, we can use metals and can take advantage of their high thermal conductivity. In addition, we have the advantage that the density of moments in these metals is substantially higher than the density of electronic moments in the highly diluted paramagnetic salts suitable for magnetic refrigeration, giving a large nuclear entropy density.

But the advantages offered by nuclear magnetic refrigeration due to the small nuclear magnetic moments are counteracted by experimental problems resulting precisely from the small size of these moments. To achieve a reduction of the nuclear magnetic entropy of, at least, a few percent we need rather demanding starting conditions for the magnetic field and for the temperature. If we take, e.g., the "work horse" of nuclear magnetic refrigeration, copper, then even with the starting conditions $B_i = 8$ T and $T_i = 10$ mK we get a reduction of the nuclear magnetic entropy of only about 9% (Fig.10.1). As shown in Fig.10.2, even at starting conditions of B_i = 8 T and $T_i = 6$ mK, the relative population of each of the Zeeman levels of Cu nuclei differs from the population of neighbouring levels by only a factor of two. The cooling power is given by $Q = n\int TdS$, and because we now also want to work at substantially lower temperature, Q is typically a factor of 1000 smaller than for electronic magnetic refrigeration. If we take the example of Fig.10.2 that, starting from $B_i = 8$ T and $T_i = 6$ mK, field and temperature are reduced by a factor of thousand to $B_f = 8$ mT, $T_f = 6$ μK (ideal adiabatic process), each spin flip associated with a transition of a nucleus from one level to the next higher one, gives a cooling power corresponding to a temperature difference of only 4.4 μK for Cu.

A final point to consider is the transfer of the spin temperature. When we demagnetize the nuclear magnetic moments the nuclear spin system may reach a very low temperature, but we have to ask how this very low nuclear spin temperature is transferred to the rest of the system, to the electrons and to lattice vibrations, which determine the "temperature" of our refriger-

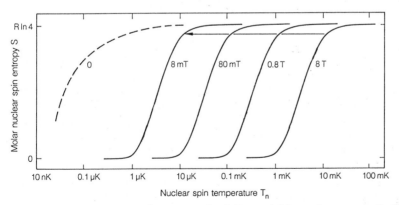

Fig.10.1. Molar nuclear spin entropy S of Cu nuclei in various magnetic fields as a function of temperature. The arrow indicates an adiabatic demagnetization process from 8 T to 8 mT. The full nuclear spin disorder entropy of copper nuclei with I = 3/2 is Rln4 as indicated on the vertical axis. The dashed line is the nuclear spin entropy of Cu in zero field according to the data of [10.1]; it indicates the spontaneous antiferromagnetic ordering of the Cu nuclear spins

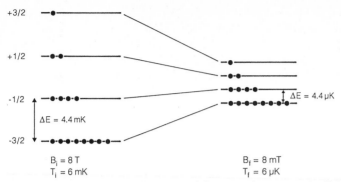

Fig.10.2. Zeeman levels of Cu nuclei in a starting magnetic field of 8 T and after demagnetization to 8 mT. The relative population of the levels and the indicated energy separation ΔE correspond to a starting nuclear spin temperature of 6 mK and a final nuclear spin temperature of 6 μK. The field to temperature ratio is chosen so that the relative population of neighboring levels differs by a factor of two

ant – unless we are only interested in the cold nuclear spin system itself. This problem will be discussed later.

Nuclear magnetic refrigeration was first proposed in 1934 by C.J. Gorter, and in 1935 independently by N. Kurti and F.E. Simon. However, due to severe experimental problems and because even the temperature range accessible by electronic magnetic refrigeration had not yet been explored, no experimental realization was tried before the end of World War II. Only in 1956 did a group at Oxford University, led by *Kurti*, try a practical application of this cooling method [10.2,3]. They succeeded in reducing the *nuclear spin temperature* to the low microkelvin temperature range by using 0.1 mm diameter copper wires as a refrigerant and starting from 12 mK and 3 T. But in their experiment the *temperature of the electrons and of the lattice vibrations* was not reduced below the starting temperature of 12 mK, and the nuclear spins warmed up from the obtained low microkelvin temperature to the starting temperature of 12 mK within a few minutes. Only about a decade later were more trials performed, in particular at Oxford, La Jolla, and Helsinki, to improve the situation. *Osgood* and *Goodkind* [10.4], and *Symco* [10.5] were the first to achieve considerable electron and lattice refrigeration by adiabatic nuclear demagnetization, in the late 1960s. Since the beginning of the 1970s knowledge and experimental equipment have been available to develop nuclear cooling to a refrigeration technology for achieving temperatures clearly below those already available by electronic magnetic refrigeration. Here, in particular, the work of *Lounasmaa* and his co-workers at Helsinki was of great importance [10.6]. They were the first to combine a ^{3}He-^{4}He dilution refrigerator for precooling with a superconducting magnet for magnetization to obtain the required starting conditions. References to the early work on nuclear refrigeration as well as credit to the pioneers of this technology can be found in [10.7,8]; these two books also contain the basic physics and many of the equations to be used in this chapter. The state of the art of nuclear demag-

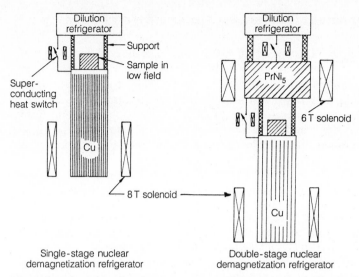

Fig. 10.3. Schematic of a single-stage Cu nuclear demagnetization refrigerator and of a double-stage $PrNi_5$/Cu nuclear demagnetization refrigerator. In the double-stage design the extra $PrNi_5$ stage decreases the starting temperature for demagnetizing the Cu stage. It also decreases the heat leaking by thermal conductance from the parts at higher temperature to the Cu stage, and to experiments and samples

netization refrigeration was reviewed in 1982 by *Andres* and *Lounasmaa* [10.9], and more recently by *Pickett* [10.10].

In principle, the procedure for nuclear magnetic refrigeration is identical to that for electronic magnetic refrigeration. However, in practice there are severe differences due to the small nuclear moments and very low temperatures involved. The schematic setup of a nuclear refrigerator is shown in Fig. 10.3. A superconducting magnet with a maximum field of typically 8 T is required in order to magnetize (polarize) the nuclear moments of typically $10 \div 100$ moles Cu. This nuclear refrigeration stage is precooled by a ^{3}He-^{4}He dilution refrigerator - which has to absorb the large heat of nuclear magnetization - to a starting temperature of typically $10 \div 15$ mK. A superconducting heat switch (Sect. 4.2.2) is used to make thermal contact between the precooling ^{3}He-^{4}He dilution refrigerator and the Cu nuclear stage. After the Cu stage has been precooled to the required starting temperature T_i, the superconducting heat switch is opened by reducing the magnetic field on it to zero to thermally isolate the nuclear refrigeration stage. Then demagnetization of the nuclear magnetic moments of the nuclear refrigerant can be started by reducing the main field slowly over several hours or days from the starting field B_i to the required low final value B_f. The experiments and thermometers are usually attached to the top flange of the refrigeration stage outside of the high-field region to avoid disturbances from the demagnetization field.

161

10.1 Some Equations Relevant for Nuclear Refrigeration

Again, in principle, we can just use the equations derived in Chap.9 for electronic magnetic refrigeration. For nuclear refrigeration we have to replace the electronic parameters by the relevant nuclear parameters, i.e., we have to replace $\mu_B g$ by $\mu_n g_n$. But we have to keep in mind that for nuclear refrigeration the moment μ and the spin I have the same direction, unlike in the electronic case, and therefore in some of the equations the sign is reversed; for example, the energies of the Zeeman levels in a magnetic field are

$$\epsilon_m = - m\mu_n g_n B , \qquad (10.3)$$

where μ_n is the nuclear magneton, $g_n = \mu/I$ is the nuclear g-factor and m runs from -I to +I. In addition, for nuclear refrigeration the requirement $\mu\mu_n B \ll k_B T I$ is usually fulfilled, due to the smallness of nuclear moments, which we consider again as non-interacting. Therefore we can expand the rather cumbersome equations of (9.15) into their high-temperature approximations, so that we have

$$S_n = R\ln(2I+1) - \frac{\lambda_n B^2}{2\mu_0 T_n^2} , \quad C_n = \frac{\lambda_n B^2}{\mu_0 T_n^2} ,$$

$$M_n = \frac{\lambda_n B}{\mu_0 T_n} , \quad \chi_n = \lambda_n/T_n \qquad (10.4)$$

with $\lambda_n = N_0 I(I+1)\mu_0 \mu_n^2 g_n^2/3k_B$, the nuclear Curie constant. The entropy and the specific heat are then functions of $(B/T)^2$ only.

Sometimes the final demagnetization field B_f is so small that the internal field b due to interactions of the magnetic or of the electric nuclear moments is not negligible and we then have to replace B in the above equations by $\sqrt{B^2 + b^2}$ giving

$$T_f = \frac{T_i}{B_i}\sqrt{B_f^2 + b^2} . \qquad (10.5)$$

As a result, the limiting temperature for nuclear refrigeration is

$$T_{f,min} = bT_i/B_i . \qquad (10.6)$$

For example, for Cu we have b = 0.34 mT. Because in an adiabatic process S = const, we should also have B/T = const., see (10.4). Therefore a plot of the B/T values achieved during magnetic refrigeration is a measure of the adiabaticity or reversibility of the process.

Recently some very powerful nuclear refrigerators have been built whose behaviour can no longer be described in the high-temperature ap-

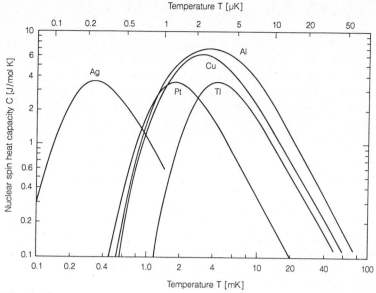

Fig.10.4. Nuclear heat capacities as a function of temperature for Al (I = 5/2), Cu (I = 3/2), Tl, Pt and Ag (I = 1/2) (remember that Pt contains only 33.8% of ^{195}Pt, its only isotope with a nuclear moment). The lower temperature scale corresponds to heat capacity data in a magnetic field of 9 T, the upper temperature scale to data in a field of 7 mT

proximation (Sects.10.7,8). Figure 10.4 shows that noticeable deviations from the high-temperature approximation occur for the specific heat of Cu in a field of 9 Tesla at T < 10 mK, for example. This can also been seen, of course, in the nuclear mangetization of Pt, Tl, Cu or In in AuIn$_2$ (Fig.10.5). Quantitively, a 1% deviation from the Curie law occurs for Cu at T < 22 mK (22μK) or in Pt at T < 9 mK (9μK) in a field of 8 Tesla (8mT). But in this chapter I will use the high-temperature approximations for our discussion. It is tedious but straightforward to use the full equations (9.15).

10.2 Differences in the Experimental Procedure for Nuclear and Electronic Demagnetization

There are two ways to precool and polarize the nuclear moments. Firstly, it can be done isothermally, as discussed for electronic magnetic refrigeration (Fig.9.1). In this case the heat of magnetization is given by

$$Q_a = nT_i\Delta S = -\frac{n\lambda_n B_i^2}{2\mu_0 T_i}. \tag{10.7}$$

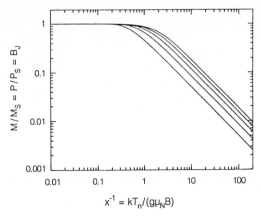

$$x^{-1} = kT_n/(g\mu_N B)$$

Fig.10.5. Relative magnetization M/M_s, see (9.15c), or relative population P/P_s, see (9.9), or Brillouin function $B_J(x)$ as a function of $x^{-1} = k_B T_N/g_n \mu_N B$ for nuclei with spins $I = 9/2$ to $1/2$ (from top to bottom). As examples, we can consider Pt ($I = 1/2$, $M_s = 0.085$mT, $g_n \mu_n/k_B = 0.42$mK/T), Tl ($I = 1/2$, $M_s = 0.36$mT, $g_n \mu_n/k_B = 1.21$ mK/T), Cu ($I = 3/2$, $M_s = 1.25$mT, $g_n \mu_n/k_B = 0.56$mK/T), and In ($I = 9/2$, $M_s = 1.02$ mT, $g_n \mu_n/k_B = 0.45$mK/T)

Another possibility is to switch on the starting field B_i at a high temperature and then precool the polarized nuclear magnetic moments by the ^{3}He-^{4}He dilution refrigerator along the entropy curve at B_i = const to the required starting temperature T_i. In this latter case the heat of magnetization is given by

$$Q_b = \int_{\infty}^{T_i} nC_{n,B} dT = - \frac{n\lambda_n B_i^2}{\mu_0 T_i} = 2Q_a . \tag{10.8}$$

In the former case, when we first precool to the starting temperature T_i, the field is slowly increased at this low temperature and the heat of magnetization has to be adsorbed by the dilution refrigerator at constant temperature T_i. The Joule heating occurring in the leads to the superconducting magnet (which is quite substantial due to the high currents, which are typically 100 A) has to be adsorbed by the ^{4}He bath for a long time. Even though in the second procedure the heat of magnetization is a factor of two larger, usually one chooses this latter procedure. Now the dilution refrigerator can start doing its work at a higher temperature, where it has a higher cooling power, and its large cooling power makes the difference in the two values for Q rather unimportant. In addition, it is then possible to avoid Joule heating in the ^{4}He bath for an extended time in the following way. The current is put into the superconducting magnet and circulates in a persistent mode through the superconduting magnet and its persistent shunt [10.11], as shown in Fig.10.6. Such a persistent switch usually consists of a small length of superconducting wire - short-circuiting the solenoid - to which a heater

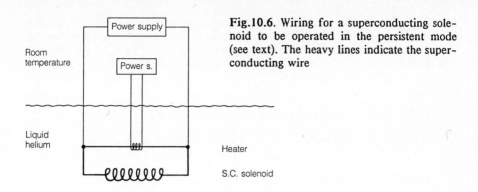

Fig.10.6. Wiring for a superconducting solenoid to be operated in the persistent mode
(see text). The heavy lines indicate the superconducting wire

Power supply

Room
temperature

Power s.

Liquid
helium

Heater

S.C. solenoid

is connected which can drive this piece of superconductor into its resistive
state, which is necessary for loading and unloading the current of the main
solenoid. We then have no current between the room temperature power
supply and the low-temperature part during the time of precooling, thus
avoiding ohmic losses. A superconducting solenoid operating in the persistent mode usually produces a field which is more stable and ripple-free than
the field of a solenoid connected to a power supply.

10.3 Interaction Between Conduction Electrons and Nuclei

In this section I shall discuss how thermal equilibrium can be established
between the various thermal reservoirs of a metal. In nuclear refrigeration
we reduce the temperature T_n of the nuclear spin system. Thermal equilibrium among the nuclear magnetic moments is established within the spin-
spin relaxation time τ_2. This relaxation time is rather short for metals, with
typical values of less than 1 ms (Table 10.1). Hence we can assume thermal
equilibrium within the nuclear spin system. For refrigeration we are usually
not interested in the final $T_{n,f}$ but much more in the electronic and lattice
temperatures of our refrigerant. Fortunately, the nuclear spin system is not
isolated from the conduction electrons. If this were the case, it would be
practically impossible to refrigerate other materials by nuclear demagnetization. Hence we have to consider how the low temperature of the nuclear
spin system can be transferred to electrons and to lattice vibrations. Because
the nuclear magnetic moments or spins do interact extremely weakly with
the lattice vibrations, the way heat or cooling is transferred is nuclei $\leftrightarrow$ conduction electrons $\leftrightarrow$ phonons.

10.3.1 Electron-Phonon Coupling

The heat flow between the electron and phonon systems for Cu, for example is given by [10.12, 13]

Table 10.1. Properties of some metals important for nuclear magnetic refrigeration and nuclear magnetic thermometry. In some cases a mean average is given if two isotopes are present. For the two compounds included (AuIn$_2$ and PrNi$_5$) the data are for the element in italics. (The nuclear properties have been taken from [10.22])

Isotope/ compound	ρ [g/cm^3]	V_m [cm^3/mol]	θ_D [K]	γ [mJ/ mol·K^2]	T_F [10^4 K]
^{27}Al	2.70	9.97	428	1.35	13.5
^{63,65}Cu	8.93	7.11	344	0.691	8.12
^{93}Nb	8.58	10.9	277	7.79	6.18
^{107,109}Ag	10.50	10.3	227	0.640	6.36
^{113,115}In	7.29	15.7	108	1.69	10.0
^{117,119}Sn	7.31	16.3	200	1.78	11.7
^{195}Pt	21.47	9.10	239	6.49	--
^{197}Au	19.28	10.2	162	0.689	6.39
^{203,205}Tl	11.87	17.2	78	1.47	9.46
Au*In*$_2$	10.3	41.5	--	--	--
*Pr*Ni$_5$	8.0	54	--	40	--

Isotope/ compound	Structure	T_c [K]	B_c [mT]	Isotopic abundance [%]	I
^{27}Al	fcc	1.18	10.5	100	5/2
^{63,65}Cu	fcc	--	--	69.1, 30.9	3/2
^{93}Nb	bcc	9.3	200	100	9/2
^{107,109}Ag	fcc	--	--	51.8, 48.2	1/2
^{113,115}In	tetr	3.41	28	4.3, 95.7	9/2
^{117,119}Sn	tetr	3.72	30.5	7.6, 8.7	1/2
^{195}Pt	fcc	--	--	33.8	1/2
^{197}Au	fcc	--	--	100	3/2
^{203,205}Tl	hcp	2.33	18	29.5, 70.5	1/2
Au*In*$_2$	cubic	0.21	1.5	4.3, 95.7	9/2
*Pr*Ni$_5$	hex	--	--	100	5/2

Isotope/compound	Q [barn]	μ [μ_n]	$\gamma/2\pi$[a] [kHz/mT]	$\gamma_m/2\pi$[b] [kHz/mT]
[27]Al	+0.15	3.64	11.09	11.27
[63,65]Cu	−0.211, −0.195	2.22, 2.38	11.29, 12.09	11.55, 12.38
[93]Nb	0.22	6.14	10.41	10.50
[107,109]Ag	--	−0.113, −0.130	1.723, 1.981	1.812, 2.084
[113,115]In	+0.82, +0.83	5.50, 5.51	9.31, 9.33	9.30, 9.41
[117,119]Sn	--	−0.99, −1.04	15.16, 15.87	15.28, 15.98
[195]Pt	--	0.597	9.094	8.781
[197]Au	+0.58	0.143	0.729	0.741
[203,205]Tl	--	1.60, 1.61	24.33, 24.57	24.73, 24.97
AuIn_2	+0.82, +0.83	5.50, 5.51	9.31, 9.33	9.38, 9.41
PrNi$_5$	−0.06	4.28[c]	13.1[c]	--

Isotope/compound	λ_n/V_m [μK]	λ_n/μ_0 [μJ·K/T^2 mol]	κ [K·s]	τ_2 [ms]
[27]Al	0.87	6.90	1.80	0.03
[63,65]Cu	0.57	3.22	1.27, 1.09	0.15
[93]Nb	1.99	17.2	0.36	0.02
[107,109]Ag	0.0020	0.016	12, 9	10
[113,115]In	1.10	13.8	0.09	0.1
[117,119]Sn	0.015	0.194	0.059, 0.054	0.10
[195]Pt	0.019	0.138	0.030	1.0
[197]Au	0.0016	0.013	4.6	–
[203,205]Tl	0.207	2.83	0.004	0.035
AuIn_2	0.83	27.8	0.09	0.6
PrNi$_5$	33[d]	1418[d]	<0.001	<0.01

[a] γ: gyromagnetic ratio of the bare nucleus
[b] $\gamma_m = \gamma \times$ Knight shift, being the gyromagnetic ratio in the metal
[c] (d) Values for the nucleus without (with) hyperfine enhancement

$$\dot{Q}_{e\text{-ph}} \simeq 600V(T_{ph}^5 - T_e^5) \quad [W] \quad \text{for} \quad T > 0.1 \text{ K},$$
$$\dot{Q}_{e\text{-ph}} \simeq 25V(T_{ph}^4 - T_e^4) \quad [W] \quad \text{for} \quad T < 0.05 \text{ K}, \tag{10.9}$$

where V is the volume [cm^3] of the sample.

This gives a rather small heat flow but fortunately the specific heat of the lattice vibrations decreases with T^3 and is very small in the temperature range of interest to us here. Therefore the phonon temperature will always follow the electronic temperature within a very short relaxation time. Henceforth we can assume that lattice vibrations and conduction electrons are at the same temperature.

10.3.2 Nucleus–Electron Coupling

The coupling between electrons and nuclei is an electromagnetic interaction acting between the nuclei and those electrons that have a finite charge density at the nucleus. In a first approximation these are only the s-electrons, because electrons with another symmetry have a node of their wave function at the side of the nucleus. In the process a nucleus and a conduction electron undergo a mutual spin flip via the contact interaction.

We will now define a time τ_1 which the nuclei need to come to thermal equilibrium with the conduction electrons at T_e = const., i.e.,

$$dT_n^{-1}/dt = - (T_n^{-1} - T_e^{-1})/\tau_1 . \tag{10.10}$$

The time τ_1 is the so-called "spin-lattice relaxation time". This name is somewhat misleading for metals because the interaction is not directly between the nuclear spins and the lattice; it is caused by hyperfine interactions between the nuclei and the conduction electrons. Only conduction electrons near the Fermi energy can interact with the nuclei and change their energy due to this interaction because the electron must find an empty energy state at an energy difference corresponding to the energy exchanged with the nucleus. Electrons which have an energy far below the Fermi energy are not accessibile for the interaction. With arguments similar to the ones which led to a linear temperature dependence of the specific heat of conduction electrons (Sect.3.1.2), we find a linear temperature dependence of the rate τ_1^{-1} at which the nuclei come into equilibrium with the electrons. This then leads to the famous Korringa law

$$\tau_1 T_e = \kappa , \tag{10.11}$$

where κ is a material constant. Note that (10.11) is valid for $T_e \gg \mu\mu_n B/Ik_B$; the general expression is [10.14-21]

$$\tau_1 = \frac{2I\kappa k_B}{\mu\mu_n B} \tanh\left(\frac{\mu\mu_n B}{2Ik_B T_e} \right) . \tag{10.11'}$$

Values of κ are given in Table 10.1 for various metals which are of interest for nuclear magnetic refrigeration. The nuclei exchange energy with each other by performing mutual spin-flips; this self-equilibration, of course, does not change the macroscopic nuclear magnetization of the sample, i.e., it keeps T_n constant. The rate of this spin-spin relaxation process is $1/\tau_2$. We see from the data in Table 10.1 that usually $\tau_1 \gg \tau_2$ at low temperatures, which means that the nuclei reach thermal equilibrium among themselves much faster than they reach equilibrium with the conduction electrons. It therefore does, indeed, make sense to speak of a "nuclear spin temperature T_n" and of an "electronic or lattice temperature T_e" [10.14-17]. We can also see from the data for κ in Table 10.1 that for some metals the relaxation time is only a few seconds, even in the low millikelvin temperature range, but it can reach, for example, about 1 h at 0.3 mK for Cu. Anyway, for metals these are experimentally accessible times. On the other hand, there are no conduction electrons in insulators and the nuclear spin-lattice relaxation time for these materials can be very large, in the range of days or even weeks at millikelvin temperatures. Therefore only metals can be used for nuclear refrigeration.

Ideally the Korringa constant is independent of temperature but depends on the magnetic field if this becomes comparable to the internal field b [10.14-17] according to

$$\kappa(B) = \kappa(\infty) \frac{B^2 + b^2}{B^2 + \alpha b^2} , \tag{10.12}$$

where the coefficient α (ca. 2 to 3) depends on the type of internal interactions. For Cu with b = 0.34 mT and α = 2.6, κ = 0.4 K·s at B = 0 and κ = 1.2 K·s at B $\geq$ 10 mT [10.1]. The discussion of the dynamics to establish thermal equilibrium between nuclei and conduction electrons becomes rather complicated if the high-temperature approximation cannot be used anymore. In such a situation rate equations have to be considered and the behavior depends on the nuclear spin I as well; for details one should consult the original literature [10.14-21].

Because τ_1 can become rather large at low temperatures, it is possible to refrigerate just the nuclear spin system to low microkelvin temperatures and leave conduction electrons and phonons at higher temperatures. This was the case in the original experiment at Oxford in 1956 [10.2,3], and has been extensively used in Helsinki in recent years in studies of nuclear magnetic interactions in Cu [10.1]. This type of experiment is called *nuclear cooling*. On the other hand, if the refrigeration is performed in such a way that the nuclei pull conduction electrons and phonons to low temperatures as well, the term used is *nuclear refrigeration* and it is the latter which we are considering in this book.

Until now we have discussed the time which "hot" nuclei need to cool to the temperature of "cold" electrons which sit at T_e = const. In the case of nuclear refrigeration it is the other way around: the cold nuclei have to pull the hotter electrons to low temperatures, and both T_n and T_e will change.

In this process we have the heat flow

$$\dot{Q} = nC_e\dot{T}_e = -nC_{n,B}\dot{T}_n \ . \tag{10.13}$$

From the definition for the spin–lattice relaxation time, (10.10,11), for κ we obtain

$$dT_n^{-1}/dt = -(T_n^{-1} - T_e^{-1})T_e/\kappa \ , \tag{10.14}$$

or

$$\dot{T}_n = (T_e - T_n)T_n/\kappa \ . \tag{10.15}$$

Note that if the nuclei experience a change of magnetic field we have

$$\dot{T}_n = (T_e - T_n)T_n/\kappa + (T_n/B)\dot{B} \ . \tag{10.15'}$$

Combining these equations (assuming $\dot{B} = 0$) we obtain an equation for the rate of change of temperature of the conduction electrons

$$\dot{T}_e = -(T_e - T_n)(T_n C_{n,B}/\kappa C_e) \ , \tag{10.16}$$

which results in $T_f = T_i B_f/B_i$, if the conduction electrons of the refrigerant do not present a noticeable heat load, i.e., if the process is adiabatic (see end of Sect. 10.4).

Finally we obtain the rate of change of the difference of the nuclear and electronic temperatures

$$\dot{T}_n - \dot{T}_e = -(T_e - T_n)(1 + C_{n,B}/C_e)T_n/\kappa \ . \tag{10.17}$$

This latter equation tells us that the hot electrons come into thermal equilibrium with the cold nuclei with an effective time constant

$$\tau_1' = \frac{\tau_1 C_e}{C_{n,B} + C_e} \simeq \frac{\tau_1 C_e}{C_{n,B}} \ , \tag{10.18}$$

where the latter approximation can be used because the specific heat of the conduction electrons is much smaller than the specific heat of the nuclear magnetic moments in an external magnetic field B. For the same reason, the effective time constant τ_1' is much shorter than the spin lattice relaxation time τ_1. This means that we need only very few nuclear spin flips to remove the electronic specific heat, i.e. T_n stays almost constant, and the electrons can follow the nuclear spin temperature rather quickly.

Everything we have discussed until now was in terms of an adiabatic, reversible process. That means electrons and nuclei are in equilibrium, and there is no external heat load. This is all right because, as mentioned, the phonon and the electronic specific heats are negligible compared to the nuclear specific heat in most cases, and we have neglected external heat loads. However, in general, there will be an external heat flow into the lattice and electron systems and from there to the nuclei, resulting in a temperature gradient between electrons and nuclei. This more realistic situation will be discussed in the next section.

10.4 Influence of an External Heat Load and the Optimum Final Magnetic Field

Let us discuss how much heat the cold nuclei can absorb or how long they will stay below a given temperature. This discussion will lead us to the optimum final demagnetization field, which is essential in determining the cooling power of the "demagnetized" nuclear magnetic moments. We discussed in Sect.9.2 that for magnetic refrigeration one has to have a finite final field to keep a reasonably large cooling power of the moments and to prevent them from warming up too rapidly.

The cooling power of the nuclei is given by

$$\int \dot{Q} dt = \int n C_{n,B} dT . \qquad (10.19)$$

Using the high-temperature approximation (10.4) for the nuclear specific heat in the final field B_f and (10.15) for the rate of change of the nuclear spin temperature, we find for the cooling power of the nuclei (neglecting the very small "load" that the electronic specific heat puts on the nuclei)

$$\dot{Q} = n C_{n,B_f} \dot{T}_n = (T_e - T_n) \frac{n \lambda_n B_f^2}{\mu_0 \kappa T_n} , \qquad (10.20)$$

or

$$\frac{T_e}{T_n} = 1 + \frac{\mu_0 \kappa \dot{Q}}{n \lambda_n B_f^2} . \qquad (10.21)$$

If the high-temperature approximation ($k_B T I \gg \mu \mu_n B$) does not apply, then (10.20) has to be replaced by

$$\dot{Q} = \frac{3 n \lambda_n B_f^2}{2 \mu_0 \kappa} \frac{e^{-x_e} - e^{-x_n}}{1 - e^{-x_e}} \frac{I(I+1) - \langle m^2 \rangle \pm \langle m \rangle}{I(I+1)} , \qquad (10.20')$$

where $+m$ ($-m$) corresponds to $m = +I$ ($-I$) being the lowest energy state, and $x_e = |g_n \mu_n| B / k_B T_e$, $x_n = |g_n \mu_n| B / k_B T_n$ [10.18-20]. We can write (10.21) as

$$T_e = T_n (1 + a/B_f^2) = (T_i/B_i)(B_f + a/B_f) , \qquad (10.22)$$

where a is a constant. Here we have used the equation $T_{n,f} = B_f T_i / B_i$, which is not quite correct if the external heat load is not zero. The error introduced by this approximation is small (typically several precent increase

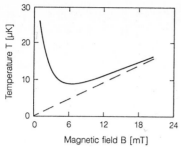

Fig.10.7. Electronic temperature (full line) and nuclear spin temperature (dashed line) as a function of magnetic field during demagnetization of Cu nuclei starting from 8 T and 5 mK and assuming a heat leak of 0.1 nW/mol Cu. The figure shows that for these parameters the lowest electronic temperature of 8 μK would be achieved at a nuclear spin temperature of 4 μK and a magnetic field of 6 mT

in $T_{n,f}$) and does not change the essential part of our result. The nuclear spin temperature is proportional to the demagnetization field and this pro-portionality also applies to the electronic temperature as long as the field is not too small. However, for small final demagnetization fields the electronic temperature increases, leading to an increasing difference between nuclear and electronic temperatures due to the heat flow between the two systems, as shown in Fig.10.7. There is an optimum final demagnetization field if we are interested in achieving the minimum electronic temperature. This mini-mum electronic temperature can be calculated from $dT_e/dB_f = 0$, resulting in

$$B_{f,opt} = \sqrt{\frac{\mu_0 \kappa \dot{Q}}{n \lambda_n}} \,, \tag{10.23}$$

(assuming b $<<$ $B_{f,opt}$ as we have done everywhere in this section).

If we use (10.21) for the ratio between electronic and nuclear tempera-tures, we find that at the optimum final demagnetization field the electrons are a factor of two hotter than the nuclei,

$$T_{e,min} = 2T_n(B_f) \,. \tag{10.24}$$

Equation (10.21) gives $T_e/T_n = 2$ for 10 moles Cu at $\dot{Q} = 1$ nW and $B_f = 6$ mT (Fig.10.7).

As a last step I want to calculate how long it takes to warm the nuclei from a temperature $T_{n,1}$ to a temperature $T_{n,2}$. This time can be computed from the equation for the rate of change of the nuclear spin temperature,

$$\dot{T}_n = \dot{Q}/C_{n,B_f} \,. \tag{10.25}$$

The warming time of the nuclei is then given by

$$t = (n \lambda_n B_f^2 / \mu_0 \dot{Q})(T_{n,1}^{-1} - T_{n,2}^{-1}) \,. \tag{10.26}$$

172

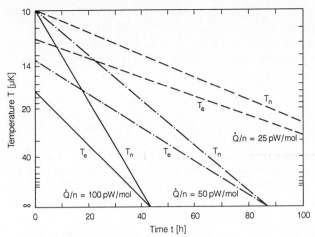

Fig.10.8. Temperatures, see (10.21), of the nuclear and electronic systems of Cu after demagnetization. The data show the warm-up rates, see (10.26), for the given molar heat leaks $\dot{Q}/n$ to the Cu refrigerant in a final field $B_f = 7$ mT [10.10]

The product tT_n is constant for a constant heat load, and can be used to determine this heat load by plotting tT_n or T_n as a function of time. If $\dot{Q}$ and the warm-up time t are known, one can calculate the total heat Q that has been absorbed by the nuclear stage. From Q and the specific heat C_{B_f} of the stage, $T_{n,f}$ the starting nuclear temperature for the warm-up of the stage can be calculated. The warm-up rates for both T_e and T_n [and therefore also their difference according to (10.21)] are shown in Fig.10.8.

Let me stress again that one has to choose the final demagnetization field very carefully if the minimum electronic temperature and a long time for the experiment are the aims of the refrigeration. The electrons and the lattice simply will not cool if B_f is too low because then the nuclear heat capacity is too small, i.e., too little heat is absorbed per nuclear spin-flip.

In the same way, as we have discussed the influence of a constant "heat-leak", we can consider the usual experimental situation that the nuclear spin system with n moles is supposed to refrigerate a load. Let this heat load be n' moles of conduction electrons or of liquid ^{3}He, so that their molar entropy can be written as $S' = \gamma'T$. For an adiabatic process from B_i, T_i to B_f, T_f we then have for the total entropies

$$n'\gamma'T_i - \frac{n\lambda_n B_i^2}{2\mu_0 T_i^2} = n'\gamma'T_f - \frac{n\lambda_n B_f^2}{2\mu_0 T_f^2} . \tag{10.27}$$

Because the molar entropies of conduction electrons or even of liquid ^{3}He are rather small compared to the entropy change resulting from nuclear refrigeration, they only represent a relatively small load on the nuclear spin system. For example, the volume of liquid ^{3}He can be up to a factor of three larger than the volume of a Cu nuclear refrigerant without deteriorat-

173

ing the performance of the latter significantly [10.10,23]. Therefore the final temperature of the load is determined by T_i B_f/B_i and, above all, by the thermal coupling of it to the refrigerant. A bad thermal coupling will lead to temperature differences between load and refrigerant and to irreversible losses during the refrigeration process.

10.5 Heat Leaks

Because the cooling power of a refrigerator is smaller the lower its temperature regime of operation, more than for all other refrigeration techniques, the success of a nuclear refrigerator depends on the reduction of heat leaks. In addition to limiting the cool-time according to (10.26), minute heat leaks can give rise to very large temperature gradients because of the small thermal conductivities and thermal contact problems at very low temperatures. Whereas in the 1970's total heat leaks of order 10^{-8} W were considered an achievement, today's best nuclear refrigerators reach values of several 10^{-10} W. They operate with heat leaks so low that the heat generated by ionization due to the penetration of the refrigerant by high-energy cosmic rays (about 10^{-14} W/g) or by residual, natural or artificial, radioactivity, can no longer be neglected [10.24,25,28]. The heat leaks in a refrigerator can be divided into "external heat leaks" and "internal heat leaks", which come from the refrigerated material itself and are usually time dependent.

10.5.1 External Heat Leaks

Obvious external heat flow to the parts at microkelvin temperatures, for example by conduction via residual gas atoms, along mechanical supports, via the heat switch, along electrical leads (typically about 100 in a large nuclear refrigerator, which may include several experiments) or fill capillaries for helium experiments (remember the high thermal conductivity of liquid helium, both ^{3}He and ^{4}He, at low temperatures; see Figs.2.11,16,17) have been reduced to a total level of $\dot{Q} < 0.1$ nW [10.23-28]. This can be done even in a complicated apparatus by choosing the proper materials and by proper thermal anchoring at intermediate cooling stages. - A 10 cm^2 surface at 4 K radiates 10 nW, far too much for a nuclear refrigerator. Therefore, all parts at microkelvin temperatures have to be guarded by a radiation shield connected to a part at lower temperature, such as the mixing chamber or at least one of the heat exchangers of the precooling dilution refrigerator. These shields can be made of brass, which has a conductivity large enough to keep temperature gradients tolerable but small enough to keep eddy current heating (see below) low while the demagnetizing field is changed. Their thermal performance can be improved by glueing highly conducting Cu foils to them. Also, brass is not magnetic (be careful with some stainless steels), which otherwise could lead to heating effects or could affect the experiments when a magnetic ordering temperature is crossed. Brass shields seem to behave as well as other sometimes more elaborate designs ("coil-foil", etc.), which are discussed in the literature [10.7]. A thermal shield not only reduces radiation but also stops "hot" gas molecules from hitting the inner low-temperature part of a cryostat. In addition, radiation shields and light traps in pumping tubes (made from semicircular baffles soldered to a wire, for example) are required.

The low-temperature parts in every cryostat are connected via transmission lines to room-temperature equipment. These lines couple to RF fields. A very serious consideration is, therefore, RF heating, in particular with regard to thermometers (for the appropriate precautions see Chap. 12). Many refrigerators have been built in an RF-shielded room with filtered electrical supplies, which can provide up to 120 dB attenuation at typically 100 kHz to 1 GHz [10.28]. Then the pumping and gas recovery lines have to be brought in by electrically non-conducting tubes. As stressed in [10.7]:

"To be effective the room must be well-made and maintained. All seams, including those around the door, must be electrically tight. Power lines to the room must be filtered and pumping and service lines electrically grounded as they pass through the walls. A shielded room can be rather easily tested by a portable FM radio which should be absolutely quiet inside. This same instrument can be employed for locating "leaks" although sometimes this is not easy. A well-made room can provide 100 dB attenuation and is obviously very useful to have. It is, however, good practice to build the room first, before the cryostat is installed, and not as an afterthought!"

But often the noise caused by instrumentation inside of the room can be at least as serious as external noise. It has turned out to be of particular importance to shield the power supplies in most instruments from the rest of the interior; often it may even be necessary to put them into a separate, shielded metal box.

Of course, the leads are usually shielded by the metal cryostat and by the metal tubes through which they run inside of it. They should be twisted pairwise and rigidly fixed. The RF noise they could transmit from their room-temperature ends may have to be cut off by RF filters, as will be discussed in Sect. 12.5.2.

A further very troublesome heat source is mechanical heating from building vibrations, from sound, or from mechanical pumps. Irreversible heating effects can arise from rubbing of adjacent parts, from inelastic bending, and from eddy current heating when electrically conducting parts move in a magnetic field; this last effect will be discussed in the next section. A systematic approach to vibration isolation of a nuclear refrigerator has not been attempted or described to my knowledge. Most nuclear refrigerators have been built in the basement or at most on the first floor, where building vibrations are smallest. They should be attached to a heavy foundation on damping material and supported by springs. Their mass should be large, so that the resonance frequency is at around 1 Hz, which is usually far below all frequencies in the surroundings [10.23-29]. The damping "springs" can be inflated metal bellows or rubber tubes or commercial pneu-

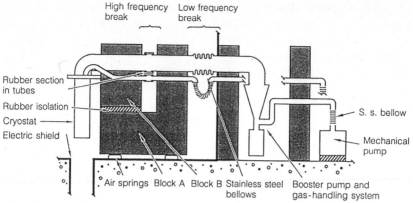

High frequency break Low frequency break

Rubber section in tubes
Rubber isolation
Cryostat
Electric shield

S. s. bellow
Mechanical pump

Air springs Block A Block B Stainless steel bellows Booster pump and gas-handling system

Fig.10.9. Schematic diagram of a support system for a nuclear refrigeration cryostat. The cryostat is mounted on a concrete block (block A) supported by air springs. On top of block A are placed two smaller blocks (only one shown, block B) resting on thick pads of rubber which carry the wooden beams supporting the cryostat. The pumping tubes are, firstly concreted, into a massive block on the laboratory floor, to remove the vibrations of the pumps, secondly, taken through metal bellows, thirdly, concreted into the main block A, and finally led via a rubber section to be fixed to the sub-blocks B [10.10, 34]

matic vibration isolators used in optics laboratories. The compressed air provides the adjustable low spring constant necessary for the isolation [10.32]. Usually the most probable paths for transmission of vibrations are pumping and gas handling lines. Mechanical pumps therefore have to be mounted separately and should sit on rubber stoppers. They should be connected to the cryostat by thick-valled rubber hoses and/or flexible soft metallic bellows with compensating bellows T's between them (for the large diameter systems) [10.32, 33] or hung in long loose loops. At some intermediate point they should be firmly attached to a large mass, like the wall or a sand-filled box. An example of such a design is shown in Fig.10.9. A last point of consideration is vibration conducted through the gas phase of the pumping system or of the ^{4}He recovery system, which sees the exhaust of rotary pumps and compressors in the recovery systems. Here, a damping element might be necessary as well.

When all these troublesome points have been considered, the effectiveness of the design should be checked with an accelerometer or a seismometer, either of the design described in [10.35] or a commercial one. Of course, the interior of the cryostat should be designed to be as rigid as possible so that vibrations still transmitted (less than $0.1\,\mu$m amplitude and $1\,$mm/s^2 acceleration in a reasonably good design) do not do too much harm; later changes - if vibration turns out to be a serious heat source - are very difficult to carry out.

10.5.2 Eddy Current Heating

Because a nuclear refrigerator contains highly conducting metals in changing magnetic fields, we have to consider eddy current heating effects. Obviously one has to operate the superconducting magnet as ripple free as possible; filtering may be necessary. The use of filamentary type superconducting wires has substantially reduced flux jumps but a small decay of the final demagnetization field B_f when the superconducting magnet is operated in the persistent mode has still been observed frequently [10.28, 36a]. However, due to the unavoidable residual vibrations of the apparatus, the highly conducting nuclear stage will always experience a changing field even if only B ≠ 0.

Eddy current heating is unavoidable when the field is changed at a rate $\dot{B}$ for demagnetization. The heat generated by eddy currents in a body of volume V and with electrical resistance ρ is

$$\dot{Q}_e = PV\dot{B}^2/\rho ,\tag{10.28}$$

where the geometry factor P is given by

$$P = \begin{cases} r^2/8 & \text{for a cylinder with radius r,} \\ (d^2/16)[k^2/(1+k^2)] & \text{for a rectangle of width w} \\ & \text{and thickness d, where } k = w/d . \end{cases} \tag{10.29}$$

For a Cu cylinder with r = 1 mm, ρ = 2 nΩ·cm (corresponding to RRR ≃ 1000 for Cu) and for $\dot{B}$ = 0.5 T/h we find

$$\dot{Q}_e/V \simeq 1 \ \frac{nW}{mol \ Cu} . \tag{10.30}$$

However, we have to keep in mind that ρ = f(B) due to the magnetoresistance of metals [10.37]. The corresponding entropy change ΔS_e due to eddy currents should be compared to the reduction of entropy ΔS_B, (10.4), in a field B and at the temperature T,

$$\frac{\Delta S_e}{\Delta S_B} = \frac{\mu_0 T r^2}{4\rho\tau\lambda_n} , \tag{10.31}$$

if the demagnetization is performed exponentially in time with τ being the demagnetization time constant. Under normal experimental conditions this ratio can be kept to a few percent [10.26]. In any case, conducting loops in which varying magnetic flux can give rise to eddy currents should be minimized.

We can ask for the optimum values for the parameters r and $\dot{B}$. Reduction of $\dot{Q}_e$ requires a small demagnetization rate $\dot{B}$. On the other hand, there are other heat sources as well and their influence accumulates if we demagnetize slowly. In practice, rates of $\dot{B}$ ≤ 1T/h seem to be appropriate. Modelling of demagnetization experiments with the aim of optimizing the rates $\dot{B}$

can be found in [10.6, 8, 38–40]. Due to a fear of eddy current heating, fine Cu wires were mainly used as a nuclear refrigerant in the early days. Nowadays demagnetization times of many hours are common and for such rates $\dot{B}$ one can show that typical dimensions of $2 \div 3$ mm for the refrigerant are optimum values if one wants a large filling factor but small r to reduce $\dot{Q}_e$.

10.5.3 Internal, Time–Dependent Heat Leaks

Once heat leaks had been reduced to the low nanowatt range, experimentalists found to their surprise that there was a residual, time-dependent heat leak which limits the minimum achievable temperature (Fig. 10.10) [10.24]. Obviously, this heat cannot come from external sources but must be released from the refrigerant or from the refrigerated parts; it depends on how long they have already been kept cold. The origin of this observation is the fact that a solid consists of various subsystems which can be at different temperatures due to very long low-temperature relaxation times. The coldest ones, of course, are the "demagnetized" nuclei in the center of the nuclear stage. The electrons there and, in particular, the electrons in the upper flange of the stage are kept by the unavoidable heat leaks at a higher temperature. However, there are other subsystems which may keep themselves at even higher temperatures due to heat releasing processes. These can be gas inclusions, like H_2 (see below), disorder due to lattice defects which may slowly relax (see below), radioactive nuclei which are always present, or other "hot" impurity atoms. The heat releasing energy sources are charged up each time the apparatus is warmed up.

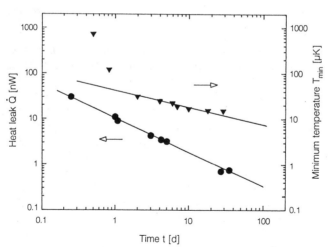

Fig. 10.10. *Left scale*: Low-temperature heat leak $\dot{Q}$ (•) in the nuclear refrigerator shown in Fig. 10.14 as a function of time t after reaching 4 K; the line is $\dot{Q} \propto t^{-3/4}$. *Right scale*: Minimum temperatures ($\blacktriangledown$) measured by Pt NMR thermometry at the top of the nuclear stage as a function of time after reaching 4 K in this refrigerator; the line is $T_{min} \propto t^{-3/8}$ [10.28]

The ortho-para conversion of H_2 has been found to be one origin of time-dependent heat release from refrigerated parts [10.41,42]. Hydrogen at typical concentrations of $10\div100$ ppm is present in some metals due to their production or purification processes. Many metals, e.g., Cu, Ag, Au, Pt and Rh, cannot dissolve hydrogen in a noticeable amount in their lattice, and H_2 molecules then precipitate in small bubbles with typical diameters of about 0.1 μm. Even though the concentration of H_2 in a metal may be rather small, the heating can be quite severe due to the large rotational energy change of $172[K]k_B$ for each converted H_2 molecule. The ortho-para conversion of 1 ppm H_2 in 1 kg Cu gives rise to a heat leak of about 5 nW even one week after cooldown (Fig.2.2). Details are discussed in Sect.2.2. To get rid of this source of energy release, one anneals the metal in vacuum at temperatures close to its melting temperature, which seems to reduce the H_2 concentration to below 0.1 ppm [10.28] (the diffusion constant of H in Cu is $D = D_0 exp(-E/k_B T)$ with $D_0 = 1.13 \cdot 10^{-2} cm^2/s$ and $E = 0.40eV$ at $T > 720$ K [10.43]).

Another group of processes giving rise to a time-dependent heat release are structural relaxations or deexcitations of low energy excitations (like tunneling transitions of protons) with long relaxation times. These occur mostly in non-crystalline materials after they have been refrigerated to low temperatures [10.44,45]. The low temperature thermodynamic properties of non-crystalline materials (Sects.3.1.4,3.3.1) are described by the two-level-system tunneling model [10.46]. Within this model, the time-dependent heat release of non-crystalline materials after they have been refrigerated from a temperature T_i to a temperature T_f is given by

$$\dot{Q} = \frac{\pi^2}{24} \frac{Vk_B^2 \overline{P}(T_i^2 - T_f^2)}{t} ,$$ (10.32)

where $\overline{P}$ is the density of two-level tunneling states. Examples of this heat release from quartz glass and from some organic materials are shown in Fig.10.11. The heat release is typically of order 0.1 (0.01) nW/g, 1 day (week) after these materials have been refrigerated to low temperatures. Because of their heat release and because of their low thermal conductivities (Figs.3.17-20), one should minimise the amount of non-crystalline, particularly dielectric materials (e.g., glues, epoxies, grease, plastics, etc.), which are often not very well-defined materials, in an apparatus which works at microkelvin temperatures. In such a cryostat the minimum achievable temperature is limited by very small heat leaks and such heat leaks can create severe temperature differences. One should also never touch the ultralow temperature parts of a cryostat with bare hands; the transferred "grease" would give rise to heat release. No heat release (to within 2 $\times 10^{-2}$ nW/g) has been observed for teflon, graphite, and Al_2O_3 [10.44], which are quite useful materials for many cryogenic purposes.

One should avoid materials with large electronic (resistance wires, Fig. 3.9) or nuclear (Be-Cu?) heat capacities and with a low thermal conductivity in a cryostat. They may store energy which is frozen in at higher tem-

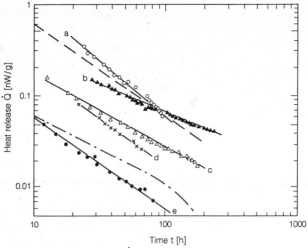

Fig.10.11. Heat release $\dot{Q}$ for (**a**) Siloxan, (**b**) Stycast 2850FT, (**c**) Stycast 1266, (**d**) Vespel SP22, (**e**) quartz glass (Suprasil W) [10.44] (*dashed line*: PMMA (Plexiglass), *dot-dashed line*: PS (Polystyrol) [10.47]) as a function of time after these materials have been cooled to below 1 K. The line through the Suprasil data and the dashed line for the PMMA data correspond to $\dot{Q} \propto t^{-1}$. Deviations from this time dependence according to (10.32) can probably be explained by the complicated nature of some of the investigated materials

peratures and release it as heat over long periods of time after cooldown, leading to a time-dependent heat leak. Simple, pure and well-characterized materials should be used and the others – if unavoidable – should be kept to a minimum. Furthermore, heat may be released by relaxation of stress, in particular, at press contacts which can be quite numerous in a complicated cryogenic apparatus.

Unfortunately, recent experiments [10.1, 28] seem to indicate that such time-dependent internal heat release also occurs in well-annealed metals; structural relaxation at grain boundaries or other lattice defects may possibly be its origin. An example is shown in Fig.10.10. The typical total heat release from the cold parts of a well-designed nuclear refrigerator during its cold time is of order 10 mJ [10.1, 24, 28]. If this heat release were to be attributed to tunneling transitions of systems with an energy separation of 30K (3K) one would need the relaxation of about 10^{-4} (10^{-3}) mols or only some ppm of the cold parts. This small concentration can easily be assigned to lattice imperfections. More research is necessary to understand this heat release and to reduce it to values below some pW/mol.

Another source of time-dependent heat leaking is insufficiently pumped exchange gas. In a nuclear refrigerator one should only use about 10^{-1} (10^{-3}) mbar of ^{3}He at 300 (10) K as exchange gas and pump on it at a temperature of $T \geq 10$ K for at least 5 h. Cooling from 10 K downwards is easy by just circulating cold gas through the dilution refrigerator because heat capacities of solids are already quite small. If too much exchange gas is left in the apparatus, the remaining atoms may desorb from hotter surfaces and condense at the parts at ultralow temperatures, leading to a heat leak which decays with time. ^{4}He should not be used because it has a lower vapour pressure, may interfere with a later mass spectroscopic leak check, and because of its superfluid film flow (Sect.2.3.5). Hydrogen should not be used as exchange gas because of its ortho-para conversion leading to a large heat release as discussed above and in Sect.2.2.

10.6 Nuclear Refrigerants

The requirements on a nuclear refrigerator can be divided into requirements on the apparatus and requirements on the material used as a nuclear refrigerant. The requirements on the apparatus are a large ratio for the starting conditions B_i/T_i and, most important, a small heat leak to the experiments, to the thermometers, and to the nuclear refrigerant. This last requirement has turned out to be the most important factor for the quality of a nuclear refrigerator.

The requirements on the refrigerant are the following [10.10]:

- It should be a metal, because we need a small Korringa constant so that the electrons will come into thermal equilibrium with the nuclei in a relatively short time and we need a high thermal conductivity to transport the cold along the refrigerant to experiments and thermometers.
- It should not be a superconductor because if a metal becomes superconducting we lose the conduction electrons for the necessary thermal conductivity (Sect.3.3.4). We would also loose them as a medium responsible for the hyperfine interaction between nuclei and electrons (τ_1 would become very long). If the material becomes superconducting, its critical field for the superconducting state has to be lower than the final demagnetization field so that we can keep the metal in its normal state.
- The material should be easy to work with mechanically and metallurgically, and should be readily available with high purity.
- It should not show an electronic magnetic ordering transition, because this would produce an internal field in which the nuclear moments would align.
- It should have a small internal field b due to nuclear interactions or a low nuclear magnetic ordering temperature because this limits the minimum achievable temperature (b should be $<1\,$mT).
- A large fraction of its isotopes should have a nuclear spin $I > 0$ and a large nuclear Curie constant λ_n for a large cooling power.
- The nuclei should either experience a cubic environment (so that electric field gradients vanish) or have a nuclear spin $I = 1/2$ (so that it has no nuclear electric quadrupole moment).

Let me elaborate on this last consideration. If neither of these last two requirements, cubic symmetry or $I = 1/2$, is fulfilled, the nuclear electric quadrupole moment Q will experience an interaction with the electric field gradient V_{zz}. The nuclei will align and nuclear magnetic refrigeration is not possible anymore. We can consider the following two cases for the nuclear interactions. If the magnetic Zeeman interaction is much larger than the electric quadrupole interaction, we have for the energies of the nuclear hyperfine levels

$$E_m = - mg_n\mu_n B + \frac{e^2 V_{zz} Q}{4I(2I-1)}[3m^2 - I(I+1)] \frac{3\cos^2\theta - 1}{2} \tag{10.33}$$

with $m = -I, -I+1, ..., +I$, and θ the angle between B and V_{zz}.

If the magnetic Zeeman interaction can be neglected compared to the electric quadrupole interaction, we have

$$E_m = \frac{e^2 V_{zz} Q}{4I(2I-1)}[3m^2 - I(I+1)] . \tag{10.34}$$

In the latter case, the nuclear quadrupole specific heat in the high temperature approximation is given by

$$C_Q = \left(\frac{11R}{480}\right)\left(\frac{e^2 V_{zz} Q}{k_B T}\right)^2 - \left(\frac{11R}{5760}\right)\left(\frac{e^2 V_{zz} Q}{k_B T}\right)^3 + ... \tag{10.35}$$

There is no material which fulfils all the above requirements. For example, indium has a large nuclear spin, a large nuclear magnetic moment, high thermal conductivity, and a very short Korringa constant (Table 10.1), but it fails to meet the requirement of absence of superconductivity and of nuclear electric quadrupole interaction, limiting its usefulness as a refrigerand to $T \geq 0.3$ mK [10.48]. Actually, some of the requirements are even contradictory. A small Korringa constant requires a large electronic density of states at the Fermi energy, as found in transition metals, but this also favors electronic magnetism or superconductivity. And the quest for a large nuclear spin and nuclear moment rules out all non-cubic crystals; otherwise there will be quadrupole interactions. If we put all the mentioned restrictive requirements together and look at the periodic system of the elements, there are not many metallic elements left which are suitable for nuclear refrigeration. The relevant parameters for most of them are collected in Table 10.1.

Figure 10.12 shows the reduction of nuclear spin entropies of Cu, In, Nb, and PrNi$_5$ in a field of 5 T; here not an equal number of moles but equal volumes are compared, which may be more relevant for practical applications. From this figure it is obvious that PrNi$_5$ is the most appropriate nuclear refrigerant if starting temperatures $T_i > 10$ mK, moderate starting fields B_i and moderate final temperatures $T_f \geq 0.4$ mK are required. The favourable properties of PrNi$_5$ and other hyperfine-enhanced van Vleck paramagnets will be discussed in the next section. The next best candidates would be Al, In and Nb, according to their rather large nuclear moments. However, superconducting transitions with critical fields $B_c > 10$ mT are the main obstacles to using In (also large quadrupole interaction [10.48]), Nb (almost type II superconductor), and Tl (poisonous and very strong oxi-

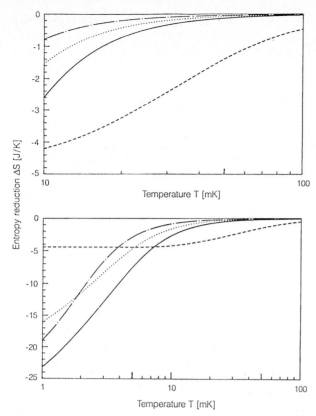

Fig.10.12. Nuclear spin entropy reduction ΔS of 1.4 mol Nb (—), 1.0 mol In (....), 2.0 mol Cu (-··-), and 0.3 mol PrNi$_5$ (- -) in a field of 5 T and at 10 mK $\leq$ T $\leq$ 100 mK (a) and at 1 mK $\leq$ T $\leq$ 100 mK (b). The amount of each material has been chosen to give the same volume of refrigerant

dation [10.36, 37]). Some of them may still be suitable nuclear refrigerants for some special applications. The disadvantages of In can be avoided by using it in the compound AuIn$_2$ (cubic; B$_c$ only 1.5 mT) [10.49], however, recent experiments [10.50] with this compound have led to a disappointingly high final temperature of about 80 μK. In addition, AuIn$_2$ is very brittle. The possible suitability of some metal hydrides with their high proton moment density remains to be demonstrated [10.51].

In the end, it turns out that at present Cu seems to be the most suitable "workhorse" for nuclear refrigeration. It has two isotopes with I = 3/2, and rather similar and reasonably large nuclear magnetic moments and nuclear Curie constants. Above all, Cu can be obtained in high purity at a reasonable price, has good metallurgical and handling properties, is not superconducting at T > 10 μK, is cubic, and has a very good thermal conductivity. Its nuclear ordering temperature is $T_{n,c}$ < 0.1 μK and the internal field is small, 0.34 mT [10.1]. Platinum would be a good candidate, too, but only 33.8% of its isotopes have a nuclear moment and above all the moment is small. In addition, Pt is very expensive. On the other hand, Pt is presently the main candidate for nuclear magnetic resonance thermometry because of its small τ_1, rather large τ_2, and because it has $I = 1/2$ (Sect. 12.9).

10.7 Hyperfine Enhanced Nuclear Refrigeration

Starting conditions for nuclear refrigeration of $B_i/T_i \sim 1000$ (T/K), corresponding to $B_i \sim 8$ T and $T_i \sim 8$ mK, for example, are at present probably an upper practical technical limit. This means that the relative reduction of nuclear magnetic entropy of Cu, for example, is restricted to $\Delta S/S \leq 0.1$ (Figs. 10.1, 22). Substantially larger entropy reductions or nuclear polarizations at less demanding starting fields B_i and starting temperatures T_i can be achieved if one uses the so-called "hyperfine enhanced van Vleck paramagnets" instead of a simple metal like Cu as a nuclear refrigerant. The potential of these materials for nuclear refrigeration was pointed out by S.A. Altshuler in 1966, and then experimentally established by *Andres* and coworkers [10.9, 52–54] and later by *Mueller* et al. [10.26, 55]. In particular, the intermetallic compound $PrNi_5$ turned out to be very suitable for the requested purpose.

Van Vleck paramagnets containing rare earth ions such as Pr^{3+} in hexagonal $PrNi_5$ have a temperature-independent electronic susceptibility at low temperatures because they have an electronic singlet non-magnetic ground state of their 4f electron shells[1]. An external magnetic field changes the electronic configuration of the 4f electrons by mixing higher non-singlet states into the ground state. This induces an electronic magnetic moment generating a hyperfine field B_{int} at the [141]Pr nucleus which is enhanced compared to the externally applied field B. For polycrystalline $PrNi_5$ the average hyperfine enhancement factor is $K = B_{int}/B = 11.2$ [10.55]. We can still use the equations deduced in the foregoing sections for magnetic refrigeration but we have to replace B by $B(1+K)$, and the nuclear Curie constant λ_n is enhanced by $(1+K)^2$ (Table 10.1). Obviously, the large internal field seen by the [141]Pr nuclei will result in a substantial reduction of the nuclear spin entropy even at rather high temperatures and in small external magnetic fields; for example, $\Delta S/S \simeq 70\%$ at $T_i = 25$ mK and $B_i = 6$ T for $PrNi_5$ (Figs. 10.12, 13, 22). The cooling capacity/volume of $PrNi_5$ is rather large. Hence a moderate dilution refrigerator and a simple superconducting magnet are sufficient to achieve the necessary starting conditions for nuclear refrigeration with $PrNi_5$; it is the "poor man's workhorse" for nuclear refrigeration. Hyperfine enhanced nuclear refrigeration is an intermediate step between paramagnetic electronic refrigeration and nuclear refrigeration with simple metals, taking advantage of some of the useful features of these two methods.

---

[1] The Ni ions in $PrNi_5$ 'behave like Cu' because the holes in its electronic d-shell which are responsible for the paramagnetic susceptibility of Ni in other compounds are filled up by the three outer $(6s^2 5d^1)$ electrons of Pr.

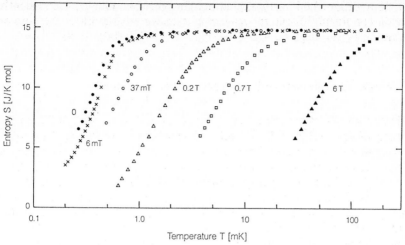

Fig.10.13. Nuclear spin entropy of PrNi$_5$ as a function of temperature in the indicated fields [10.55]

The minimum temperature that can be achieved is, of course, again given by the nuclear magnetic ordering temperature $T_{n,c}$. Due to the strong hyperfine interaction in rare earth van Vleck compounds, $T_{n,c}$ is in the millikelvin range for relevant Pr compounds; for example, $T_{n,c}$ = 0.40 (2.6) mK for PrNi$_5$ (PrCu$_6$) [10.55, 56]. The internal field will then be quite large; b = 65 mT in PrNi$_5$, for example. The minimum temperature which has been achieved with such compounds is 0.19 mK for PrNi$_5$ [10.26]. Recent experiments on Pr$_{1-x}$Y$_x$Ni$_5$ have shown that the nuclear spin ordering temperature, and therefore the accessible temperature range, can be substantially reduced by diluting Pr by a few percent of the non-magnetic Y, still keeping a rather high cooling power/volume [10.57]. This is quite different to the dilution of Ce by La in LCMN, where substantial reductions of T_c can only be achieved by a very high degree of dilution (see references quoted in Sect.9.4). Of course, at the conditions accessible with these compounds, the high temperature approximations used in this chapter cannot be used anymore; we have to take the full equations, such as (9.15).

· Some practical aspects to be considered in the use of PrNi$_5$ as a nuclear refrigerant are listed below. It has a very small, and still unknown, nuclear spin-lattice relaxation time, but due to its small thermal conductivity (about 0.5 W/Km [10.26, 58, 59], something like brass) usually a long thermal relaxation time. It is very brittle, and the use of H$_2$ gas for thermal coupling in the cooldown process should be avoided because PrNi$_5$ adsorbs H$_2$ strongly and may then crack. The compound can be soldered with Cd (use ZnCl flux) to Cu wires for thermal contact; the Cd should be kept in its normal conducting state by a high enough final demagnetization field. A complete coating of PrNi$_5$ with Cd keeps possibly cracked parts together. PrNi$_5$ is usually used in the form of rods of 6÷8 mm diameter and typically 10 cm length, and because of the low thermal conductivity of PrNi$_5$ it is advisable to solder high-purity Cu wires along the entire length for thermal anchoring [10.26,27]. Good PrNi$_5$ samples should have RRR $\geq$ 20; lower values may indicate the presence of excess Ni or of other Pr-Ni compounds, which may cause trouble in the demagnetization, limiting the cooling power and the minimum temperature[2]. A good test of the quality of the compound is to check whether the electronic magnetization is a linear, reversible function of magnetic field. Minicracks developing with time and number of cooldowns can also deteriorate the thermal conductivity of such stages.

10.8 Nuclear Demagnetization Refrigerators

The progress of nuclear refrigeration is particularly due to the development of filamentary wire superconducting magnets to produce the required fields and of ^{3}He-^{4}He dilution refrigeration to produce the required starting temperatures. This combination in a nuclear refrigerator was first used at Helsinki, as described in [10.6-9].

In the early 1970's, the Cu nuclear refrigeration stage was almost exclusively a bundle of insulated fine Cu wires to reduce eddy current heating [10.6-9]. Only later was it realized that this problem is not as serious as anticipated and today favourite designs consist of an assembly of Cu rods [10.26, 27], see Figs. 10.23,24, or of a slit Cu block [10.1,28], see Figs. 10.14, 15,19, to improve structural stability and filling factor, to reduce the number of joints, and to avoid the wire insulation. One can show that with typical experimental parameters [RRR$_{Cu}$ $\sim$ $10^2 \div 10^3$, T_i $\sim$ 10 mK, demagnetization rate $\sim$1 T/h] a thickness of the Cu rods or sheets of about 3 mm is the optimum when maximum filling factor and eddy current losses are compared (Sect. 10.5.2).

A review on some of the successful nuclear refrigerators built before 1981 has been published by *Andres* and *Lounasmaa* [10.9]. Since then the technology has been advanced, in particular by the Cu nuclear demagnetization refrigerators built at *Lancaster* [10.23] and *Bayreuth* [10.28].

In the nuclear demagnetization refrigerator at Bayreuth [10.28] (Figs. 10.14,15), the ^{3}He-^{4}He dilution refrigerator - whose cooling power is shown in Fig. 7.19 (T_{min} = 4.5mK, $\dot{Q}$ = 2.5μW at 10mK) - is able to precool the 104 mol of the 275 mol Cu stage (RRR $\sim$ 1000) which are in a field of 8 T to a temperature of 13 (10) mK within 1 (4) day(s) (Fig. 10.16). The temperature of the magnetized Cu stage during the precooling phase decreases with time according to T $\propto$ $t^{-1/3}$. This is the expected behaviour at least as long as the cooling power of the dilution refrigerator varies as T^2 [Fig. 7.19 and (7.38)], the nuclear specific heat of the magnetized nuclear stage varies as T^{-2}, (10.4), and they are connected by a metallic link of

---

[2] The nominal composition should contain some excess Pr, as in PrNi$_{4.98}$, because some of it will be oxidized during the arc-melting production process from the constituent elements or may already be present as oxide.

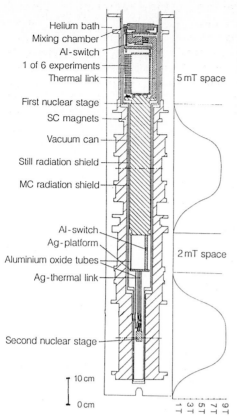

Helium bath
Mixing chamber
Al-switch
1 of 6 experiments
Thermal link

5 mT space

First nuclear stage
SC magnets
Vacuum can

Still radiation shield

MC radiation shield

Al-switch
Ag-platform
Aluminium oxide tubes
Ag-thermal link

2 mT space

Second nuclear stage

10 cm

0 cm

1 T
3 T
5 T
7 T
9 T

Fig.10.14. Schematic of the low-temperature part of the nuclear refrigerator at the University of Bayreuth with the two superconducting magnets and their field profiles. The first nuclear stage contains 17 kg or 275 mol Cu, of which 6.6 kg or 104 mol Cu are effectively in a field of 8 T. The second nuclear stage contains 0.13 kg or 2 mol Cu in a field of 9 T [10.28]

thermal conductivity $\kappa \propto T$. Demagnetization of the 104 mol Cu from 10 mK/8 T ($\Delta S/S \sim 9\%$) to 4 mT results in a *measured* minimum electronic temperature of 15 μK in the low-field experimental region of the refrigerator containing nine sites for experiments and thermometers (Fig.10.17), and a *calculated* minimum electronic temperature of 5 μK at the centre of the stage. This powerful Cu nuclear stage has also been used to precool a 2 mol Cu stage in 9 T to 3.5 mK. The demagnetization of the latter stage gave *measured* electronic temperatures between 10 and 12 μK [10.28].

If it is intended to refrigerate ^{3}He by demagnetizing a metallic nuclear refrigerant, the contact area between ^{3}He and the refrigerant has to be large to overcome the thermal boundary resistance problem (Sect.4.3.2). In this situation a metallic refrigerant of Cu (or PrNi$_5$ [10.60]) in the form of compressed powders or sinters is most appropriate. This design has similarities to that for refrigerating and making thermal contact to liquid helium using CMN powder (Sect.9.4). The Lancaster group [10.23] has developed very efficient Cu sinter nuclear refrigeration stages for this purpose. They use a nested rather than a series design for the nuclear stages, using the outer one as a thermal guard. The stages contain a mixture of Ag and Cu sinters on 1 mm Cu plates in epoxy cells acting both as a refrigerant and as

Fig.10.15. Photograph of the first nuclear stage (17 kg Cu) of the nuclear refrigerator shown in Fig.10.14. On the top flange one can see the large crystallites which result from annealing the Cu stage. The various holes are for mounting experiments and thermometers. The stage is slit, except at the flanges, to reduce eddy current heating. The total length of the stage is 525 mm [10.28]

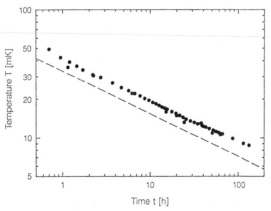

Fig.10.16. Precooling of 104 mol Cu magnetized in 8 T in the nuclear refrigerator shown in Fig.10.14 by a ^{3}He-^{4}He dilution refrigerator with the cooling capacity indicated in Fig.7.19 as a function of time. The dashed line represents $T \propto t^{-1/3}$ for comparison [10.28]

heat exchangers for thermal contact to the liquid helium to be refrigerated and investigated in the cells (Fig.10.18). Of course, the cells are demagnetized together, and the liquid sample and the thermometers are exposed to the changing demagnetizing field. The electrical conduction of the sinter is low enough that eddy current heating during demagnetization is negligible. As shown by (10.27), only a comparatively small amount of Cu is needed to

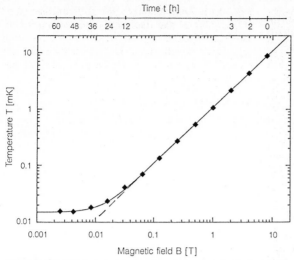

Fig.10.17. Temperature measured by a pulsed Pt NMR thermometer in the experimental region of the first nuclear refrigeration stage of the Bayreuth nuclear refrigerator (Fig.10.14) as a function of the applied magnetic field. The demagnetization behaves in an ideally adiabatic way, B/T = const., and there are no temperature differences between demagnetized Cu nuclei and Pt thermometer to within 3% to at least 70 μK [10.28]

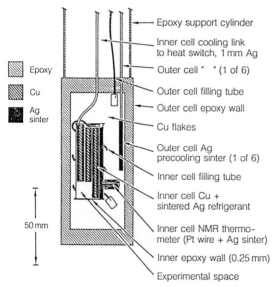

Fig.10.18. Nuclear refrigeration stage used at the University of Lancaster for refrigerating liquid ^{3}He (see text) [10.10,23]

refrigerate some cm^3 of liquid ^{3}He. According to the authors [10.10,61] this cryostat has refrigerated liquid ^{3}He to about 100 μK.

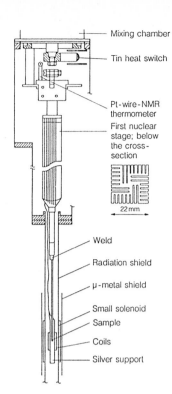

Mixing chamber

Tin heat switch

Pt-wire-NMR thermometer

First nuclear stage; below the cross-section

22 mm

Weld

Radiation shield

μ-metal shield

Small solenoid

Sample

Coils

Silver support

Fig.10.19. Double-stage nuclear demagnetization refrigerator at the Technical University of Helsinki (see text) [10.1]

In this book I shall not discuss the methods of nuclear *cooling* by which only the nuclear spin temperature is reduced, leaving the lattice and electrons at a higher temperature. This can be achieved by the method of dynamic polarization and demagnetization in the rotating frame for insulators, as developed by *Abragam, Goldman,* and their coworkers [10.14-16], or by the usual "brute force" demagnetization procedure discussed here for metals if the nuclear spin-electron coupling is weak enough (large Korringa constant) and the demagnetization is performed within a few minutes instead of many hours [10.1]. Nuclear cooling is important for the study of nuclear cooperative phenomena but not suitable for refrigerating other samples. A two-stage Cu-Cu nuclear demagnetization refrigerator intended solely for studies of nuclear magnetic ordering phenomena has been built in Helsinki and is described in [10.1] (Fig.10.19). The first Cu stage consists of a slit Cu block ($22 \times 22 \times 250 \, mm^3$) with 10 moles of Cu in 8 T. It precools a small (about 2g Cu) second stage in 7 T to about 0.1 mK. The two stages are directly thermally coupled (without a heat switch), and the Cu nuclei in the small second stage are rapidly demagnetized from 7 T to a nuclear spin temperature of some ten nanokelvins while leaving electrons at the starting temperature which is the final temperature of the demagnetized first stage. The apparatus has recently refrigerated the nuclear spins of a Ag sample to even about 0.5 nK [10.62].

If moderately low final temperatures of the order of 0.4 mK are required, these temperatures can be achieved using $PrNi_5$ with its large

190

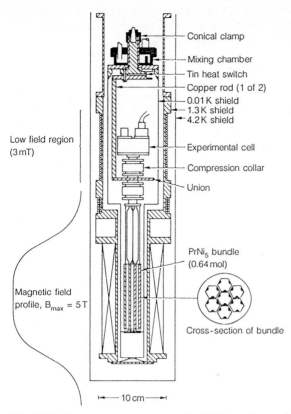

Low field region (3 mT)

Magnetic field profile, B_{max} = 5 T

Conical clamp
Mixing chamber
Tin heat switch
Copper rod (1 of 2)
0.01 K shield
1.3 K shield
4.2 K shield
Experimental cell
Compression collar
Union

$PrNi_5$ bundle (0.64 mol)

Cross-section of bundle

├──── 10 cm ────┤

Fig. 10.20. Low-temperature part of a $PrNi_5$ nuclear refrigerator. The refrigerant consists of 0.64 mol $PrNi_5$ in the form of seven 8 mm dimeter hexagonal rods of 95 mm length. This refrigerator has cooled ^{3}He samples to below 0.3 mK [10.63]

hyperfine enhancement of fields as a refrigerant with rather modest superconducting magnets and dilution refrigerators for the starting conditions, see Sect. 10.7. Simple $PrNi_5$ nuclear refrigerators have been described by *Andres* [10.9, 54] and by *Greywall* [10.63] (Fig. 10.20). Recently, a compact 0.9 mol $PrNi_5$ nuclear refrigeration stage (31 bars of 6 cm length and 7 mm diameter) has been described [10.64]. This stage, together with its 4 T, 5 cm bore demagnetization solenoid, is mounted in the free volume of the heat exchangers of a dilution refrigerator used for precooling (Fig. 10.21). This design allows the construction of a very compact nuclear refrigerator which is less susceptible to vibrations than usual cryostats where the nuclear stage is mounted below the mixing chamber of the dilution refrigerator. This apparatus has recently been modified by mounting a 6 T magnet to the still of the ^{3}He-^{4}He dilution refrigerator and a 61 mols Cu nuclear stage inside of the heat exchangers of the dilution refrigerator [10.65]. The torus-shaped mixing chamber [10.29] allows easy access to the nuclear stage and to the experiments on its bottom.

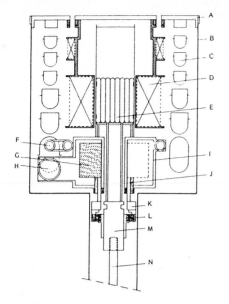

Fig.10.21. Lower part of the dilution refrigerator of [10.29,64] with a PrNi₅ nuclear demagnetization stage. (A: cold plate; B: cold plate thermal radiation shield; C: heat exchanger of dilution refrigerator; D: demagnetization magnet; E: PrNi₅ stage; F: input tube connection; G: heat exchanger for nuclear stage; H: output tube connection; I: mixing chamber (epoxy); J: leg of heat exchanger; K: copper ring for thermal anchoring; L: heat switch; M: silver post; N: cold finger extending to the high field region)

If very low temperatures are required, the compound PrNi₅ can bridge the gap in temperature where the cooling power of dilution refrigerators for precooling a Cu nuclear stage becomes very small, which is at around 10÷15 mK, but where one would like to have a powerful precooling refrigerator to reduce the nuclear magnetic entropy of copper as a nuclear refrigeration stage (Fig.10.22). In this situation one can build a rather powerful two-stage nuclear refrigerator using a dilution refrigerator as the first precooling stage, a PrNi₅ nuclear refrigeration stage as the second precooling stage, bridging the gap between the dilution refrigerator and the copper, and then the final copper nuclear refrigeration stage to reach the final minimum temperature [10.24, 26, 27, 66]. With such a combination substantially higher entropy reductions can be achieved. The large hyperfine enhanced nuclear heat capacity of the intermediate PrNi₅ stage can also be used as a very efficient thermal guard for the Cu stage and experiments, as well as thermal anchor for everything leading to lower temperatures. The design of such a two-stage nuclear refrigerator built in Jülich [10.24, 26] is shown in Figs.10.23,24. It requires two superconducting magnets (6 T for the PrNi₅ and 8 T for the Cu) and two superconducting Al heat switches. The Jülich refrigerator contains 4.3 mol PrNi₅ (60 rods, 6.4mm diameter, 120mm length each soldered with Cd to six 1mm diameter Cu wires) and effectively 10 mol Cu (96 rods of $2 \times 3 \text{mm}^2$ and 245mm length of which about 120mm are inside of the field region of 8T), welded at one end and electrically isolated but bolted together at the other. The PrNi₅ stage (starting from 25mK, 6T corresponding to $\Delta S/S \sim 0.7$) precools the Cu stage in 8 T to typically 5 mK, reducing the Cu nuclear spin entropy by about 26%. Figure 10.25 shows the development of the temperature of the experiments in this refrigerator after a demagnetization from 3.8 mK/8 T to 0.01 T. The

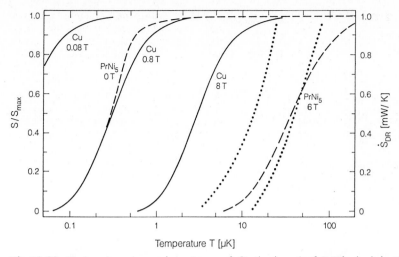

Fig.10.22. Reduced nuclear spin entropy of Cu (—) and of PrNi$_5$ (--) in the indicated magnetic fields compared to the rate of entropy reduction of typical ^{3}He-^{4}He dilution refrigerators (....). The reduction of the nuclear spin entropy of PrNi$_5$ occurs at a higher temperature than that for Cu because the ^{141}Pr nuclei see an effective field which is a factor of 12 enhanced compared to the externally applied field [10.24, 26]

minimum temperature which the PrNi$_5$ stage in this refrigerator has reached is 0.19 (0.31) mK starting from 10 (23) mK and 6 T, and the Cu stage of it has refrigerated experiments to 38 μK [10.24, 26]. The low heat leak in this refrigerator results from its rigid construction (reducing eddy current heating) and the very small quantity of "ill-defined" materials. The refrigerator can stay below 0.3 mK for about 1 month. Similar two-stage nuclear refrigerators have been built in Tokyo (11 mol PrNi$_5$ 19 mol Cu; T$_{min}$ = 27 μK) [10.27] and in Nagoya (2.6 mol PrNi$_5$, 8 mol Cu) [10.66]. With the advent of more powerful dilution refrigerators [10.29-31, 34, 67] the advantage or necessity of an intermediate PrNi$_5$ precooling stage for the final Cu nuclear refrigeration may disappear [10.28].

In all these nuclear refrigerators the thermal path between refrigerant and samples/thermometers in the experimental space should be kept as small as possible to keep temperature differences between them small. Most experiments and thermometers should not be exposed to the large and changing demagnetization fields. Therefore the superconducting main magnet for demagnetization has to be compensated at its end(s) to reduce the field in the experimental space to a tolerable level, typically ≤ 5 mT when the coil is fully energized.

The best temperature stability in magnetic refrigerators is achieved if the magnetic field itself is used as the control parameter. An automated temperature regulation system for an adiabatic paramagnetic demagnetization refrigerator achieving a temperature stability of 2 μK at 100 mK has been described in [10.68].

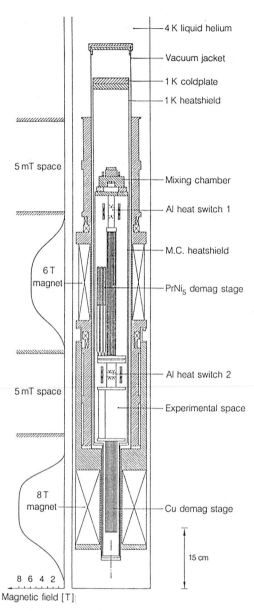

4 K liquid helium

Vacuum jacket

1 K coldplate
1 K heatshield

5 mT space

Mixing chamber

Al heat switch 1

M.C. heatshield

6 T
magnet

PrNi$_5$ demag stage

Al heat switch 2

5 mT space

Experimental space

8 T
magnet

Cu demag stage

15 cm

8 6 4 2
Magnetic field [T]

Fig. 10.23. Schematic of the low-temperature part of the PrNi$_5$/Cu nuclear refrigerator at the KFA Jülich and field profiles of its two superconducting magnets (see text) [10.26]

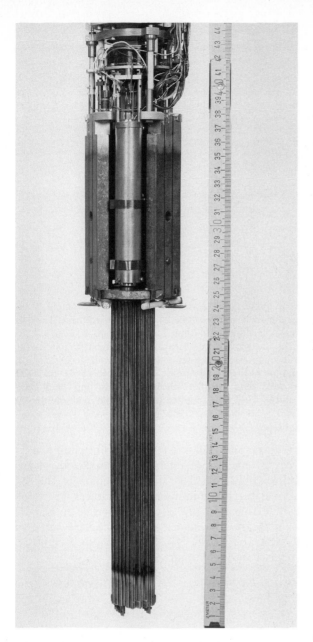

Fig.10.24. Copper nuclear demagnetization stage welded to the bottom of the experimental region of the nuclear refrigerator shown in Fig.10.23. At the top the lower end of the second superconducting heat switch can be seen. In the experimental region, a Nb tube contains a NMR thermometer. The thermal connection between the heat switch and the Cu nuclear stage is made by three massive Cu legs with two grooves reducing eddy current heating in each of them. At the bottom of the experimental region the centring device can be seen [10.26]

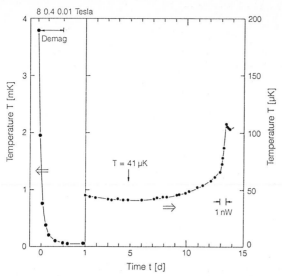

Fig.10.25. *Left*: The decrease of temperature, starting at 3.8 mK, of a sample in the double stage nuclear refrigerator shown in Figs.10.23,24 when the magnetic field on the Cu refrigerant is decreased exponentially in time for 10 h from 8 T to 0.01 T. *Right*: The development of the sample temperature after demagnetization on an expanded temperature scale and compressed time scale. It takes about 4 days for the apparatus to relax to its minimum measured electronic temperature of 41 μK. The sample was kept below 50 μK for 10 days. On the 13th day after starting the demagnetization an additional heat input of 1 nW was supplied to the sample to accelerate the warm-up [10.24]

Figure 10.26 shows the development of the *measured* minimum equilibrium temperatures achieved by nuclear refrigeration of nuclei in metals and available for refrigerating samples in the field-free region of the refrigerators. Table 10.2 summarizes the minimum temperatures to which various materials have been refrigerated; the given references should be consulted for information on the present state of the art. Somewhat pessimistic [10.24] as well as rather optimistic [10.10] predictions have been made for further improvement of these minimum values.

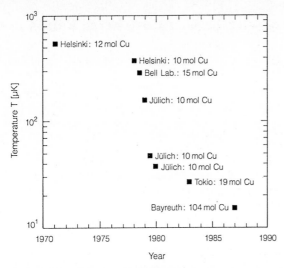

Fig.10.26. Minimum temperatures *measured* in the experimental *field-free region* of nuclear refrigerators of the indicated laboratories. In each case the number of moles of Cu used as refrigerant are indicated. In addition to these results the nuclear refrigerator at the University of Lancaster [10.23] has reached 13 μK (0.1 mol Cu) and the nuclear refrigerator at the Universtiy of Bayreuth [10.28] has reached a temperature of 10 to 12 μK (2 mol Cu) in the *high-field region* All these temperatures have been measured with Pt NMR thermometers

Table 10.2. Minimum temperatures to which the given materials have been cooled by nuclear magnetic refrigeration

Refrigerated material	Minimum temperature	Reference
Liquid ^{3}He-^{4}He	0.15 mK	10.69
Liquid ^{3}He	0.10 mK	10.61,69
Solid ^{3}He	38 μK	10.70
Metals	12 μK[a]	10.28
Nuclear moments in metals	0.5 nK	10.62

[a] This value is an upper limit [10.28] measured by a Pt NMR thermometer (Sect. 12.9.3) mounted in the high-field experimental region of the refrigerator and indicating minimum temperatures between 10 and 12 μK. The minimum electronic temperature in the low-field region of the Cu nuclear refrigerator is 15 μK and the electronic temperature in the center of the stage calculated from its thermal behaviour is 5 μK [10.28]

11. Temperature Scales and Temperature Fixed Points

In low-temperature physics and technology the measurement of a temperature is very often as difficult and, of course, as important as actually reaching that temperature. Therefore, low-temperature physicists have to spend a
substantial part of their time considering thermometry. Before we can talk
about thermometry we have to talk about temperature; we have to define a
temperature scale. Actually, temperature is one of the most important parameters in physics and technology. It is one of the basic units in all systems
of units. In spite of this fact - as we will see in the following - the absolute
temperature is not very accurately known; our knowledge of temperature is
much less precise than our knowledge of time, length, mass, voltage, etc.
But let me start with a recollection of the definition of the temperature
scale and some temperature fixed points.

11.1 Thermodynamic Temperature

The definition of the temperature scale is obtained from the Carnot cycle,
which is based on the second law of thermodynamics. This reversible cycle
gives

$$\oint T^{-1} dQ = 0 , \tag{11.1}$$

which is equivalent to

$$T/Q = \text{constant} . \tag{11.2}$$

Hence, this or any other process gives the temperature only in terms of
ratios or to within a multiplicative constant; the absolute values in a temperature scale have to be fixed by definition.

The most important proposal for the definition of a temperature scale,
in general everyday practical use, was made in 1742 by A. Celsius, who
proposed that the range of temperature between that at which water boils
and that at which ice melts should be divided into 100 degrees:

$$1742 \text{ Celsius: } T(H_2O \text{ boiling}) - T(H_2O \text{ melting}) = 100 \text{ degrees} . \tag{11.3}$$

In 1887 the name "centigrade" and in 1948 the name "degree Celsius" were
internationally accepted for the unit of this scale. Of course, we know that

we have to decide at which pressure this definition should be valid; the accepted value is 1 bar.

Physicists know that the definition of a temperature scale in which the temperature of melting ice is set at 0° C is not very appropriate for physics and for many processes in nature, because we have an absolute zero in temperature. That an absolute zero exists had actually already been realized 40 years before Celsius' proposal, in 1702, by the French scientist Amontons. He found from his experiments with gases that there must be a lower limit for the temperature, and he estimated this lower limit to be at around -240° C. This was an outstanding achievement for that time.

Almost 150 years passed before Lord Kelvin made the proposal in 1854 to take absolute zero, T_0, as the starting point of a thermodynamic temperature scale. It was not until 100 years later, in 1954, that this and the proposal that one should count from T_0 in steps of

$$1 \text{ degree} = 1 \text{ K} = T_{triple}(H_2O)/273.16 \tag{11.4}$$

was internationally adopted. Thus the unit of the thermodynamic temperature is defined as 1/273.16 of the temperature of the triple point of water which is taken as the second fixed point of the Kelvin scale. A degree in this scale is the same size as in the Celsius scale. The following values relate the Celsius to the Kelvin scale

$$1848 \text{ Kelvin: } T(H_2O \text{ melting}) = 0° \text{ C} = 273.15 \text{ K },$$
$$T_0 = 0 \text{ K} = -273.15° \text{ C} . \tag{11.5}$$

So, we have a point for the zero of our temperature scale, and in principle we can use an experiment which is related to a Carnot cycle to establish the temperature scale, but this is rarely done by experimentalists. A handier procedure is to establish a number of fixed temperature points and to use them to calibrate the chosen thermometric method, which makes use of some temperature dependent property of a suitable material in the desired temperature range.

11.2 The International Temperature Scale ITS-90

In 1968 international agreement was reached on the definition of an offical temperature scale, at least for temperatures above about 14 K. This temperature scale, the IPTS-68 (amended in 1975) [11.1] is given by fixed temperature points which are defined by equilibrium phase transitions of pure substances. It superseded the earlier scales IPTS-48, ITS-48 and ITS-27. There was no internationally adopted and binding temperature scale for temperatures lower than 14 K, only recommendations for temperatures between 0.5 K and 30 K. One was the "provisional 0.5 K to 30 K temperature scale (EPT-76)" [11.2,3], which again is given by fixed points which are defined by equilibrium phase transition temperatures of pure substances, in particular the transition temperatures into the superconducting states of five metals at 0.5 K $\leq T < 10$ K (Table 11.5). In addition, it was recommended to use the vapour pressures of ^{4}He and ^{3}He at 0.5 K $\leq T \leq T_{crit}$ whose temperature dependences are given with a very high accuracy in tables (Tables 11.3,4).

Unfortunately, already at the time of the international agreement on IPTS-68 it was realized that there are substantial errors (up to the order of several 10^{-4}) in this temperature scale, deviations from the thermodynamic temperature which are too large for an international standard. It was also obvious that the deviations of the helium vapour pressure scale from IPTS-68 and EPT-76 were a few millikelvins. Even though EPT-76 was established substantially later than IPTS-68 and had a much higher accuracy, the need for a new international scale was obvious. After substantial efforts in various laboratories, the *International Temperature Scale of 1990*, ITS-90, was established recently [11.4-6]. It was adopted by the Comité International des Poids et Messures at its meeting in September 1989 and has been

Table 11.1. Defining fixed points of the temperature scale ITS-90 [11.4-6]

Material[a]	Equilibrium state[b]	Temperature [K]
He	VP	$3 \div 5$
e-H$_2$	TP	13.8033
e-H$_2$ (or He)	VP (or CVGT)	≈ 17
e-H$_2$ (or He)	VP (or CVGT)	≈ 20.3
Ne	TP	24.5561
O$_2$	TP	54.3584
Ar	TP	83.8058
Hg	TP	234.3156
H$_2$O	TP	273.16
Ga	MP	302.9146
In	FP	429.7485
Sn	FP	505.078
Zn	FP	692.677
Al	FP	933.473
Ag	FP	1234.93
Au	FP	1337.33
Cu	FP	1357.77

[a] All substances (except ^{3}He) are of natural isotopic composition. e-H$_2$ is hydrogen at the equilibrium concentration of the ortho and para molecular forms

[b] The symbols have the following meanings:
VP: Vapour pressure point
TP: Triple point
CVGT: Gas thermometer point
MP, FP: Melting point, freezing point (at a pressure of 1 bar)

Table 11.2. Values of the coefficients A_i, and of the constants B and C for the ^{3}He and ^{4}He vapour pressure equations and the temperature range for which each equation is valid [11.4-6]

Coeff. or constant	^{3}He 0.65÷3.2 K	^{4}He 1.25÷2.1768 K	^{4}He 2.1768÷5.0 K
A_0	1.053 477	1.392 408	3.146 631
A_1	0.980 106	0.527 153	1.357 655
A_2	0.676 380	0.166 756	0.413 923
A_3	0.372 692	0.050 988	0.091 159
A_4	0.151 656	0.026 514	0.016 349
A_5	-0.002 263	0.001 975	0.001 826
A_6	0.006 596	-0.017 976	-0.004 325
A_7	0.088 966	0.005 409	-0.004 973
A_8	-0.004 770	0.013 259	0
A_9	-0.054 943	0	0
B	7.3	5.6	10.3
C	4.3	2.9	1.9

the official international temperature scale since 1 January 1990. There are significant differences between the new ITS-90 and the earlier scales; for example, 0.6 mK at 10 K between ITS-90 and EPT-76, and 9 mK at 20 K between ITS-90 and IPTS-68.

The ITS-90 extends from 0.65 K to the highest temperatures practicably measurable in terms of the Planck radiation law using monochromatic radiation. The defining fixed points of the ITS-90 are mostly phase transition temperatures of pure substances, given in Table 11.1. In its overlapping ranges the ITS-90 is defined in the following ways [11.4-6]:

a) 0.65÷5.0 K: Vapour pressure/temperature relations of ^{3}He (0.65÷3.2 K) and of ^{4}He (1.25÷5.0 K) given by

$$T = \sum_{i=0}^{9} A_i \left[\frac{\ln P - B}{C} \right]^i , \qquad (11.6)$$

with the constants A_i, B and C given in Table 11.2 (T in Kelvin, P in Pascal, 1 Pa = 10^{-5} bar). The equation is, in fact, valid to 0.5 K.

Tables 11.3 and 4 give the new ^{3}He and ^{4}He vapour pressure-temperature values for ^{3}He and ^{4}He in the range from 0.6 to 5.2 K calculated from (11.6). These tables supersede the former $T_{58}(T_{62})$ scale for the ^{4}He (^{3}He) vapour pressure.

Table 11.3. Helium-3 vapour pressure [kPa] according to ITS-90 [11.4-6]

T [K]	0.00	0.01	0.02	0.03	0.04	0.05	0.06	0.07	0.08	0.09
0.6	0.071	0.079	0.087	0.096	0.105	0.116	0.127	0.139	0.152	0.166
0.7	0.180	0.195	0.211	0.229	0.247	0.267	0.287	0.308	0.330	0.353
0.8	0.378	0.404	0.431	0.459	0.489	0.520	0.552	0.586	0.621	0.657
0.9	0.695	0.734	0.775	0.817	0.861	0.907	0.954	1.003	1.054	1.106
1.0	1.160	1.216	1.274	1.333	1.395	1.459	1.523	1.590	1.660	1.731
1.1	1.804	1.880	1.957	2.037	2.118	2.202	2.288	2.376	2.466	2.559
1.2	2.654	2.752	2.851	2.954	3.059	3.165	3.275	3.387	3.501	3.618
1.3	3.738	3.860	3.985	4.112	4.242	4.375	4.511	4.649	4.790	4.934
1.4	5.081	5.231	5.383	5.538	5.697	5.858	6.022	6.189	6.360	6.533
1.5	6.709	6.889	7.071	7.257	7.446	7.638	7.834	8.033	8.235	8.440
1.6	8.649	8.861	9.076	9.295	9.517	9.742	9.972	10.20	10.44	10.68
1.7	10.92	11.17	11.42	11.68	11.93	12.19	12.46	12.73	13.00	13.28
1.8	13.56	13.84	14.13	14.42	14.72	15.02	15.32	15.63	15.94	16.26
1.9	16.58	16.99	17.23	17.56	17.90	18.24	18.58	18.93	19.28	19.64
2.0	20.00	20.37	20.74	21.11	21.49	21.87	22.26	22.65	23.05	23.45
2.1	23.85	24.26	24.68	25.10	25.52	25.95	26.38	26.82	27.26	27.71
2.2	28.16	28.61	29.08	29.54	30.01	30.49	30.97	31.45	31.94	32.44
2.3	32.94	33.44	33.95	34.47	34.99	35.51	36.04	36.58	37.12	37.67
2.4	38.22	38.77	39.33	39.90	40.47	41.05	41.63	42.22	42.82	43.41
2.5	44.02	44.63	45.24	45.87	46.49	47.12	47.76	48.40	49.05	49.71
2.6	50.37	51.04	51.71	52.38	53.07	53.76	54.45	55.15	55.86	56.58
2.7	57.29	58.02	58.75	59.49	60.23	60.98	61.74	62.50	63.27	64.04
2.8	64.82	65.61	66.41	67.21	68.01	68.83	69.65	70.47	71.30	72.14
2.9	72.99	73.84	74.70	75.57	76.44	77.32	78.21	79.10	80.00	80.91
3.0	81.83	82.75	83.68	84.61	85.96	86.51	87.46	88.43	89.40	90.38
3.1	91.37	92.36	93.37	94.38	95.39	96.42	97.45	98.49	99.54	100.60
3.2	101.66	102.73	103.82	104.90	106.00	107.10	108.22	109.34	110.47	111.61

b) $3.0 \div 24.5561$ K (triple point of Ne): Constant-volume helium gas thermometer (Sect.12.1) calibrated at points number 1, 2 and 5 (Table 11.1), and with the P/T relation given in [11.4-6].

c) 13.8033 (triple point of H_2) $\div$ 1234.93 K (freezing point of Ag): Electrical resistance of platinum (Sect.12.5.1), calibrated at defining fixed points and with various Pt resistance thermometers designed for the particular T ranges. For the determination of temperatures, various relations of temperature to resistance ratio $W(T_{90}) = R(T_{90})/R(273.16$ K) are given.

d) Above 1234.93 K (freezing point of Ag): Planck's radiation law.

The ITS-90 contains detailed instructions about how to calibrate a thermometer relative to it in the various temperature ranges, as well as differences to earlier scales.

Table 11.4. Helium-4 vapour pressure [kPa] according to ITS-90 [11.4-6]

T [K]	0.00	0.01	0.02	0.03	0.04	0.05	0.06	0.07	0.08	0.09
1.2	0.082	0.087	0.093	0.100	0.107	0.115	0.123	0.131	0.139	0.148
1.3	0.158	0.168	0.178	0.189	0.201	0.213	0.226	0.239	0.252	0.267
1.4	0.282	0.298	0.314	0.331	0.348	0.367	0.387	0.407	0.428	0.449
1.5	0.472	0.495	0.519	0.544	0.570	0.597	0.625	0.654	0.684	0.715
1.6	0.747	0.780	0.814	0.849	0.885	0.922	0.961	1.001	1.042	1.084
1.7	1.128	1.173	1.219	1.266	1.315	1.365	1.417	1.470	1.525	1.581
1.8	1.638	1.697	1.758	1.820	1.883	1.948	2.015	2.084	2.154	2.226
1.9	2.299	2.374	2.451	2.530	2.610	2.692	2.776	2.862	2.949	3.039
2.0	3.130	3.223	3.317	3.414	3.512	3.613	3.715	3.818	3.925	4.032
2.1	4.141	4.253	4.366	4.481	4.597	4.716	4.836	4.958	5.082	5.207
2.2	5.335	5.465	5.597	5.731	5.867	6.005	6.146	6.288	6.433	6.580
2.3	6.730	6.882	7.036	7.192	7.351	7.512	7.675	7.841	8.009	8.180
2.4	8.354	8.529	8.708	8.889	9.072	9.258	9.447	9.638	9.832	10.03
2.5	10.23	10.43	10.64	10.84	11.05	11.27	11.48	11.70	11.92	12.15
2.6	12.37	12.60	12.84	13.07	13.31	13.55	13.80	14.05	14.30	14.55
2.7	14.81	15.07	15.33	15.60	15.87	16.14	16.42	16.70	16.98	17.26
2.8	17.55	17.84	18.14	18.44	18.74	19.05	19.36	19.67	19.98	20.30
2.9	20.63	20.95	21.28	21.61	21.95	22.29	22.64	22.98	23.33	23.69
3.0	24.05	24.41	24.77	25.14	25.52	25.89	26.27	26.66	27.05	27.44
3.1	27.84	28.24	28.64	29.05	29.46	29.87	30.29	30.72	31.14	31.58
3.2	32.01	32.45	32.89	33.34	33.79	34.25	34.71	35.17	35.64	36.11
3.3	36.59	37.07	37.56	38.05	38.54	39.04	39.54	40.05	40.56	41.08
3.4	41.60	42.12	42.65	43.18	43.72	44.26	44.81	45.36	45.92	46.48
3.5	47.05	47.62	48.19	48.77	49.35	49.94	50.54	51.13	51.74	52.35
3.6	52.96	53.57	54.20	54.82	55.46	56.09	56.73	57.38	58.03	58.69
3.7	59.35	60.02	60.69	61.37	62.05	62.73	63.43	64.12	64.83	65.53
3.8	66.25	66.96	67.69	68.41	69.15	69.89	70.63	71.38	72.14	72.90
3.9	73.66	74.43	75.21	75.99	76.78	77.57	78.37	79.17	79.98	80.80
4.0	81.62	82.44	83.27	84.11	84.95	85.80	86.66	87.52	88.38	89.26
4.1	90.13	91.02	91.91	92.80	93.70	94.61	95.52	96.44	97.37	98.30
4.2	99.23	100.18	101.13	102.08	103.04	104.01	104.98	105.96	106.95	107.94
4.3	108.94	109.94	110.95	111.97	113.00	114.03	115.06	116.11	117.15	118.21
4.4	119.27	120.34	121.42	122.50	123.51	124.68	125.79	126.89	128.01	129.13
4.5	130.26	131.40	132.54	133.69	134.84	136.01	137.18	138.36	139.54	140.73
4.6	141.93	143.13	144.35	145.57	146.79	148.03	149.27	150.52	151.77	153.04
4.7	154.31	155.58	156.87	158.16	159.46	160.77	162.09	163.41	164.74	166.08
4.8	167.42	168.78	170.14	171.51	172.89	174.27	175.66	177.07	178.47	179.89
4.9	181.32	182.75	184.19	185.64	187.10	188.56	190.04	191.52	193.01	194.51
5.0	196.08	197.53	199.06	200.59	202.13	203.68	205.24	206.81	208.39	209.97

11.3 Practical but Not Officially Accepted Low-Temperature Fixed Points

There are various very useful temperature fixed points for low-temperature thermometry which are in wide use but which are not officially accepted or officially recommended.

11.3.1 Fixed Points of EPT-76

Even though the low-temperature scale EPT-76 [11.2,3] is not an official scale anymore, it contains a number of fixed points which are very useful for low-temperature thermometry. These fixed points are given in Table 11.5. They differ from ITS-90 by less than 1 mK at T < 13 K, which is close to the uncertainty of EPT-76 at these temperatures.

Table 11.5. Some fixed points (in K), mostly from the superseded low-temperature scale EPT-76 [11.2,3] (the difference to the new scale ITS-90 [11.4-6] is less than 2 mK)

T_b (H_2)[a]	T_{tr} (H_2)	T_c (Pb)	T_b (^4He)[a]	T_c (In)	T_λ (^4He)[b]	T_c (Al)	T_c (Zn)	T_c (Cd)
20.27	13.80	7.20	4.21	3.415	2.1768	1.180	0.851	0.519

[a] At a pressure of 1 bar
[b] At saturated vapour pressure

11.3.2 The NBS Superconducting Fixed-Point Device

The American National Bureau of Standard (NBS; now National Institute of Standards and Technology, NIST) offers a device (NBS-SRM 767 a) containing the five superconductors with transitions between 0.5 K and 7.2 K of the EPT-76 temperature scale, as well as Nb with T_c = 9.3 K. However, thermometry in the Kelvin range is not too great a problem and is widely performed with the helium vapour pressure scale.

For a number of years the NBS (NIST) offered a very useful superconducting fixed-point device for the millikelvin temperature range (NBS-SRM 768) [11.7,8]. The temperatures for the superconducting transitions of five metals contained in this device together with other relevant information are given in Table 11.6. The temperature scale of this device is based on a scale called "NBS-CTS-1" established at 0.01÷0.5 K by the American National Bureau of Standards by ^{60}Co γ-ray anisotropy (Sect. 12.10), by Josephson noise thermometry (Sect. 12.6), and the paramagnetic susceptibility of CMN (Sect. 12.8) [11.9]. Each device is individually calibrated. The reproducibility and traceability to the NBS temperature scale is about 0.1÷0.2 mK. This device is very useful for calibrating other millikelvin thermometers and it is a simple standard, now widely used in low-temperature laboratories working in the millikelvin temperature range.

Table 11.6. Properties of the superconductors in the NBS superconducting fixed point device SRM 768 [11.7,8]

Material	T_c [mK]	B_c [mT]	RRR
W	15.5÷15.7	0.12	10^3
Be	22.6÷22.8	0.114	79
$Ir_{0.8}Ru_{0.2}$	99÷100	(type II)	2.5
$AuAl_2$	159÷161	1.21	50
$AuIn_2$	203÷206	1.45	50

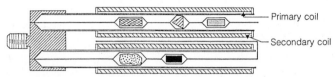

Fig.11.1. Schematic of the superconducting fixed-point device SRM 768 of the Nat'l Bureau of Standards (now Nat'l Institute of Standards and Technology) containing five superconducting samples as well as the primary and secondary coils for measuring the transition temperatures of these metals in a Cu holder [11.7,8]

The design of this device, a self-contained assembly of coils and samples, is shown in Fig.11.1. Thermal contact between the samples and the Cu body is provided by Cu wires welded to the body and connected to the samples by varnish. The device contains two primary coils to generate a magnetic field (B = 0.016·I) and two secondary coils wound directly on the primary coils. The coils are connected in series opposition, so that only four leads are required. When a sample enters the superconducting state it expels the magnetic field (Meissner effect) generated by the primary coil, which is observed as a change in the mutual inductance of the secondary coils. A typical electronic setup to measure the superconducting transitions is shown in Fig.11.2; the generated signals are 0.1÷1 μV.

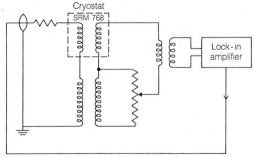

Fig.11.2. Mutual inductance bridge for detecting the superconducting transitions of a superconducting fixed-point device like the SRM 768 shown in Fig.11.1.

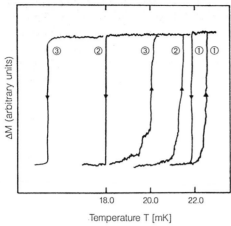

Fig. 11.3. Superconducting transitions of pure Be indicating the influence of a magnetic field. The data in cooling and warming are taken in fields of 0.5 μT (1), 9.5 μT (2) and 19 μT (3) [11.7, 8]

The NBS (NIST) has put substantial effort into the selection of samples with reproducible, sharp superconducting transitions and into investigations of external influences on these transitions, in particular by a magnetic field. The influence of an external magnetic field on the transition of Be is shown in Fig. 11.3. An external magnetic field shifts the superconducting transition to lower temperatures. Even more important, in an external magnetic field the superconducting transition is a first-order phase transition. Therefore supercooling effects can occur for pure elements, as is shown for pure Be. In the device this effect is reduced by spot-welding small pieces of Al to the W and Be samples so that Al, with $T_c \simeq 1$ K, serves as a nucleation centre to induce superconductivity in the samples by the proximity effect. Because the earth's magnetic field (about 50μT) is substantially larger than fields which have a substantial influence on some of the transitions of the metals in this device, one has to shield carefully (to less than 10^{-7}T) against the earth's magnetic field. This shielding is of course even more important in an experimental setup where large fields are applied, as in a magnetic refrigerator. I shall discuss magnetic field shielding in Sect. 13.5.

The experimental conditions recommended by the NBS (NIST) for use of their device are:

a) ambient magnetic field: ≤ 1 μT

b) peak-to-peak field in primary coil: ≤ 2.3 μT for tungsten, ≤ 0.40 μT for the other superconductors (Joule and eddy current heating: 1.8 and 0.08 nW, respectively).

The reproducibility and the shifts in T_c in a 1 μT field are about 0.1 mK. The sweep rate used to trace out the superconducting transitions should be less than 0.1 mK/min (for Be and W) to avoid hysteresis effects; then widths of the transitions of less than 1 mK are achievable. Unfortunately this very useful superconducting fixed point device is no longer pro-

206

duced by the NBS (NIST). We can just hope that another laboratory or company will start to offer such a very useful device in the future. Experience in the last two decades has shown that superconducting transitions seem to be very suitable fixed points for low-temperature thermometry, owing to their ease of detection, their reproducibility, their accuracy and fast response time, if the precautions discussed above are taken into account.

The simple critical field/temperature relation of type-I superconductors

$$B_c(T) = B_c(0)[1 - (T/T_c)^2]$$ (11.7)

could be, and indeed has been, used to provide a continuous thermometer reading with at least 1% resolution for $0.1\,T_c \leq T \leq T_c$.

11.3.3 Fixed Points of Liquid and Solid ^{3}He

Due to its outstanding nuclear magnetic and superfluid phase transitions, ^{3}He offers various fixed points for establishing a millikelvin temperature scale (Fig.2.3b). The history of the phase transition temperatures of ^{3}He indicates the problems of establishing a temperature scale at very low temperatures. At the beginning of the 1980's it became apparent that there were differences of up to 40% in the specific heat of liquid ^{3}He measured at various laboratories. It became obvious that these differences result from the different temperature scales used by the various groups. *Greywall* then performed very accurate measurements of the specific heat of liquid ^{3}He to establish a new millikelvin temperature scale [11.10]. His results for the transition temperatures of ^{3}He are given in Table 11.7.[1]

I shall now reproduce one of the arguments given by *Greywall* [11.10] to demonstrate the thermodynamic consistency of his temperature scale and of the input data. He measured the specific heat of liquid ^{3}He in the temperature range 7 mK to 2.5 K. From these data he was able to calculate the entropy of liquid ^{3}He along the melting curve

$$S_{liq,m} = \int_0^{T_m} \left(\frac{C_{v,liq}}{T'}\right)_m dT' .$$ (11.8)

---

[1] Recently detailed investigations were performed at the NIST comparing noise thermometry, the ac susceptibility of CMN, the melting curve data of ^{3}He, the resistance of Rh-Fe and superconducting fixed points (the latter two determine the EPT-76 scale) to establish a millikelvin temperature scale. These experiments gave $T_{min} = (3164\pm0.3)$ mK, $P_{min} = (29.311\pm0.001)$ bar. Their temperature values agree with the 'Greywall scale' to within 0.1% at 15 mK $\leq$ T $\leq$ 200 mK, but are higher at lower temperatures (by 0.8% at 10 mK and 1.8% to 6.3 mK, their minimum temperature) [11.11].

Table 11.7. Fixed points of liquid and solid ^{3}He according to [11.10, 12, 13]

Minimum of melting curve	316 ± 1 mK	29.318 bar
Superfluid A-transition at P_{melt}	2.49 ± 0.02 mK	34.338 bar
Superfluid B-transition at P_{melt}	1.93 mK	34.358 bar
Superfluid B-transition at S.V.P.	0.93 ± 0.02 mK	0
Nuclear magn. transition of solid ^{3}He at P_{melt}	0.97 mK	34.391 bar

With the Clausius-Clapeyron equation

$$S_{sol,m} = S_{liq,m} - (V_{liq,m} - V_{sol,m}) \left(\frac{dP}{dT}\right)_m , \qquad (11.9)$$

and the known values of the slope of the melting curve [11.12, 13] and the difference of the molar volumes of ^{3}He in the liquid and solid phases along the melting curve (1.31 m^3/mol) [11.14, 15], he was able to calculate the entropy of solid ^{3}He along the melting curve. This calculation gave the values (Fig. 11.4)

$$S_{sol,m}/R = 0.688 \ (0.693) \quad \text{at} \quad T = 0.02 \ (0.32) \text{ K} . \qquad (11.10)$$

These values are in excellent agreement with the value which is expected between about 10 mK (which is substantially above the nuclear magnetic ordering temperature of 0.97 mK) and 0.32 K (which is below a temperature where other excitations, e.g. phonons, start to contribute), which would be

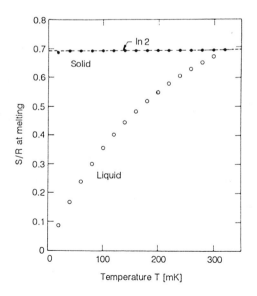

Fig. 11.4. Entropies of liquid and solid ^{3}He along the melting curve [11.10a]

$$S_{sol,m}/R = \ln(2) = 0.693 \qquad (11.11)$$

for the fully disordered ^{3}He nuclear spins. Together with the continuous temperature-pressure relation of the ^{3}He melting curve (Sect. 12.3), the ^{3}He temperature fixed points (possibly along with transition temperatures of some superconducting metals (Sect. 11.3.2) may become the basis for a future internationally accepted temperature scale for the millikelvin temperature range.

12. Low-Temperature Thermometry

A thermometer is a device by which we can measure a property of matter which is connected via a physical law to the concept of "temperature", where the latter is defined by thermodynamics. Therefore knowledge about the obtained temperature depends both on the quality of the measurement and on the theory on which this physical law is based. In general, thermometers can be divided into two groups.

For *primary thermometers* our theoretical knowledge about the measured property of matter is good enough to calculate the thermodynamic temperature from it without any calibration. Examples of primary thermometers are gas thermometers (using the relation between pressure, volume and temperature for gases) (Sect. 12.1), measurements of the velocity of sound in a gas [$c = (\kappa\rho)^{-1/2}$], thermal noise of an electrical resistor (using the Nyquist equation, see Sect. 12.6), and the angular anisotropy of gamma rays emitted from radioactive nuclei (using the Boltzmann population of the various hyperfine levels, see Sect. 12.10). Usually primary thermometry is difficult and mostly left to specialized national standards laboratories. Therefore the *secondary thermometers* are the "workhorses" of thermometry. For these thermometers, theory is not at a stage such that we can calculate the temperature directly from the measured property. Secondary thermometers have to be calibrated with a primary thermometer and/or at fixed points, as discussed in Chap. 11. Secondary thermometers are often much more sensitive than primary thermometers, and usually they are much more convenient to use. Examples will be discussed in this chapter.

There are various requirements which a useful thermometer has to fulfil:
- The property x to be measured must be easily, quickly and exactly accessible to an experiment.
- The temperature dependence of the measured property, x(T), should be expressible by a reasonably simple law.
- The sensitivity $(\Delta x/x)/(\Delta T/T)$ should be high.
- The thermometer should reach equilibrium in a "short" time, both within itself and with its surroundings whose temperature it is supposed to measure. Therefore it should have a small heat capacity, good thermal conductivity and good thermal contact to its surroundings. In particular, the thermal contact problem is ever present for thermometry at T < 1 K.
- The relevant measurement should introduce a minimum of heat to avoid heating of the surroundings of the thermometer and, of course,

above all, heating of itself; this becomes more important the lower the temperature.

There are many possible choices for a thermometer, and one of the first considerations has to be to select the one most appropriate for a particular experiment and temperature range. The recent achievements in refrigeration have required corresponding progress in thermometry. The substantial advancements in this field are reflected by the enormous number of papers on low-temperature thermometry published in recent years in journals such as *Journal of Low Temperature Physics, Review of Scientific Instruments* and *Cryogenics*. It is impossible to give sufficient credit to all this work by citing an adequate number of publications. I shall therefore give just a relatively small number of appropriate references to original papers. Much of the information in this chapter dating back to work before 1980 can be found in [12.1-10].

The oldest methods of thermometry use thermometers based on the expansion of gases, liquids or solids when the temperature is changed. I discuss one of them here in the first section of this chapter.

12.1 Gas Thermometry

The gas thermometer [12.1, 2, 8, 10], in principle, is a primary thermometer based on the relation for an ideal gas

$$PV = nRT .$$
(12.1)

Real gases, of course, deviate from the behaviour of an ideal gas, and therefore corrections to this equation ("virial coefficients") have to be applied. The measurement can be performed either at constant pressure or at constant volume. Figure 12.1 schematically illustrates the setups for these two procedures.

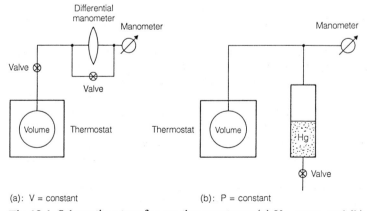

(a): V = constant   (b): P = constant

Fig. 12.1. Schematic setups for gas themometry at **(a)** V = const. and **(b)** P = const.

One of the requirements for gas thermometry is that the dead volumes (valves, tubes, manometers) are small and hopefully constant, because one has to correct for them. In addition, the thermal and elastic volume changes of the various components, and absorption and desorption of gas from the container walls have to be taken into account and, last but not least, the deviations from the ideal gas behaviour, which are particularly important at low temperatures, must be known. In general, high-precision gas thermometry is very difficult and therefore the gas thermometer is mostly used by national laboratories for calibration purposes or to establish the temperature scale. As discussed in Sect.11.2, it is one of the devices used to establish the ITS-90, and that is the main reason for mentioning it here.

12.2 Helium Vapour Pressure Thermometry

Another method relying on the behaviour of the gas phase and on the Clausius-Clapeyron equation (2.7) is the determination of temperature by measurement of the vapour pressure above a cryogenic liquid. It is less complicated and more accurate than gas thermometry because the vapour pressure depends strongly on the temperature, see (2.9). Here one has to use the liquid which is appropriate for the relevant temperature range. Vapour pressure data for H_2, N_2 and O_2 can be found in *White's* book [12.1], but, of course, these temperatures have to be converted to the new ITS-90 scale (Sect.11.2). Most frequently used for low-temperature physics is the measurement of the vapour pressure of the liquid helium isotopes (Sects.2.3.2 and 11.2). Helium vapour pressure thermometry is of particular importance for the calibration of resistance thermometers in the range from 0.5 to 4.2 K (Sect.12.5). A vapour pressure thermometer has to be calibrated. It is a secondary thermometer because our theoretical knowledge about the temperature dependence of the vapour pressure is not such that we can write down a complete and simple equation for it from first principles. The equation that we derived in Sect.2.3.2 was a very rough approximation, assuming ideal gas behaviour for the vapour and assuming the latent heat of evaporation to be temperature independent. Fortunately, calibration of the helium vapour pressure has been done very carefully by various laboratories in recent years to establish the ITS-90, where the P-T relations for the helium isotopes are given (Sect.11.2). The new P-T values for the ^{3}He and ^{4}He vapour pressures calculated with (11.6) and with the coefficients given in Table 11.2, are listed in Tables 11.3,4.

To perform vapour pressure thermometry one needs data relating vapour pressure to temperature as well as a sensitive, calibrated manometer, and one has to minimize experimental errors. Usually it is not sufficient just to measure the vapour pressure above the boiling cryoliquid because liquids have a low thermal conductivity (except superfluid helium), and therefore substantial temperature gradients may develop within them. For example, liquid ^{3}He at SVP shows a pronounced maximum in its density at

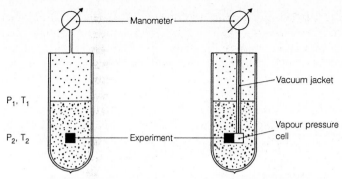

P_1, T_1

P_2, T_2

Manometer

Vacuum jacket

Vapour pressure cell

Experiment

Fig.12.2. Schematic setups for vapour pressure thermometry. *Left*: The vapour pressure above an evaporating cryoliquid is measured. Substantial temperature differences between the top of the liquid and the experiment can result due to the hydrostatic pressure head and temperature gradients in the liquid, which is usually not a good conductor (except for superfluid helium). *Right*: A small vapour pressure cell is connected to the experiment to avoid these problems. The capillary from this cell to the manometer at room temperature is vacuum jacketed to avoid changes due to a change in height of the cryoliquid

0.5 K. This anomaly and the low thermal conductivity of liquid ^{3}He (Fig. 2.16) at those temperatures can lead to a severe temperature (density) gradient in ^{3}He baths at T < 0.5 K, with the coldest part at the bottom, because in this case gravitationally driven convection does not occur. As a result, the temperature at the top of the liquid which determines the vapour pressure may be substantially different from the temperature lower down in the bath where the experiment is situated. The problem can be reduced by using only a thin layer of ^{3}He and well-conducting container walls. These problems are absent when superfluid ^{4}He with its very large thermal conductivity is used, but here problems may arise from the superfluid helium film (Sect.2.3.5) creeping to warmer parts of the apparatus, where it evaporates. Also, one should never use the pumping tube to connect the cryogenic liquid to the manometer, because there is usually a pressure gradient along it. The connecting capillary should also not be connected to a point at a temperature lower than the one to be measured because here part of the vapour would recondense. This problem can be eliminated by using a vacuum jacket around the capillary. Figure 12.2 shows an improved method of vapour pressure thermometry. Even doing it in this way may introduce errors if the capillary - connecting the vapour pressure bulb at low temperatures with the manometer at room temperatures - has a small diameter and if the vapour pressure is low. A so-called "thermomolecular pressure difference" between the low-temperature bulb and the room-temperature manometer will develop when the mean free path λ of the gas particles becomes comparable to the radius r of the connecting capillary [12.4, 11, 12]. The equation for this difference is

$$\frac{dP}{dT} = \frac{P}{2T} f(r/\lambda) , \qquad (12.2)$$

213

Table 12.1. Thermomolecular pressure correction for ^{3}He in a tube of radius r and with $T_{warm} = 300$ K and $T_{cold} = 2$ K at its ends [12.4, 11, 12]

rP_{warm} [mm·mbar]	0.1	0.3	0.7	1.5	4
P_{cold}/P_{warm}	0.59	0.82	0.92	0.97	0.995

where f is a function of the ratio r/λ. Table 12.1 lists some values for this correction for ^{3}He vapour with $T_{cold} = 2$ K and $T_{warm} = 300$ K.

All these problems can be avoided if the pressure is measured not with a manometer at room temperature but with a cold manometer connected in situ directly to the refrigerated experiment. This low-temperature manometric vapour pressure thermometry can be done with very high precision with capacitive manometers, which will be discussed in Sect. 13.1. A capacitive vapour pressure thermometer with a resolution of about 10^{-9} over the limited temperature range 1.6 K $\leq$ T $\leq$ 2.2 K that uses a low temperature capacitive pressure transducer has been described in [12.13]. The design is similar to the earlier one of *Greywall* and *Busch* [12.14] to be discussed in Sect. 13.1, which has been used for vapour pressure thermometry below 1 K, but the new design has a better long-term stability and resolution. Of course, it is only possible to take advantage of such a high-sensitivity thermometric device when an adequately designed stable thermal environment is available. This can be obtained by shielding the experiment with one or more temperature-regulated platforms or shields to which it is weakly thermally coupled [12.15].

12.3 Helium-3 Melting Pressure Thermometry

The physics of liquid and solid ^{3}He determining the shape of its melting curve has already been discussed in Chap. 8; the melting curve is described by the Clausius-Clapeyron equation (8.2). The melting pressure of ^{3}He exhibits a pronounced temperature dependence (Fig. 8.1), which can be used as a rather precise thermometric standard, particularly in the temperature range 1 mK < T < 250 mK [12.16-24]. In addition, as discussed in Sect. 11.3.3, the temperature of the minimum of the melting curve, the superfluid transitions of liquid ^{3}He, and the nuclear antiferromagnetic ordering transition of solid ^{3}He on the melting curve provide well-defined temperature fixed points independent of the pressure measurement, which can easily be detected using a melting curve thermometer [12.16, 17]. Alternatively, the pressures at which these transitions occur (Table 11.7) can be used to check the pressure calibration.

As a result of the above considerations, several groups investigating the properties of ^{3}He along the melting curve have used the melting pressure for thermometry in a similar way as helium vapour pressure is used for thermometry. The pressure is measured as a function of temperature in situ capacitively with a capacitive manometer, like the ones discussed in Sect. 13.1, filled with a mixture of liquid and solid ^{3}He. With a pressure resolution of 10 μbar, the precision of temperature measurement is $3\cdot10^{-4}$ at 1 mK, $3\cdot10^{-5}$ at 10 mK and $5\cdot10^{-6}$ at 100 mK [12.19]. *Greywall* has recently determined the melting pressure/temperature relation for ^{3}He, particularly from his accurate data for the specific heat C of normal fluid ^{3}He and the constraint C $\propto$ T at T $\ll$ T_F [12.16]. In the temperature range 1÷250 mK he has fitted the following formula to his data:

$$ P = P_A + \sum_{i=-3}^{5} a_i\, T^i , \qquad\qquad (12.3) $$

where P_A is the pressure on the melting curve at which the transition from normal fluid to superfluid ^{3}He-A occurs, which is P_A = 34.3380 bar. Alternatively, one can use the pressure at the melting curve minimum, 29.3175 bar, instead of P_A as the reference. The coefficients a_i given by *Greywall* are reproduced in Table 12.2. These melting curve data are consistent with the revised temperature fixed points of the NBS superconducting fixed point device (Sect. 11.3.2); they are also in remarkably good agreement with the earlier, less accurate data of *Grilly* near the minimum of the melting curve [12.25]. At present this is probably the most reliable millikelvin temperature scale.

^{4}He impurities in ^{3}He would depress the melting curve, but due to phase separation (Sect. 7.1.1) they should have no noticeable effect on the melting curve data at low enough temperature [12.23]. For high-field experiments we have to keep in mind that the melting pressure is slightly depressed by a magnetic field [12.26,27].

The advantages of a ^{3}He melting pressure thermometer are the high resolution (about 1 μK) and reproducibility (about 1 ppm), essentially zero power dissipation, insensitivity to RF radiation and (almost) to magnetic fields. A drawback is the rather large specific heat of liquid ^{3}He in the thermometer, the need of ^{3}He, of a fill capillary, and of a gas handling system. If the properties of ^{3}He can be well enough established theoretically, the ^{3}He melting curve will become a primary thermometer. Furthermore, the ^{3}He melting curve thermometer, together with the ^{3}He temperature fixed points (Sect. 11.3.3) and possibly transition temperatures of some

Table 12.2. Coefficients of (12.3) for the ^{3}He melting pressure curve [12.16]

a_{-3} = - 0.019 652 970	a_{-2} = 0.061 880 268
a_{-1} = - 0.078 803 055	a_0 = 0.130 506 00
a_1 = - 0.043 519 381	a_2 = 0.137 527 91$\cdot10^{-3}$
a_3 = - 0.171 804 36$\cdot10^{-6}$	a_4 = - 0.220 939 06$\cdot10^{-9}$
a_5 = 0.854 502 45$\cdot10^{-12}$	

superconductors (Sect.11.3.2), may be of importance in a future establishment of an internationally accepted millikelvin temperature scale. For this reason, one could well argue that this section should have been put in Chap.11 on temperature scales and temperature fixed points. A further advantage of the ^{3}He melting curve as a temperature scale is the fact that it can easily be transferred between laboratories without requiring the exchange of calibrated devices. It may therefore become for the millikelvin temperature range what the helium vapour pressure curves have already become for the Kelvin temperature range (Sect.11.2). Until then more work is necessary, and the presently existing discrepancies (about 1 mK at T_{min} and 1% at $T \sim 10 mK$, see [12.16, 23, 24] and the footnote in Sect.11.3.3) have to be removed.

12.4 Thermoelectricity

If the ends of a metallic wire are at different temperatures a voltage will develop along the wire. This voltage ΔU is the absolute thermoelectric force; the corresponding thermoelectric power is defined as

$$S = \frac{\Delta U}{\Delta T}. \tag{12.4}$$

Generally the thermoelectric power between two different metals is measured with a reference junction at a reference temperature, usually at 0° C (Fig.12.3).

The advantages of thermometry based on thermoelectric power are: it is a local measurement using a point sensor; the device and the measurement are simple (but see below); the device is rather insensitive to magnetic fields (except for magnetic alloys, see below); the device has a small specific heat; the measurement occurs essentially without heat input; the results are reproducible, because in general there is no change even after the device has been warmed up and cooled down repeatedly.

Unfortunately the thermoelectric power vanishes for $T \rightarrow 0$. Therefore, thermometry based on thermoelectric measurements with one of the usual combinations of thermocouple wires - for example, Constantan/Cu - becomes insensitive below 10 K (Fig.12.4). Recently new materials and very sensitive voltage measuring devices have been developed allowing thermoelectric thermometry to be extended even to the millikelvin temperature range. The newly developed suitable alloys are highyl diluted magnetic systems like Au + 0.03 at.% Fe [12.1, 2, 28–30], or Pd + (typically) 0.01 at.% Fe [12.31, 32]; usually commercially "pure" Au or Pd contain enough Fe. The first is a so-called Kondo alloy, where the magnetic moment of Fe in the Au matrix is strongly temperature dependent. Values for its thermoelectric power can be found in [12.1, 2], see Fig.12.4. Of course, these still small voltages cannot be measured relative to a reference point at 0° C, because

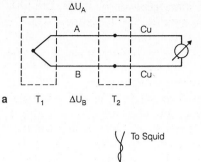

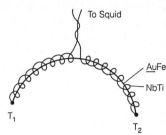

a T_1 ΔU_B T_2

b

Fig.12.3. Wiring for thermoelectric thermometry. *Top*: The general setup, where the thermoelectric power is created at the welded junction between wires A and B, which is at a temperature T_1. These two wires are connected to the Cu leads which eventually lead to the measuring instrument. *Bottom*: Wiring suitable for thermoelectric thermometry at very low temperatures. Here the thermopower of a wire of *Au*Fe, for example, is compared to that of a superconducting wire of NbTi, which does not create any thermopower. At low temperatures the small thermopowers have to be measured with a SQUID

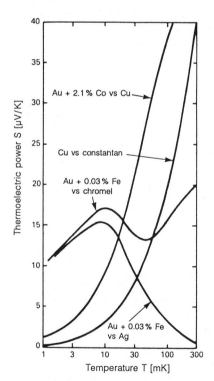

Fig.12.4. Thermoelectric powers of some metal pairs at low temperatures [12.1]

there the thermopower is very large so that the reference temperature would have to be extremely well regulated. For these low-temperature thermocouples the reference junction is usually kept in a liquid ^{4}He bath at 4.2 K. The second alloy, whose thermopower is shown in Fig.12.5, is a so-

217

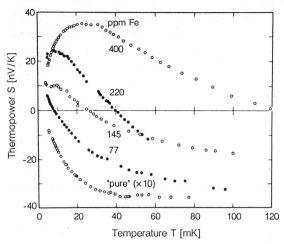

Fig.12.5. Thermoelectric power of Pd doped with the indicated amounts of Fe (in ppm) as a function of temperature. The values for the "pure" sample have been multiplied by 10 for clarity [12.32]

called giant moment spin glass. Here the Fe impurity polarizes the highly paramagnetic Pd matrix, giving rise to a giant magnetic moment of about 10 μ_B. These giant moments freeze in at low temperatures with statistical orientations ("spin glass freezing") [12.33].

Spurious thermoelectric voltages may develop in a wire due to chemical inhomogeneity or physical strain if it is exposed to a temperature gradient; these effects in the leads to room temperature may be larger than the desired low-temperature signal from the junction. The leads have therefore to be carefully selected and fixed when they have to be brought out to room temperature. To avoid nuisance thermopowers one should join the various metals without using a third metal. Welding is the most appropriate joining procedure for a thermocouple. Very often thermopowers are a problem if one has to measure small voltages, because thermopower develops at soldering joints, at switches, and other contacts between different metals. Therefore sensitive measurements, for example in bridges, mostly have to be AC measurements. Because no voltage drop can be developed along a superconducting wire, a superconductor with S = 0 is the appropriate reference wire in a low-temperature thermocouple (Fig.12.3b). - The high-sensitivity device for measuring very low thermoelectric voltages at low temperatures is the so-called SQUID (Superconducting Quantum Interference Device), allowing a resolution of 1 μK at 1 K with a Au + 0.03 at.% Fe thermocouple, which has a thermopower of about -9 μV/K at 1 K [12.1, 2, 28-30].

Generally, a practical low-temperature limit for the use of thermocouples is 10 K, with some effort and the use of magnetic alloys the temperature range can be extended to about 1 K, and the practical limit for thermoelectric thermometry is about 0.1 K. It has been shown that, in principle, thermopower can be used for thermometry to about 10 mK (Fig.12.5). This has not been applied in routine temperature measurements because there are more suitable methods available, which will be discussed in the following sections. However, thermoelectric thermometry can be attractive in situations where temperature differences have to be measured.

12.5 Resistance Thermometry

Resistance thermometry is based on the temperature dependence of the electrical resistance of metals or semiconductors. It is probably the simplest and most widely used method of low-temperature thermometry. The devices are readily available and the measurements are easy. As we will see below, the problems at very low temperatures are thermal conductivity, thermal contact, and self-heating of the device due to the measuring current and RF absorption. In addition, the resistivity usually has no simple, known temperature dependence, therefore a resistance thermometer is a secondary thermometer.

12.5.1 Metals

The pure metal most commonly used for resistance thermometry is platinum [12.1]. It is one of the standards for interpolation between fixed points of the ITS-90 (Sect.11.2). Platinum is chemically resistant; it can be obtained with high purity (diminishing the temperature-independent residual resistivity part); it is ductile, so it can be drawn into fine wires; and its resistance has a rather large temperature coefficient. The temperature-dependent resistance of a commercial Pt-100 thermometer shown in Fig.12.6 illustrates the linear R-T dependence over an appreciable temperature range. A Pt-100 thermometer is a platinum resistor with a resistance of exactly 100 Ω at 0° C. Values at other temperatures are given in Table 12.3. Pt-100 thermometers are available commercially with calibration tables. They are well annealed and either fused in quartz glass or encapsulated in a quartz or metal tube which is filled with helium gas for thermal coupling of the Pt wire to its surroundings. It is rather important that the Pt wire is supported strain-free so it does not change its properties on repeated cooling and warming.

As can be seen from Figs.12.6,7, sensitive thermometry with a Pt resistor or with other pure metals is only possible down to about 10 K; at lower temperatures we are in the temperature-independent residual resistivity range. As in the case of the thermopower, one can increase the sensitivity of the resistance of a metal to temperature changes at low temperatures by introducing magnetic impurities. This is shown for Cu with Fe impurities in Fig.3.22. Like *Au*-Fe, the alloy *Cu*-Fe is a Kondo alloy, where the Fe moment is strongly temperature dependent at low temperatures, leading to an *increase* of the resistance with decreasing temperatures below about 15 K. The magnetic alloy most widely used for resistance thermometry at low temperatures is the commercially available alloy *Rh*-0.5% Fe

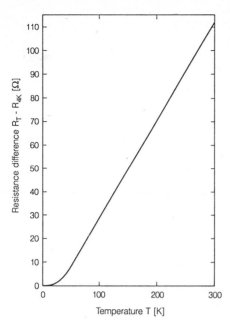

Fig.12.6. Difference of the resistances at temperature T and 4 K of platinum as a function of temperature. The resistance difference varies linearly with temperature between room temperature and about 50 K. (Data from [12.1])

Table 12.3. Temperature-resistance values of a Pt-100 resistance thermometer. (For more points see [12.1])

T [K]	10	15	20	25	30	40	50	60	77(!)	100
R [Ω]	0.09	0.19	0.44	0.94	1.73	4.18	7.54	11.45	18.65	28.63

T [K]	125	150	175	200	225	250	273.2(!)	300
R [Ω]	39.33	49.85	60.23	70.50	80.66	90.72	100.00	110.63

[12.8]. Above 30 K its resistance behaves similarly to Pt, whereas below 10 K its resistance is much more sensitive to temperature changes due to magnetic scattering of conduction electrons at the Fe impurity atoms; it then increases almost linearly with decreasing temperature at 0.1 K < T < 1 K (Fig.12.7). *Rh*-Fe resistance thermometers are also in use to realize the EPT-76 scale (Sect.11.3.1) and to transfer it between various laboratories.

12.5.2 Semiconductors, Carbon Resistors and RuO$_2$

The resistance of a semiconductor does not *decrease* with temperature as it does for a pure metal; it *increases* with decreasing temperature. For an "ideal" intrinsic semiconductor the temperature dependence is given by

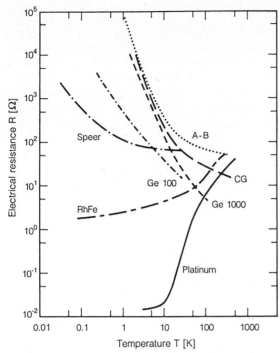

Fig.12.7. Temperature dependence of the electrical resistances of some typical low-temperature thermometers. A-B denotes an Allen-Bradley carbon resistor, Speer is also a carbon resistor and CG is a carbon-in-glass thermometer; Ge 100 and Ge 1000 are two commercial germanium thermometers. The lower two curves are for the two indicated metals [12.1]

$$R(T) = \alpha \exp\left[\frac{\Delta E}{2k_B T}\right], \tag{12.5}$$

where ΔE is the energy gap between the valence and conductance bands, and α depends on the doping of the semiconductor. However, the resistance of materials used for thermometry usually does not agree with this relation, and empirical equations between R and T have to be used. One can reach very high resistances and, above all, very high sensitivities at low temperatures where the conductivity is no longer intrinsic ($\Delta E \gg k_B T$) but results from impurities donating or accepting electrons. Actually, very often the resistance of a semiconductor becomes too high below 1 K to be suitable for a temperature measurement. Due to its advantageous properties, resistance thermometry with semiconductors is today the most important and most widely used secondary thermometry technique in the temperature range between about 10 mK and 10 K. The two materials most widely in use are germanium, specifically doped for low-temperature thermometry, and carbon in the form of commercial carbon resistors from the electronics industry.

a) Doped Germanium

Germanium used as a low-temperature thermometer is specially doped with $10^{15} \div 10^{19}$ atoms/cm^3 of As ("n-type") or Ga ("p-type"). Below 100 K the conductance is due to holes or electrons which the dopant delivers. Such a thermometer is particularly suited for the temperature range 0.3 K $\leq$ T $\leq$ 40 K. At lower temperatures the resistance often becomes too large ($>1\,M\Omega$), but with special doping these thermometers have been used to 30 mK. The temperature dependences of various Ge thermometers are shown in Figs. 12.7,8.

A great advantage of the germanium thermometers is their stability. Even after repeated cyclings between room temperature and low temperatures, or after an extended time on the shelf, the deviations at 4 K are typically only about 1 mK or, more generally, about 0.1%. Therefore these thermometers can be bought calibrated with a computer fit for the resistance/temperature relation (but this increases their price by at least an order of magnitude!). Such a computer fit has to be performed, because, unlike an "ideal" semiconductor, the T-R relation for a doped germanium thermometer is not simple, but given, for example, by

$$\ln R = \sum_{n=0}^{m} \alpha_n (\ln T)^n \quad \text{or} \quad T^{-1} = \sum_{n=0}^{m} \alpha_n (\ln R)^n \ . \tag{12.6}$$

To assure the reproducibility and stability of the device, the encapsulated single crystal Ge chip has to be supported strain-free on its four gold leads (Fig.12.9). Again, for an encapsulated Ge thermometer the thermal coupling is provided by helium exchange gas as well as by its leads. This coupling and the thermal conductivity of the chip are weak. Therefore one has to keep the measuring current and hence the Joule heating low. Typical, safe values for the allowed measuring current and power are 10 (1; <0.1) μA and 10^{-7} (10^{-10}; $<10^{-12}$) W at 10 (2; <1) K. Another point of importance is the strong and orientation-dependent magnetoresistance of germanium thermometers, which increases with temperature sensitivity (Fig. 12.10) [12. 34,35]; at low temperatures they should not be used in the Tesla range.

b) Carbon Resistance Thermometers

In contrast to Ge thermometers, carbon composition resistors widely applied for low-temperature thermometry are not specially manufactured for thermometry but are taken from the mass production of the electronics industry. Therefore their price is less than 1 DM each, which is two orders of magnitude lower than the price of the specially produced Ge thermometers. Due to this low cost and their very suitable R-T behaviour, carbon resist-

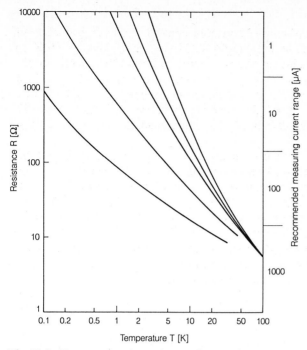

Fig.12.8. Temperature dependence of the resistances of some commercial germanium thermometers. The right-hand vertical scale shows the recommended measuring current for these thermometers

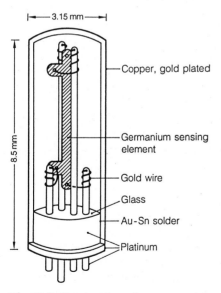

Fig.12.9. Construction of a commercial germanium thermometer

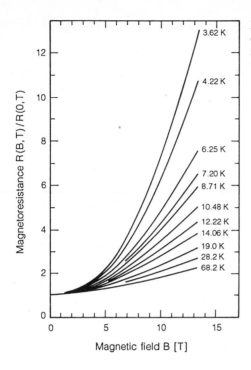

Fig.12.10. Magnetic field dependence of the electrical resistance of a germanium thermometer ($R_{4K} = 856\Omega$) at the indicated temperatures [12.34]

ance thermometers are the most widely used secondary thermometers in the upper millikelvin and Kelvin temperature ranges. Very often, particularly in a complicated multistage refrigerator, one has to monitor temperatures at various positions. For such a purpose the cheap and simple-to-use carbon thermometers are indispensable.

Pure carbon is not a semiconductor. The negative R-T characteristic of commercial carbon resistors results from their production process, which consists of pressing and sintering fine carbon particles together with some glue. The resistance is probably mostly determined by the contact resistance between the particles and by composition. Particle size and production method have an essential influence on the behaviour of carbon resistors. As a result, the resistance of carbon resistors changes from sample to sample and often is not very reproducible after thermal cycling due to the stresses involved. Furthermore, they show ageing and sometimes even changes during a low-temperature experiment. One therefore should repeatedly cycle a carbon resistor between room temperature and liquid-nitrogen temperature before using it as a thermometer. And one has to avoid overheating it while soldering on its leads. Anyway, the calibration should be repeated in each run if temperature has to be measured to within a few percent or even better. For these reasons these resistors cannot be bought with calibration as the much more reproducible Ge thermometers.

For low-temperature thermometry almost exclusively the following three commercial types of carbon thermometers with the given properties are in use:

Allen-Bradley: 1/8 W; small, cheap; good at T > 1 K; too large R (and dR/dT) at lower T [12.4, 36].

Matsushita: 1/8 W; types ERC 18 GK and ERC 18 SG; small; not produced anymore, small stocks at various low-temperature laboratories; useful at T ≥ 10 mK [12.37-39].

Speer: 1/2 W; type 1002; larger; not produced anymore; available at a higher price from some suppliers of low-temperature equipment; particularly useful in the millikelvin temperature range to about 10 mK [12.40, 41].

Typical temperature dependences of the resistance of these thermometers are shown in Figs. 12.11-14. With such thermometers, a resolution of order 10 μK at T ≤ 1 K is possible. The particular type most suited for the desired purposes - most importantly the temperature range of interest - has

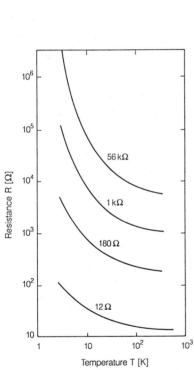

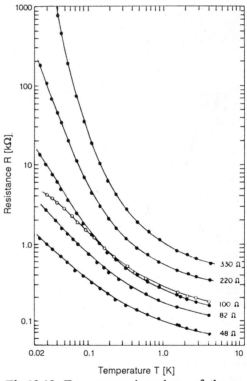

Fig.12.11. Temperature dependence of the resistances of four Allen-Bradley carbon resistors (1/8W) with the indicated room-temperature resistances [12.10]

Fig.12.12. Temperature dependence of the resistances of several Matsushita carbon resistors (grade ERC-18 SG, 1/8W) with the indicated room temperature resistances (full points). For comparison the temperature dependence of a Speer carbon resistor (grade 1002, 1/2W, 100Ω) is shown as open points [12.38]

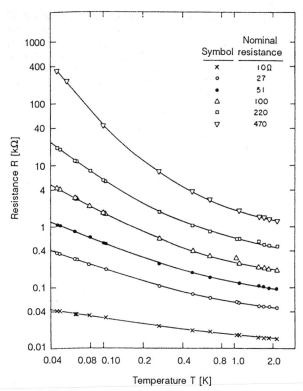

Fig.12.13. Temperature dependence of the resistances of various Speer carbon resistors (grade 1002, 1/2 W) with the indicated room temperature resistances [12.40]

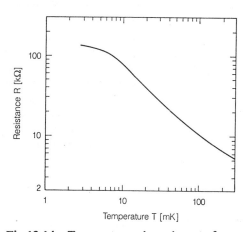

Fig.12.14. Temperature dependence of a ground-down Speer carbon resistor (Fig.12.16c). The resistance seems to saturate below about 7 mK due to a heat input of about 10^{-14} W from the measuring current and from the RF-noise pick-up [12.47]

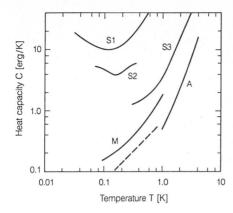

Fig.12.15. Heat capacity of modified carbon resistors. S1: Speer 220 Ω (about 30mg) [12.42]; S2: Speer 220 Ω (25mg) [12.43]; S3: Speer 220 Ω (17mg) [12.44]; A: Allen Bradley 116 Ω (11mg C and 2mg Cu) [12.45]; M: Matsushita, 100 Ω (about 5.5mg C and Cu each) [12.46]. The *dashed curve* is an estimate of the contribution of the copper leads to the heat capacity of the Matsushita resistor

to be chosen. Because the well-investigated Matsushita and Speer types are not produced anymore, it is hoped that a search for other suitable carbon thermometers from the electronics industry will be started. Otherwise, carbon thermometers may have to be replaced, e.g., by RuO_2 resistors which will be discussed shortly.

Application of carbon thermometers for thermometry *below* 1 K presents some problems. These are their rather high heat capacity (Fig.12.15) and their low thermal conductivity. These two intrinsic properties, as well as the difficulty of thermal coupling of the thermometers to their environment while avoiding electrical contact can lead to very long thermal relaxation times and, even worse, to thermal decoupling from their environment. This may lead to saturation of the resistance at low temperatures, mostly due to pick-up of RF noise (Fig.12.14). Typical values for the thermal resistance of Speer resistors are $R \simeq 10^4 T^{-3}$ (K/W) [12.41]; in this reference it was shown that the bottleneck for Speer carbon resistors is the thermal resistance in the carbon itself rather than the Kapitza boundary resistance.

The most difficult problem for carbon thermometry in the millikelvin temperature range is therefore establishing thermal equilibrium within the thermometer and between the thermometer and its surroundings. The problem of coupling these thermometers thermally to the area whose temperature is supposed to be measured has the consequence that Joule heating from the measuring current or due to pick-up of RF waves has to be kept very small. As a general rule the heat input to the thermometers should be at most

$$\dot{Q}\,[\text{W}] < 10^{-6} T^4 \quad [\text{K}^4]\,, \tag{12.7}$$

if overheating of the resistor is to result in a temperature error of not more than about 1%. This limit gives, for example, $\dot{Q} < 10^{-14}$ W (10^{-10} W) for a well-shielded and well-coupled piece of carbon at 10 mK (100mK) [12.36, 41, 47, 48]. In any case, one should check for overheating effects by measuring the resistance at various power levels and, if possible, assure that at the used power the thermometer is not overheated. If this is not possible,

227

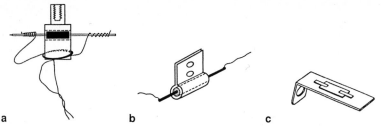

a   b   c

Fig.12.16a–c. Recommended designs for the use of a carbon resistor as low-temperature thermometers. For the Kelvin temperature range it is sufficient to put it in a hole of a Cu holder which can be filled with grease for thermal coupling [12.49] (**a**) or to glue the unmodified carbon thermometer into a Cu foil (**b**). The leads to the thermometer should be thermally heat sunk to the Cu holder. For the millikelvin temperature range one should use only a 0.1 mm thick slice of a carbon resistor to achieve adequate thermal contact (**c**). For this purpose one side of the resistor should be ground down. The remaining semicircular piece should then be glued with a thin layer of epoxy to a metal heat sink for protection against breakage (put a cigarette paper in between for electrical isolation). Then the second side of the resistor can be ground down to give the required thickness of the thermometer. It should then be covered with a copper foil for shielding against RF pick-up. The leads, of course, should again be heat sunk to the place whose temperature the carbon slice is supposed to measure. From there on the leads should be superconducting to reduce heat transmitted along them

one has to perform the calibration of the thermometer and the later temperature measurements at the same power so that overheating is at least comparable in both cases.

For the Kelvin temperature range it is adequate to put the carbon thermometer into a tightly fitting hole filled with vacuum grease (Fig. 12.16a) [12.49] or to glue it into a Cu foil for thermal contact (Fig.12.16b). However, these thermometers should not be used in their original form if temperatures below 1 K are to be measured. For the millikelvin temperature range one should use carbon slices about 0.1 mm thick to achieve adequate thermal response and contact [12.47, 48, 50]. For this purpose first the phenolic cover should be removed from the resistor. Then one side of the carbon core should be ground down with fine sandpaper. The resulting semicircular piece of carbon can be glued to a Cu sheet (separated by a thin cigarette or lens paper) for mechanical strength and for better thermal contact. Then the second side of the carbon can be ground down to a remaining thickness of $0.05 \div 0.1$ mm (or a resistance of $1 \div 2$ kΩ if Speer resistors are used), see Fig.12.16c. Finally a thin Cu foil should be glued to the upper side for electrical and thermal shielding of the thermometer. The varnish or epoxy will penetrate the carbon, giving it a better mechanical stability and preventing microcracks. Such thermometers have been found to have much more reproducible characteristics than in their original shape; they keep their calibration for years and through many cooldowns to within about 1%. The leads to the thermometer have to be well heat sunk at various points along their way in the cryostat and eventually to the area whose temperature is supposed to be determined. Only with such a design, the

228

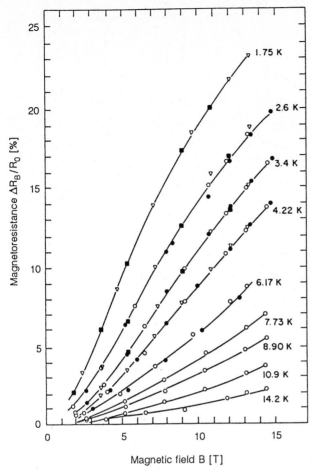

Fig. 12.17. Magnetoresistances of 47 Ω, 1/4 W Allen-Bradley carbon thermometers [12.35]

sensitivity and the thermal coupling can be maintained even in the low mil-likelvin range (Fig. 12.14), and a thermal time constant of some minutes is possible even at 10 mK [12.48]. - Of course, the temperature dependence of the resistance of a carbon thermometer is not simple; one has to fit an equation like (12.6) to obtain their R(T) dependence. - Carbon thermome-ters show an often nonmonotonic magnetoresistance of typically only a few percent per tesla [12.8, 10, 35, 37, 39, 51], see Figs 12.17-19.[1]

In low-temperature resistance thermometry one has to measure very small voltages, often in the nanovolt range, because low-temperature resist-ance thermometry has to be performed at very low powers (see above). Therefore, in general a direct current/voltage measurement is not applica-

---

[1] Actually, the smallest magnetoresitance at low temperatures is exhibited by carbon glass thermometers [12.52] or by dielectric constant thermometers (Sect. 12.7).

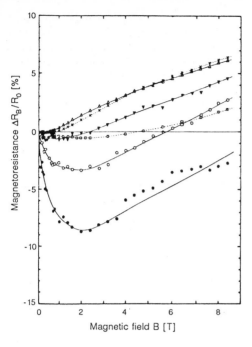

Fig.12.18. Magnetoresistances of a Matsushita carbon resistor (68 Ω, 1/8W) at 0.05 K (•), 0.1 K (○), 0.25 K (∇), 0.5 K (Δ), 1.0 K (x), and 4.2 K (□) [12.39]

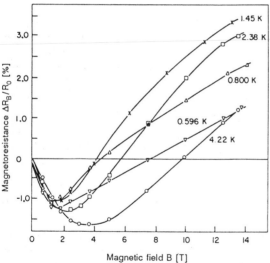

Fig.12.19. Magnetoresistances of a 220 Ω, 1/2 W, grade 1002 Speer carbon resistor [12.35]

ble. The solution is to resort to a suitable bridge design for the electronic equipment [12.6, 15, 36]. The measurement should be performed with AC current to avoid problems arising from thermoelectricity and to obtain higher sensitivities. The measurements are performed at low frequency, e.g. 40 Hz, to keep capacitive effects leading to out-of-phase signals at a low

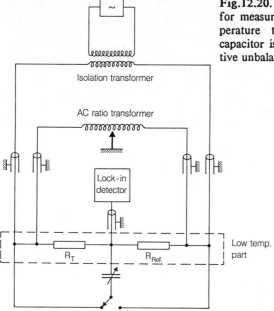

Fig.12.20. Schematic diagram of a bridge for measuring the resistance of low-temperature thermometers. The adjustable capacitor is used to compensate a capacitive unbalance in the bridge

level. The simple design of the usual Wheatstone bridge has to be improved for adequate low temperature resistance thermometry. Some of the possible problems and possibilities for improvements are the following. One has to be very careful about grounding; ground loops have to be avoided to keep nuisance currents in the thermometer small. All leads and the thermometer have to be shielded from RF, because the thermometer often has a rather high resistance and, together with its leads, it may be well matched to absorb sizable amounts of RF energy floating around in the laboratory. Figure 12.20 shows a bridge design which avoids some of the problems that may arise with a standard Wheatstone bridge. In particular, it reduces the influence of the resistances r_i of the leads on the cold sensor because the equation for the resistance R_T of the thermometer is given by

$$R_T + r_1 = R_{Ref} + r_2 , \tag{12.8}$$

whereas for a simple Wheatstone bridge r_1 and r_2 both add to R_T. This design also decouples the power supply from the bridge and it uses an inductive voltage divider ("ratio transformer") to null the voltage across the bridge. A ratio transformer has a very small error per reading, is nearly unaffected by age, temperature and voltage, and it has a low impedance. The null detector is a phase-sensitive lock-in amplifier with a high voltage sensitivity. Finally, the reference resistor, which may be a stable metal film resistor, is kept at low temperatures to keep its resistance constant and the lead resistances in the two arms of the bridge as equal as possible to reduce the noise signal and improve the stability. A variable capacitor is included to null out the out-of-phase signal. Such a bridge can be home-made, with the lock-in amplifier and the ratio transformer as the most expensive components, or one can buy a complete four-wire AC bridge commercially.

The leads into the cryostat should be twisted pairwise, rigidly fixed and well shielded to avoid induced currents due to movements in electromagnetic fields which are always present. In the low-temperature part they should be superconducting if the working range is $T < 0.1$ K to keep the heat flow to the thermometer small, and they have to be thermally anchored, preferably at a temperature as close as possible or slightly below the temperature the thermometer is exposed to. This thermal anchoring of the leads can be performed by glueing them on a Cu rod to which a layer of lens or cigarette paper has been glued with GE 7031 varnish (diluted by a toluene/methanol mixture). The Cu rod should be well annealed to keep its thermal conductivity high.

Equipment for very low temperature experiments is very often installed in a shielded room. The main advantage of such a setup is not so much that the shielded room keeps RF power away from the refrigerator, but that it keeps RF power away from the leads and from the thermometers to avoid heating of the temperature sensors. A final step to keep nuisance RF heating to the low-temperature sensor at a tolerable level is to instal a low-pass filter at low temperatures just in front of the low-temperature resistive elements. A design of such a filter is shown in Fig.12.21 [12.6,36, 41,48].

A very successful design of a thermometer made from a Speer grade 1002-100Ω-1/4W resistor with appropriate thermal anchoring and shielding of it as well as of its leads has been described in [12.48]. The thermometer is ground down to 0.15 mm and fixed with Stycast 1266 epoxy; it showed a response time of 5 min at its lowest useful temperature of 5 mK, where it still did not show any saturation effects, which is attributed to the cold filter, the careful electromagnetic shielding of thermometer and leads, and the small measuring power of 4 fW.

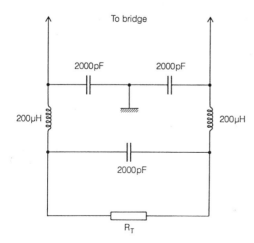

Fig.12.21. Low pass filter between a resistor R_T used as a low-temperature thermometer and the bridge by which its resistance is measured. The cutoff frequency for the shown values of capacitors and inductances is about 0.1 MHz. The filter should be put into a Cu case to which all elements are well heat sunk. The inductances can be homemade and for the capacitors one could use commercial mica or, better, styroflex capacitors

c) Thick-Film Chip Resistors Based on RuO_2

Recently, commercial thick-film chip resistors based on RuO_2 have been successfully tested as low-temperature thermometers [12.53-56]. They are a metal-ceramic consisting of a mixture of conducting RuO_2, Bi_2RuO_2 and a lead silicate glass ($PbO-B_2O_3-SiO_2$) which has been heated to above its glass point. The resulting resistance depends mostly on the metal-to-glass ratio. Their resistance has been fitted to (12.6) at 35 mK $\leq$ T $\leq$ 800 mK to within 2% and at 25 mK $\leq$ T $\leq$ 800 mK to within 0.5% to

$$R(T) = R_0 \exp[(T_0/T)^{0.345}] . \qquad (12.9)$$

The latter result is shown in Fig. 12.22. The advantages of these resistors are their small size (resulting in a weight of only a few milligrammes), the repoducibility of their behaviour after thermal cycling (better than 0.5%), and their low price. The former feature makes them very suitable as thermometers in calorimeters. In the most recent work it was found that the low-temperature behaviour of these chips can be related to within 2% to their room temperature resistance. References [12.53-56] also report on the magnetoresistance of these thermometers; typically it is $\Delta R_B/R \sim 0.5\%$ at B = 5 (1) T and T = 4.2 (0.1) K.

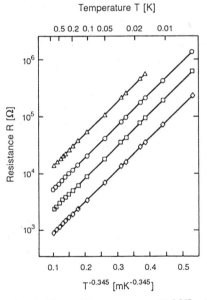

Fig. 12.22. Resistances versus $T^{-0.345}$ of four different RuO_2 resistors with approximate room temperature values of 0.5 kΩ ($\diamond$), 1 kΩ ($\square$), 2 kΩ ($\circ$), and 4.7 kΩ ($\triangle$), respectively. The upper horizontal scale shows the temperature in Kelvin [12.56]

12.6 Noise Thermometry

The conduction electrons in a metal perform random thermal movements ("Brownian motion"), which result in statistical voltage fluctuations of a resistive element. Therefore all resistive elements of an electronic circuit are noise sources. This noise is statistical, therefore we cannot make statements about its value at a fixed time, and the mean value of the noise voltage vanishes. However, we can calculate an effective time averaged mean square noise voltage

$$U_{rms} = \sqrt{\langle u^2 \rangle_t} \; . \tag{12.10}$$

This noise voltage was investigated in 1928 by J.B. Johnson ("Johnson noise") and H. Nyquist ("Nyquist theorem"). Nyquist arrived at the following equation for the component of the time averaged noise voltage within the frequency band from ν to $\nu+d\nu$ of a resistor with value R at temperature T:

$$\langle u^2(\nu) \rangle_t = 4k_B T R d\nu \; . \tag{12.11}$$

If we measure within a frequency band of width $\Delta\nu$ we obtain

$$\langle u^2 \rangle = \int_\nu^{\nu+\Delta\nu} 4k_B T R d\nu = 4k_B T R \Delta\nu \; . \tag{12.12}$$

This relation between noise voltage and resistance as well as temperature can be obtained by the following reasoning [12.57, 58]. If we connect two resistors - which act as noise sources providing random AC voltages of uncorrelated frequencies and phases - via lossless leads (Fig. 12.23), the power transported from R_1 to R_2 and vice versa is

$$\dot{Q}_{12} = R_2 I_1{}^2 = \frac{R_2 U_1{}^2}{(R_1 + R_2)^2}$$

and $\qquad\qquad\qquad\qquad\qquad\qquad\qquad\qquad\qquad\qquad\qquad$ (12.13)

$$\dot{Q}_{21} = R_1 I_2{}^2 = \frac{R_1 U_2{}^2}{(R_1 + R_2)^2} \; ,$$

respectively. In thermal equilibrium $\langle \dot{Q}_{12} \rangle = \langle \dot{Q}_{21} \rangle$, and we have

$$\frac{\langle U_1{}^2 \rangle}{R_1} = \frac{\langle U_2{}^2 \rangle}{R_2} \; , \tag{12.14}$$

the R dependence of the noise voltage we were looking for.

234

Fig.12.23. Wiring to obtain the Nyquist theorem (see text)

To obtain the temperature dependence of the noise voltage we set the two resistances equal to each other, and join them by a connection with vanishing ohmic resistance but with an impedance $Z = R$. If we short the leads at time t, then the total transported energy at this time is trapped, and the enclosed wave train can be written as a sum of the eigenfrequencies of the transforming leads with length L,

$$\nu_n = \frac{nv}{2L} \tag{12.15}$$

with $n = 1,2, \ldots$ and v being the transport velocity in the leads.
For large n, we can write

$$d\nu = \frac{vdn}{2L} . \tag{12.16}$$

In thermal equilibrium at temperature T each mode has an electric and a magnetic degree of freedom with a mean energy $k_B T/2$. Therefore the total energy in the interval $d\nu$ is given by

$$\langle dQ \rangle = 2dnk_B T/2 = 2k_B TLd\nu/v , \tag{12.17}$$

which is just the energy Q transported from R_1 to R_2, or vice versa, during the time $t = L/v$,

$$\langle d\dot{Q}_{12} \rangle = \langle d\dot{Q}_{21} \rangle = \langle dQ \rangle/2t = k_B Td\nu . \tag{12.18}$$

Therefore we have, with (12.13) and $R_1 = R_2$,

$$\langle u^2(\nu) \rangle = 4\dot{Q}R = 4k_B TRd\nu . \tag{12.19}$$

If we perform a quantum mechanical calculation, the result is the replacement of $k_B T/2$ (valid at $h\nu \ll k_B T$) by

$$\frac{h\nu/2}{\exp(h\nu/k_B T) - 1} \rightarrow \frac{k_B T}{2} \quad \text{for} \quad h\nu \ll k_B T , \tag{12.20}$$

where the last requirement, $\nu/T \ll 20$ GHz/K, is always fulfilled in practice. Equations (12.11, 12) are also obtained for this limit.

235

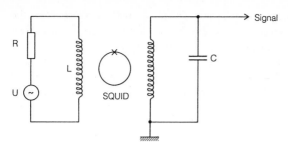

Fig.12.24. Schematic of low-temperature wiring using a SQUID to measure noise voltages (see text) [12.59.60]

The experimental problems in using noise voltages for thermometry result from the rather small size of the effect [12.3, 4, 57-60]. If we take, for example, R = 1 kΩ and $\Delta\nu$ = 1 kHz, then

at 4 K: $U_{rms} \simeq 10^{-8}$ V , $\dot{Q} \simeq 10^{-19}$ W ,

and

at 10 mK: $U_{rms} \simeq 10^{-10}$ V , $\dot{Q} \simeq 10^{-23}$ W .

At least the latter values are usually not measurable with semiconductor amplifiers and one has to use a SQUID as the amplifying element. The SQUID can be employed either to measure variations in the magnetic flux induced by the noise current or by allowing the voltage fluctuations to produce variations in the oscillation frequency of a biased Josephson junction [12.3, 59, 60] We can use a design as shown in Fig. 12.24, where a SQUID magnetometer detects the magnetic field resulting from the noise current $\langle I^2 \rangle^{1/2} = \langle U^2 \rangle^{1/2}/R$. It is a resonance circuit, and we find for the current in the primary coil of inductivity L

$$\langle i^2(\nu) \rangle = (4k_B T/R)d\nu , \qquad (12.21)$$

with $d\nu^{-1} = \tau = L/R$, giving

$$\langle I^2 \rangle = \frac{4k_B T}{R} \int_0^\infty d\nu = \frac{4k_B T}{L} , \qquad (12.22)$$

which is independent of the resistance R. A rather small value for R has to be chosen to match the circuit to the SQUID. For typical values R ~ 0.1 mΩ, τ ~ 0.1 s, 0.2 Hz ≤ ν ≤ 20 Hz, we have $\langle I^2 \rangle/T$ ~ 10^{-20} A^2/mK. In [12. 59, 60] all the required parameters were measured or calculated, and the device was indeed used as a primary thermometer with an accuracy of ±3% from 4 mK to 4 K.

In principle, a noise thermometer is a primary thermometer. In practice there are many severe experimental problems besides the small volt-

236

ages, so that this method is not in wide use. Some of these problems are the following. All resistive elements of the electronic setup for noise thermometry are noise sources themselves. This situation has been improved by using a SQUID as a low-temperature amplifier whose noise can be kept at a very low level; a value of 0.05 mK for the device noise temperature has actually been achieved [12.59, 60]. The remaining equipment is at temperatures between 4 K and 300 K and noise from the resonance circuit, for example, may affect the performance of the SQUID as well. Another important parameter is the effective bandwidth of the electronics and, last but not least, one has to determine the amplifying factor V of the total system, which enters the noise voltage by the equation

$$\langle U^2 \rangle = 4k_B TR \int V^2(\nu) d\nu . \tag{12.23}$$

If noise thermometry is used as secondary thermometry, the system is calibrated by putting the resistor at a known temperature. Another possibility is to build two identical electronic circuits and calibrate the two against each other, where one of them has the sensor as the noise source at unkown temperature and the other one has its sensor at a known temperature.

If we detect noise voltages, we are detecting statistical events, which have to be time averaged and, as for all statistical events, the accuracy depends on the measuring time t. If $t\Delta\nu \gg 1$, then the standard deviation for the temperature measurement via noise thermometry is given by

$$\Delta T/T = (2t\Delta\nu)^{-1/2} . \tag{12.24}$$

This means that the accuracy does not depend on temperature, which is an advantage if we want to apply this method at low temperatures. For 0.1% accuracy, a measuring time of at least 1 h is typical. This is a rather long time and is another disadvantage for the practical application of noise thermometry.

Because of the mentioned experimental problems, at present it looks as if mostly standards laboratories will use noise thermometry for calibration purposes, while the usual experimenter will resort to some simpler means. Today, national calibration laboratories use noise thermometry with an accuracy of ±0.1% at 10 mK < T < 1 K [12.23, 24].

12.7 Dielectric-Constant Thermometry

Capacitance measurements are as simple as resistance measurements and they usually have the advantage of negligible heating of the investigated samples. Actually these measurements can be performed with very high precision, in general much more accurately than a resistance measurement with comparable electronic effort. Therefore, if one has a material whose dielectric constant changes with temperature this will be a very attractive

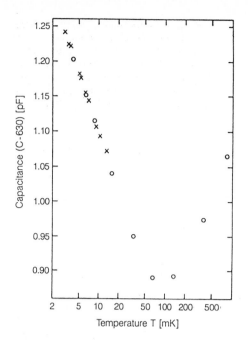

Fig.12.25. Capacitance (minus 630pF) of a capacitive glass thermometer as a function of temperature. The data points were obtained at excitation frequencies of 1.0 and 4.7 kHz, at zero magnetic field (x) and at B = 9 T (○) [12.64]

thermometric parameter to be measured in a capacitor. Indeed, some dielectric materials, in particular amorphous or glassy materials, show changes of their dielectric constant down to the lowest investigated temperatures [12.61-65]. A recent investigation by *Frossati* and coworkers [12.63,64] of the low-frequency capacitance of a glass thermometer made from SiO_2 which contained about 1200 ppm OH^- gave very encouraging results in the temperature range from 4 mK to 100 mK (Figs.12.25,26). In particular, they showed that such a thermometer is field independent for fields up to 9 T (within 5%), and it has a time constant of order 1 s to the lowest investigated temperatures [the specific heat is typically 10 T (erg/g·K), see Sect. 3.1.4]. In addition, heating effects are negligible, typically $<10^{-12}$ W, because of the very small dielectric losses of vitreous silica, and because it is almost not affected by stray RF fields which limit the use of carbon resistors to T > 5 mK, for example (Sect.12.5.2). The measurements can be performed with a commercial capacitance bridge or a bridge, as shown in Fig.12.33 (with the inductances replaced by capacitors), see also the end of Sect.13.1.

The dielectric constant ϵ of glasses (for example, Spectrosil, BK 7, Kapton, smoky quartz [12.61-65]) as a function of temperature passes through a minimum whose position depends on frequency ν as $T_{min} \underset{\sim}{\propto} \nu^{1/3}$ [12.63,64]; at lower temperatures ϵ is independent of frequency for $h\nu \ll k_B T$, with a slope $d\ln\epsilon/d\ln T \sim -10^{-4}$ (Fig.12.25). It was found that the dielectric constant can depend on the excitation voltage [12.63-65] (Fig. 12.26). Therefore these thermometers should be operated at constant voltage. The latter nuisance effect is influenced by the design of the glass thermometer (construction of electrodes, contacts, leads, etc.). Typical shapes of

238

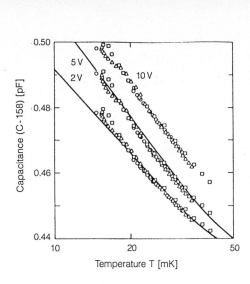

Fig.12.26. Capacitance (minus 158 pF) of a capacitive glass thermometer as a function of temperature at the three indicated measuring voltages but all at the same frequency (4.7 kHz). The measurements were performed in magnetic fields of 0.0 T ($\circ$), 0.25 T ($\triangle$), and 6.0 T ($\square$) [12.63]

these thermometers are plates or tubes of $10 \div 40$ mm length and width, and some 0.1 mm thickness, covered with fired or sputtered noble metal electrodes, giving typical capacitances of $0.1 \div 1$ nF. The measurements are performed at some kilohertz and with voltages of 0.1 V to some volts applied to the electrodes, giving a sensitivity of about 10^{-4} pF at 100 pF and a temperature resolution of 0.1 μK at some millikelvins, even though the absolute changes of ϵ with T are small (Figs.12.25, 26). Unfortunately, the thermometers usually have to be recalibrated in each cooldown, mostly due to changing contributions from the leads. - The recent result [12.66] that the velocity of sound and the internal friction of metallic and dielectric glasses change with temperature to at least 0.1 mK may make these thermometers suitable even for the microkelvin temperature range.

A suitable temperature dependence of ϵ down to 7 mK and the absence of a field dependence had been demonstrated earlier by *Lawless* and coworkers for $SrTiO_3$ glass-ceramic thermometers [12.67]; such thermometers are now available commercially.

More investigations are necessary to establish the potential of the capacitive thermometric technique with its particular importance for thermometry in high magnetic fields. However, the thermal coupling of a dielectric material whose capacitance is supposed to be measured and hysteresis effects have to be investigated. In addition the time-dependent heat release of non-crystalline solids (Sect.10.5.3) has to be taken into account.

12.8 Magnetic Thermometry with Electronic Paramagnets

The magnetic thermometric method to be discussed in this section is the conventional way to measure temperatures below 1 K. Its basis is the T^{-1} dependence of the magnetization

$$M = \frac{\lambda B}{\mu_0 T} ,$$

(12.25)

or of the susceptibility

$$\chi = \mu_0 M/B = \lambda/T ,$$

(12.26)

of a paramagnet with the Curie constant

$$\lambda = \frac{N_0 J(J + 1)\mu_0 \mu_B^2 g^2}{3k_B} .$$

(12.27)

These equations are valid in the high-temperature approximation $\mu\mu_B B \ll k_B T$ I, where the susceptibility follows the Curie law. The above relations were deduced in Chap.9 for non-interacting magnetic moments in an external magnetic field.

Due to the simple relation between the measured parameters χ or M and temperature, magnetic thermometry, in principle, is a primary method. However, again there are problems and deviations, making magnetic thermometry in practice a secondary method. The moments in a paramagnetic material experience a local magnetic field B_{loc} which is different from the externally applied field B_{ex} and which has the following three components [12.3, 4, 68]:

$$B_{loc} = B_{ex} + B_d + B_w .$$

(12.28)

The demagnetization field B_d resulting from the magnetization of the paramagnet in a field is given for an ellipsoid magnetized in the direction of its symmetry axis by

$$B_d = - f\mu_0 M/V .$$

(12.29)

The geometry factor f can be calculated for various ratios of length to diameter of an ellipsoidal sample:

ℓ/d:	1	1.5	2	3	4	5	6	∞
f:	0.333	0.233	0.174	0.108	0.075	0.056	0.043	0

This geometry effect is of great importance, of course, for superconductors (which are ideal diamagnets) as well as for ferromagnets. As can be seen from the above values of f, it can be quite appreciable for paramagnets as well.

The Weiss field B_w results from the neighbouring partially aligned dipoles and is

$$B_w = \alpha\mu_0 M/V .$$

(12.30)

The parameter α depends on the symmetry of the crystal; for a cubic crystal $\alpha = 1/3$. We then have

$$B_{loc} = B_{ex} - (f - \alpha)\mu_0 M/V .$$ (12.31)

The local susceptibility

$$\chi_{loc} = \mu_0 M/B_{loc} = \lambda/T$$ (12.32)

follows the Curie law. Actually we are measuring

$$\chi = \mu_0 M/B_{ex} ,$$ (12.33)

which leads to

$$\chi = \chi_0 + \frac{\lambda}{T - (\alpha - f)\lambda/V} = \chi_0 + \frac{\lambda}{T - \Delta} ,$$ (12.34)

where a (hopefully temperature independent) background contribution χ_0 resulting from other parts of the experimental setup - besides the thermometric sample - has been included. The latter relation is known as the Curie-Weiss law. The Weiss constant Δ depends on the shape of the sample, the symmetry of the crystal, and the interactions between the moments. It can be small or may even vanish for a sphere of a crystal with cubic symmetry, where $B_{loc} = B_{ex}$. In addition, of course, it is small for small Curie constants λ. Because of the usually unknown parameters in (12.34), we have to calibrate our thermometer at several temperatures, making it a secondary thermometer. This calibration can be performed against the ^{3}He vapour pressure at $T \geq 0.4$ K, against a superconducting fixed point device or the ^{3}He melting pressure at $T \leq 0.3$ K, etc.

Substances suitable for electronic magnetic thermometry are paramagnets containing elements with partly filled 3d or 4f electronic shells. As mentioned in Chap.9, the paramagnetic salt with the lowest ordering temperature is CMN with $T_c \simeq 2$ mK. This value can be further reduced by partly replacing the magnetic Ce^{3+} ions in CMN by nonmagnetic La^{3+} ions, possibly to $T_c \leq 0.2$ mK if only 5% or less cerium remains [12.69-72]. These salts can be used over the widest temperature range known and indeed it is the most widely applied paramagnetic thermometer [12.3, 4, 7, 8, 18, 23, 24, 59, 68-77]. A CMN single crystal is a nearly perfect paramagnet if the temperature is not too low, say for $T > 5$ mK. The use of a single-crystal sphere is, of course, inconvenient. Therefore, in most cases powders compressed to a cylindrical shape have been used. However, its thermal conductivity is low and it is difficult to make thermal contact to it. Therefore, usually a mixture of CMN powder plus grease (or another suitable liquid) has been compressed together with a brush of fine metal wires (Fig.12.27). Thermal contact is then made via these wires. Of course, if the temperature of liquid ^{3}He is to be measured, CMN powder can be immersed in the

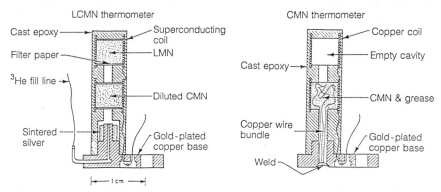

Fig.12.27. Schematic of setups for paramagnetic thermometry with paramagnets such as LCMN and CMN; for details see text [12.18]

liquid itself (Fig.12.27), taking advantage of the low thermal boundary resistance between these two materials (Sect.4.3.2). Many groups have used such a thermometer in the shape of a cylinder with its diameter equal to its length to keep deviations from the Curie law small and to make their temperature scales comparable [12.73,74]. It has been found that the Weiss constant $|\Delta|$ is in the range of several 0.1 mK and that such a CMN thermometer can follow the thermodynamic temperature scale to 3 mK to within about 0.2 mK, but a more typical limit is 5÷8 mK. The thermal time constant of such thermometers still is of order 10 (10³) s at 40 (10) mK (Fig.12.28) [12.18,75,77]. This has recently been improved by a design described in [12.75], see Fig.12.29. For this thermometer, thin pads of a 1:1 by volume mixture of about 0.1 g CMN powder (d ≃ 37 μm) and Ag powder (3 μm) were pressed to perforated Ag foils. Thirty of these foils separated by paper insulation were then epoxied to one piece and machined to a cylindrical shape. The lower free ends of the Ag foils were laser welded to a Ag base for thermal contact. This thermometer follows a Curie-Weiss law between 7 and 250 mK with $\Delta = -0.004$ mK. To obtain a resolution of 10^{-4} at 8 mK, a drive level in a bridge of the design shown in Fig.12.33 was necessary which gave a heating of 10 pW (probably mostly eddy currents in the Ag). Most important, this CMN thermometer has a time constant of only 10 s at 2 mK (Fig.12.28). With a modified fitting equation, it has been used to 1 mK, and, with the Ce^{3+} ions partly replaced by La^{3+} ions, even to 0.4 mK. With the improvement of measuring techniques the use of salts with larger Curie constants than CMN - and correspondingly higher ordering temperatures [12.3,4,7] - does not seem to be warranted anymore, so CMN seems to remain unrivalled among the salts.

To avoid the thermal equilibrium and chemical stability problems, in particular dehydration, (at 25° C the water vapour pressure of CMN corresponds to 25% humidity) encountered when paramagnetic salts are employed for thermometry, various dilute paramagnetic *alloys* have been used for magnetic thermometry. These metallic alloys have a reasonably good thermal conductivity, and it is easy to make thermal contact to them. An

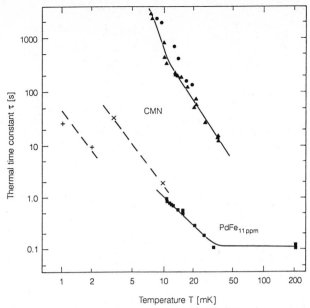

Fig.12.28. Thermal time constant of the indicated paramagnetic thermometers. The data (+, x, •, ▲) for CMN are from [12.75b, 75a, 18, 77] respectively. The *Pd*Fe data are from [12.77]

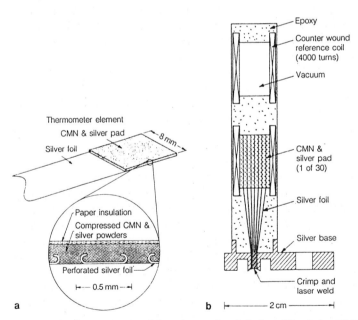

Fig.12.29. Single element (**a**) and completed design (**b**) of the CMN thermometer of [12.75b] (for details see text)

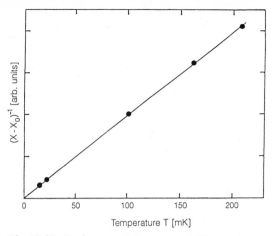

Fig.12.30. Reciprocal of the susceptibility χ minus a background susceptibility χ_0 of a *Pd*Fe sample containing 15 ppm Fe as a function of temperature. The temperatures for calibration of the susceptibility thermometer are obtained from a superconducting fixed-point device such as the one shown in Fig.11.1 [12.77])

example is Cu with some ppm of Mn [12.78]. With such a sample, 1% accuracy in a field of 0.1 mT at 5 mK can be obtained using a SQUID as the detecting element; but more information is necessary before it can be proposed for thermometry. Recently we have very successfully used *Pd*Fe alloys with Fe concentrations of the order of $10 \div 15$ at.ppm [12.77,79]. If one buys "pure" Pd of 4N (or 5N) purity it usually contains just the right concentration of Fe impurities. In these alloys, the Fe and its Pd surroundings have a "giant" magnetic moment of 10 μ_B, giving a rather large signal. The spin glass freezing occurs at T_f [mK] $\simeq 0.1$ x_{Fe} [ppm] (where x_{Fe} is the concentration of Fe in ppm) [12.33], and the susceptibility follows a Curie (!) law ($\chi - \chi_0 = \lambda/T$) to quite low temperatures (Figs.12.30,47); the data indicate that $|\Delta| < 0.1$ mK. The accuracy of the calibration is better than one percent, and the sensitivity is about 10^{-4} at 10 mK and 10^{-3} at 100 mK, comparable to CMN thermometers. The very simple design of such a thermometer is shown in Fig.12.31. Due to its good thermal conductivity and ease of making thermal contact, such a thermometer has a rather short time constant of at most 1 (0.1) s at temperatures above 10 (30) mK (Fig. 12.28). Such a *Pd*Fe thermometer calibrated with a NBS superconducting fixed-point device (Sect.11.3.2) is now our standard thermometric method for the temperature range between about 5 mK (it should work to 1 mK) and 500 mK. The only drawbacks of a *Pd*Fe thermometer are its sensitivity to magnetic fields (it has to be shielded from stray fields but the earth's field is OK, therefore one can use a superconducting shield) [12.33], and possibly a frequency-dependent diamagnetic contribution to the signal.

The lower limit for a paramagnetic thermometer is given by the deviation of χ from a Curie-Weiss law. The upper limit of the thermometer's temperature range is governed by the loss in sensitivity due to $\chi \propto T^{-1}$,

244

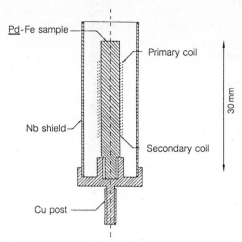

Pd-Fe sample

Primary coil

30 mm

Nb shield

Secondary coil

Cu post

Fig.12.31. Design of a *Pd*Fe susceptibility thermometer. The sample is a palladium rod containing 10÷20 ppm Fe. If the susceptibility is measured with a SQUID then the primary coil may contain two layers of 0.1 mm NbTi wire and the secondary coil ten layers of 25 μm Cu wire. If the susceptibility is measured with a mutual inductance bridge the number of windings should be increased, e.g., to 400 and 10^4, respectively. The sample is protected against magnetic fields by a superconducting Nb shield

which is usually at about 1 K, depending on the material and on the electronic equipment.

Examples of typical electronic setups for measuring electronic susceptibilities of paramagnets suitable for thermometry are shown in Figs.12.32 –34. With the availability of ratio transformers and phase-sensitive detectors, AC mutual inductance bridges of the Hartshorn type have become quite popular, reliable and convenient [12.1, 80]. Care must be taken to avoid heating effects due to relaxation in the sample or eddy currents in it, if it is a metal, or in other components of the setup. These and also capacitive leakage effects are reduced by operating the bridge at low enough frequencies (20÷300Hz). In addition to the conventional AC mutual inductance bridges, another favourite setup measures the resonant frequency (~1MHz) of a tank circuit driven by a tunnel diode whose inductance contains the paramagnetic sample [12.4].

In recent years much higher sensitivities have been achieved using a SQUID as the detecting element [12.3, 7, 59]. The static magnetization of only a few milligrammes of sample can then be measured. Figure 12.34

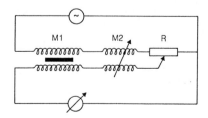

M1   M2   R

Fig.12.32. Hartshorne mutual inductance bridge for measuring magnetic susceptibilities (for details see e.g. [12.1, 2, 4])

245

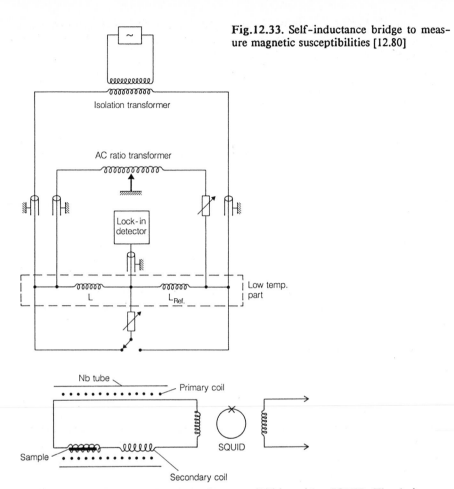

Fig.12.33. Self-inductance bridge to measure magnetic susceptibilities [12.80]

Isolation transformer

AC ratio transformer

Lock-in detector

L $L_{Ref.}$

Low temp. part

Nb tube

Primary coil

SQUID

Sample

Secondary coil

Fig.12.34. Circuit to measure magnetic susceptibilities with a SQUID. The design uses an astatic pair of pick-up coils with the sample in one of them. Because of the high sensitivity of the SQUID a few milligrammes of a paramagnetic material is sufficient. The astatic pair, which can be made with an accuracy of about 1%, reduces the sensitivity of the device to external disturbances and also compensates the influence of the magnetization of the construction materials. The principle of the design is to keep the total flux constant, which makes it necessary to make the low-temperature wiring from a superconducting material (for further details see [12.3, 59, 60])

shows a self-explanatory example of a setup for this method. The sample is exposed to a small DC field and the change of its magnetization changes the current in a superconducting flux transformer. The resulting flux change in the signal coil (to keep the total flux constant) is sensed by the SQUID; changes as small as 10^{-4} but typically more like $10^{-3} \div 10^{-2}$ flux quanta can be detected. Because of the very high sensitivity, the circuit has to be well shielded against nuisance magnetic signals.

If an inductance measurement is performed, then the following relations are relevant. In the primary coil we generate a current $I = I_0 \sin(\omega t)$ which produces a change of magnetic flux

$$\frac{d\phi_1}{dt} = \frac{A_1 (dI/dt) N_1^2}{L_1} , \tag{12.35}$$

where A_1 is the area, N_1 the number of windings and L_1 the length of the primary coil. This flux change induces a voltage in the secondary coil given by

$$U_2 = \mu_0 (1 + \chi) \frac{N_2^2 A_2 \omega I_0}{L_2} \cos(\omega t) , \tag{12.36}$$

where A_2 is the area, N_2 the number of windings and L_2 the length of the secondary coil, and χ is the susceptibility of the sample in the secondary coil.

The mutual inductance of two secondary coils sitting inside of a primary coil and with one of them containing a cylindrical sample of susceptibility χ is [12.81]

$$M_s = \pi \mu_0 n_p n_s r_s^2 f_1 (1 - D + f_2) q \chi$$

with $n_{p(s)}$ being the number of turns per cm of the primary (of one of the secondary) coil, r_s the radius of the sample, D the mean demagnetization factor (typically $1/3$), and q the filling factor of the sample in one of the secondary coils (typically $1/2$). The geometric factors f_i depend on the lengths of the sample, primary and secondary coils, and were given in [12.81]. A similar equation for a spherical sample in one of the secondary coils can be found in [12.59].

Magnetic thermometry has the advantages that it is based on a simple and quick measurement, one can have a rather large sensitivity of typically 10^{-4}, there is essentially no heating due to the measurement, one has a simple T-χ relation (therefore calibration is easy), and the thermometer can be home-made. Another advantage of magnetic thermometry for low-temperature physics is the increase of its sensitivity with decreasing temperature. If well designed, such a thermometer will have a rather short thermal response time of a few seconds at 10 mK. - Recently, a resolution of about 10^{-10} K has been obtained by measuring the susceptibility of a paramagnetic salt in a narrow temperature range near 1.8 K in 50 mT with an astatic pair of superconducting Nb coils connected to a SQUID as detector [12.82, 83].

All the described methods, of course, "see" not only the sample but all other magnetization in the neighbourhood as well (see the appendix for materials with very small magnetization); hence one should avoid other magnetic materials rather carefully or choose a design so that their contributions are cancelled, for example, as is the case in a carefully wound astatic pair of seconary coils. For very-high-sensitivity measurements one may even consider to regulate the temperature of these coils.

12.9 Magnetic Thermometry with Nuclear Paramagnets

The low-temperature limit of magnetic thermometry is given by the ordering temperature of the magnetic moments; for electronic magnetic moments this is about 1 mK for the CMN and PdFe thermometers discussed above. With the extension of the accessible temperature range to lower and lower temperatures thermometric methods for lower and lower temperatures have to be invented. To extend magnetic thermometry to temperatures below 1 mK one has to switch from electronic paramagnets to nuclear paramagnets. The change to the much smaller nuclear magnetic moments allows the use of magnetic thermometry to at least the low microkelvin temperature range. Due to the small nuclear magnetic moments we now have a much smaller susceptibility and therefore much smaller signal, requiring more sensitive detection methods; these are SQUID or resonance techniques, which will be described in this section [12.84-88]. In addition to the extension of the temperature range, we can now switch to pure metals with their good thermal conductivity and contact and fast nuclear spin-lattice relaxation, resulting in fast thermal response times - as we did when going from electronic magnetic refrigeration to nuclear magnetic refrigeration.

The parameter to be measured is the nuclear susceptibility

$$\chi_n = \lambda_n / T_n \qquad \text{with} \tag{12.37}$$

$$\lambda_n = \frac{N_0 I(I+1)\mu_0 \mu_n^2 g_n^2}{3k_B} . \tag{12.38}$$

In most metals this nuclear Curie law should be valid to at least a few microkelvin (or possibly even 0.1 μK). This seems to be true for Cu and Pt to within about 1% in fields of less than 1 mT (see Sect. 10.1 and Figs. 10.4,5) [12.89]. However, recently some deviations have been observed for the intermetallic compound AuIn$_2$ [12.90] and for Tl [12.91], for example, already at about 100 μK in fields of some millitesla, therefore some caution may be appropriate when new materials are introduced for thermometry.

Requirements for the validity of the nuclear Curie law are the absence of changing internal fields due to nuclear magnetic or electronic magnetic ordering in the relevant temperature range, the absence of nuclear electric quadrupole interactions (which means cubic lattice symmetry or, better, I = 1/2; see Sect. 10.6),[2] and in addition a short τ_1 (because we are measuring

---

[2] This, of course, does not apply if 'nuclear quadrupole resonance' is applied for thermometry, as recently suggested even for very low temperatures [12.92].

nuclear spin temperatures T_n but are usually interested in the electronic temperature T_e or in the equilibrium temperature of the material) and the absence of a superconducting transition. Nuclear magnetic thermometry dominates the submillikelvin temperature range but at higher temperatures the signals can become rather weak and may be dominated by contributions from electronic magnetic impurities. Therefore an adequate measuring technique - mostly a resonance method - is of utmost importance.

12.9.1 Non–Resonant, Integral Detection of Nuclear Magnetization

Of course, we can directly measure M_n or χ_n statically as we do in electronic magnetic thermometry. However, now due to the small nuclear moment necessarily we need a SQUID with its high sensitivity to measure nuclear magnetization. In the experiment whose results are shown in Fig. 12.35 [12.93], the magnetization of a 6N pure Cu sample in a field of 0.25 mT was investigated with a sensitivity of 10^{-3} flux quanta ($\phi_0 = 2 \cdot 10^{-8}\,mT \cdot cm^2$), resulting in $\Delta T/T = 5 \cdot 10^{-4}$ or 5 μK at 10 mK in a field of 1 mT. The result gave agreement with the calculated nuclear Curie constant of Cu and $M_n \propto 1/T$ in the investigated temperature range even up to 0.9 K! In general, one measures a combination of nuclear and electronic magnetizations $M_n(T) + M(T)$ in a direct measurement and then 1 ppm Fe or Mn in Cu would give the same signal as the 100% Cu nuclei. As shown by *Hirschkoff* et al. [12.94, 95], electronic contributions from the wire of the primary or secondary coils or from the insulation may cause serious prob-

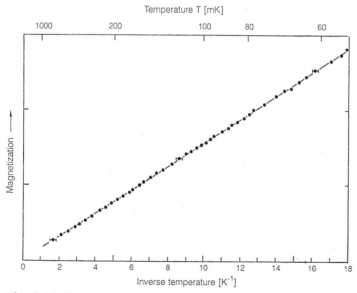

Fig. 12.35. Temperature dependence of nuclear magnetization of copper as a function of inverse temperature (the temperature scale is shown on the top horizontal axis). The static nuclear magnetization of Cu in a field of 0.25 mT was measured with a SQUID. The temperatures were deduced from the ^{3}He melting pressures [12.93]

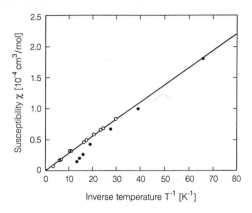

Fig.12.36. Molar nuclear susceptibility of AuIn$_2$ in different magnetic fields plotted against T^{-1}. The measuring fields are 20 mT (•), 193 and 640 mT (∘), respectively. The last two magnetic fields are strong enough to saturate the electronic moments, so that only the changes in nuclear susceptibility are measured (data from [12.96])

lems. These problems can mostly be eliminated by measuring in a magnetic field large enough to saturate the large electronic moments at the temperatures involved (also at the calibration points!), which, for example, is B/T $\geq$ 1 T/K for 3d elements in the cubic intermetallic compound AuIn$_2$ (Fig.12.36), [12.96]. In this latter work a simpler but much less sensitive commercial fluxgate magnetometer was used instead of a SQUID in the temperature range 15÷500 mK. If the electronic moments are saturated, they only give a temperature-independent background to the signal. Of course, there is the possibility of other background contributions from the sample holder, coils, etc., which may give temperature-independent as well as temperature-dependent contributions. The direct method has experimental problems but, unlike the following methods, it does not lead to heating of the sample due to the measuring process.

12.9.2 Selective Excitation but Non-Resonant Detection of Nuclear Magnetization

A variation of the method discussed above, avoiding the problem of background contributions, is the resonant, selective destruction of the nuclear polarization in an external field B$_z$ by irradiating the sample with a RF field at resonance. The frequency of the RF field has to be in resonance with the Zeeman splitting

$$h\nu = \mu\mu_n B_z/I \,. \tag{12.39}$$

It has to be perpendicular to the polarizing static field B$_z$, so it can induce transitions from the lower to the upper nuclear levels. In this way the static magnetization of the nuclei is changed and this change can be detected with a SQUID (Fig.12.37) [12.97,98]. The method combines the high sensitivity

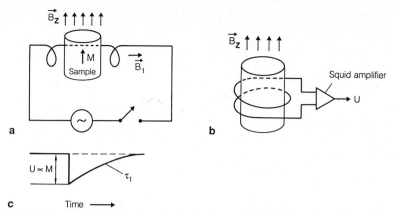

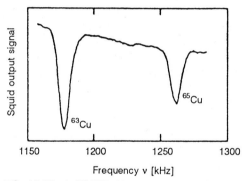

Fig.12.37a-c. Schematic for the technique of SQUID NMR thermometry. (a) The magnetization of the sample induced by the static field B_z is destroyed by applying a RF pulse of strength B_1 at the resonance frequency. (b) The resulting change of the magnetization is detected by a SQUID amplifier. (c) The voltage detected by the amplifier - which is proportional to the magnetization M - changes with time when the magnetization recovers with the spin lattice relaxation time τ_1

Fig.12.38. A SQUID NMR spectrum of Cu taken at a sweep rate of 15 kHz/s at 0.65 K in $B_0 = 104$ mT. The vertical signal represents the total nuclear magnetization of the specimen which is reduced when the frequency is swept through the resonance of the two Cu isotopes [12.97]

of the SQUID with the selectivity of resonant excitation; electronic contributions or contributions from other nuclei are not detected because they are not in resonance. Some results for "SQUID NMR" on Cu are shown in Fig. 12.38. The destroyed nuclear magnetization recovers with the spin-lattice relaxation time τ_1. This method is often applied when the more conventional NMR techniques to be discussed below are inappropriate; for example, for very broad resonances, experiments at very low frequencies [12.99] or when heating effects are a problem. A disadvantage of this method is that a change of magnetization of all the materials within the SQUID sensing volume will lead to changes in the baseline of the signal (Fig.12.38).

12.9.3 Resonant Excitation and Resonant Detection of Nuclear Magnetization

The most commonly used method in nuclear magnetic thermometry are Nuclear Magnetic Resonance (NMR) techniques which avoid electronic or any other non-resonant contributions. There are two ways to do nuclear magnetic resonance: in the continuous wave mode or with pulses. Excellent books describe these very important methods which are not only of relevance for thermometry but have found many applications in physics, chemistry and biology. I can not discuss these methods in as much detail as their importance would require but refer to relevant books and review articles (see, e.g., [12.3, 4, 7, 84-88]).

a) Continuous Wave Nuclear Magnetic Resonance

For Continuous Wave NMR (CW NMR) [12.84-87, 100, 101] we consider a sample whose nuclear moments are magnetized by a static field B_z in the coil of a resonance circuit. The sample changes the inductance of the coil by the factor $(1+\chi_n)$. When the static magnetic field applied to the sample is swept through the nuclear magnetic resonance, transitions between the nuclear energy levels are induced by a RF field

$$B_y = B_1 \sin(\omega t) \tag{12.40}$$

applied perpendicular to the static field. The necessary energy is taken from the resonance circuit, resulting in a decrease of its quality factor. Assuming that the line shape at resonance is temperature independent, the amplitude of the signal is proportional to χ_n and therefore to T_n^{-1}. The electronics for this method is shown in Fig.12.39. One has to use small RF power to keep eddy-current heating small [12.102] and to avoid disturbing or heating the nuclear spin system from thermal equilibrium; therefore the signals are rather small. To increase the sensitivity, very often the frequency or the magnetic field is modulated at audio frequencies and the signal is detected with lock-in techniques.

It can be shown that the signal at resonance, $\omega = \omega_0$, in CW NMR is proportional to the imaginary part of the dynamic nuclear susceptibility

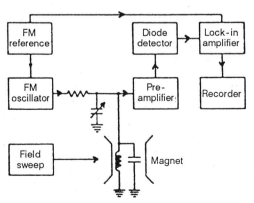

Fig.12.39. Block diagram of the electronics used by *Corruccini* et al. [12.101] for CW NMR. The cw oscillator is frequency modulated at 100 Hz as the magnetic field is swept through the resonance of the sample inside of the coil of the resonance circuit

$$\chi_n(\omega_0) = \chi_n' - i\chi_n'' \,, \qquad \text{with} \tag{12.41}$$

$$\chi_n''(\omega_0) = \frac{\omega_0 \tau_2^*}{2} = \frac{\chi(0)B_z}{\Delta B_z} \propto T^{-1} \,, \tag{12.42}$$

in the case that the signal is not saturated; here ΔB_z is the resonance width at half maximum. Hence the dynamic susceptibility is enhanced with respect to the static one by the ratio $B_z / \Delta B_z$ which can be of order $10^2 \div 10^3$ for Cu or Pt, for example.

b) Pulsed Nuclear Magnetic Resonance

In pulsed nuclear magnetic resonance [12.84-88, 103-106], again a static field B_z keeps a nuclear magnetization M_n in the z-direction. But now we apply perpendicular, in the y-direction, a short pulse of a sinusoidal field $B_y = B_1 \sin(\omega t)$ at the resonance frequency given by (12.39). This RF pulse tips the nuclear magnetization by an angle

$$\theta = \pi B_1 / B_z \tag{12.43}$$

away from the z-direction. The magnetization M_n then precesses around B_z at the resonance frequency ω_0; the resulting transverse component $M_n \sin\theta$ rotates in the xy-plane and is detected in a receiver coil (Fig.12.40). The magnetization along B_z has been reduced from M_n to $M_n \cos\theta$. The coil for

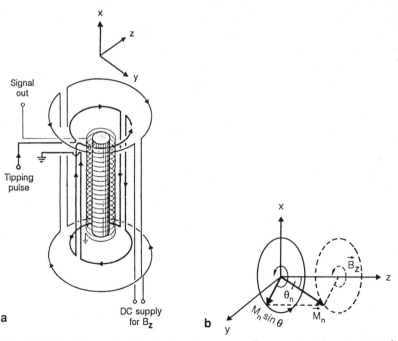

Fig.12.40a,b. Schematic of pulsed nuclear magnetic resonance thermometry. (a) Principle of the method. (b) Schematic of the coil arrangement. (See [12.3, 4, 105, 117])

253

the tipping pulse and for detection of the signal can be identical (Figs. 12.45, 46) because the tipping and detection do not occur simultaneously. The precession signal in the receiver coil decays with a characteristic time given by the transverse spin-spin relaxation time τ_2 due to the dephasing of the rotating spins. An always present inhomogeneity δB_z of the static field will speed up the dephasing. The effective decay time [12.84-88] is then given by

$$\frac{1}{\tau_2^*} = \frac{1 - P^2}{\tau_2} + \frac{\mu\mu_n}{\hbar I} \delta B_z \ , \tag{12.44}$$

where P is the polarization, hence

$$M_{xy}(t) = M_n(0)\, e^{-t/\tau_2^*} \ . \tag{12.45}$$

Such a free induction decay signal is shown in Fig. 12.41. The pulse length $(\tau_p = \theta\hbar/\mu\mu_n B_1$ at resonance) should therefore be short compared to τ_2^*.

The voltage induced in a detection coil in the x-direction around the sample is given by

$$U = \alpha\omega M_n \sin\theta \propto T_n^{-1} \ , \tag{12.46}$$

where α is the geometry or coil constant. The behaviour of the important quantity $M_n\sin\theta$ can be calculated from its equation of motion (Bloch equations) [12.3, 4, 84-87, 102, 103].

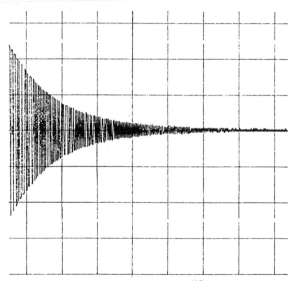

Fig. 12.41. Free precession signal of ^{195}Pt nuclear spins (2000 wires of $25\,\mu$m diameter in a 5mm long secondary coil of several thousand windings of $25\,\mu$m Cu wire, see Fig. 12.45) at T = 45 μK and in B = 13.8 mT (125kHz). The excitation pulse was 64 μs long and had about 0.2 V_{pp} amplitude. The horizontal scale is 0.5 ms/div

In the NMR methods discussed above one is determining the nuclear spin temperature T_n from a measurement of the nuclear susceptibility. By measuring the spin lattice relaxation time τ_1 and applying the Korringa law $\kappa = \tau_1 T_e$, one can also use NMR to measure the temperature T_e of the electrons. This can be done by using either SQUID NMR or pulsed NMR. In the latter method one applies a 90° pulse at the resonance frequency to destroy the magnetization in the z-direction. Afterwards, small, e.g. 10°, inspection pulses are applied to record the recovery of M_z according to

$$M_z(t) = M_n(0)(1 - e^{-t/\tau_1}) . \tag{12.47}$$

An example of such a measurement is illustrated in Fig.12.42. A determination of the electronic temperature from nuclear magnetic properties by observing the nuclear spin lattice relaxation time τ_1 has been popular for many years [12.47, 103, 105-107]. The results of successful examples are shown in Figs.12.43,44. However, in some experiments substantial deviations from the Korringa law have been observed for Cu [12.108] and Pt [12.79, 103, 107, 109-111], showing that κ can be strongly temperature and field dependent, so that this method should only be used with great caution. These deviations have been attributed to the Kondo effect of magnetic impurities in the host lattice [12.112] but details are not yet understood. The early optimism about being able to double-check the NMR temperature scale by measuring $T_n = \lambda_n / \chi_n$ and $T_e = \kappa / \tau_1$ seems to have faded.

NMR at very low temperatures is not a simple method, and the electronic setup can be quite sophisticated. However, it is the *only* method available at present for thermometry below 1 mK. There are a number of requirements which have to be fulfilled in order to obtain reliable results

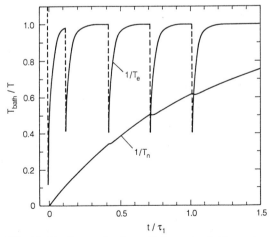

Fig.12.42. Determination of the spin lattice relaxation time τ_1 from pulsed NMR measurements. The figure shows the calculated time behaviour of T_n^{-1} and T_e^{-1} during a τ_1 determination [12.106])

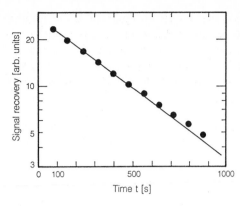

Fig.12.43. Relaxation of the nuclear magnetization of a ^{195}Pt NMR sample after applying a 60° pulse. From the measured relaxation time τ_1 and the Korringa relation for platinum, $\tau_1 T_e = 30$ mK·s, one finds $T_e = 61.5$ μK; the Pt nuclear magnetization gave $T_n = 60.5$ μK [12.47]

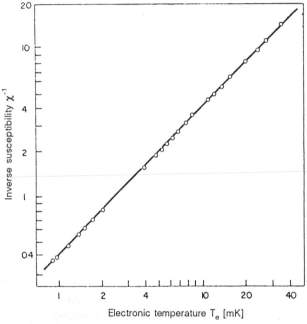

Fig.12.44. A comparison of the reciprocal of the nuclear spin susceptibility χ_n of Pt (proportional to its nuclear spin temperature T_n) versus the reciprocal of the spin lattice relaxation time τ_1^{-1} of Pt (which is proportional to the shown electronic temperature T_e of Pt) to show that the nuclear spins and the conduction electrons are at the same temperature [12.118,119]

with pulsed NMR, which is mostly applied. Particular care has to be taken if a large temperature range is investigated. Firstly, we have to remember that the tipping pulse reduces the nuclear magnetization M_n to $M_n \cos\theta$; this increases the nuclear spin temperature from T_n to $T_n/\cos\theta$. For a 90° pulse this would be $M_n = 0$ and $T_n = \infty$; generally, $\Delta T/T = (\cos^{-1}\theta) - 1$ ($\approx \theta^2/2$ for small θ). One has to search for a compromise between a small increase of T_n (proportional to $1/\cos\theta$) and a large enough signal (proportional to $\sin\theta$).

256

Typically a 10° pulse is applied, giving cos 10° = 0.985 or $\Delta T/T \simeq 1.5\%$ only. Calibration is always carried out at temperatures higher than the investigated temperature range and the tipping angle has to be changed to keep the signal at a reasonable level. Even more important, we have to take into account that the RF field of the tipping pulse increases the electronic temperature due to eddy current heating [12.102, 106]. This eddy current heating is proportional to ω^2 (Sect.10.5.2). Again a compromise between a large enough signal and small enough eddy current heating has to be found. Typical heat depositions are $0.1 \div 1$ nJ per pulse for Pt NMR thermometry at $T \leq 1$ mK [12.47, 79, 103, 113].

Besides taking a low frequency and a small tipping angle, even more importantly, one has to use small dimensions of the sample, which very often means taking a bundle of thin insulated wires (or powder) for the NMR thermometry sample, to keep RF eddy current heating small and to let the electromagnetic field penetrate the sample (skin depth $\delta = \sqrt{2\rho/\mu_0\omega}$). Then we have to bear in mind that after each pulse, nuclei and electrons have to recover and should be in thermal equilibrium before the next pulse is fired. Therefore the repetition rate has to be small compared to τ_1^{-1}. We would also like the heat capacity of the thermometric sample (and addenda) to be small, so that we have a small thermal time constant for its thermal recovery; this means, the static field B_z should be kept as small as possible. The last requirment is in accordance with our desire to keep the frequency for the NMR low. Last but not least, the static field should be homogeneous (to at least 10^{-4}) to give a sharp resonance and to keep τ_2^* large, see (12.44).

A main advantage of this transient method is the fact that it measures the state of the nuclear spin system before the (short!) pulse is applied and that the detection can occur when the tipping field has been switched off. The pulsed technique seems to be more appropriate for thermometry at very low temperatures than the CW method under the usual experimental conditions [12.102].

Owing to recent advances in attaining very low temperatures, one can now perform experiments where the high–temperature approximations (10.4) used to describe the thermodynamic properties of a sample cannot be applied anymore. The spin dynamics can then become rather complicated because after a disturbance the nuclei will *decay exponentially with a single decay time only for I = 1/2* [12.114-116]. Eventually, at $g_n\mu_n B > k_B T$, the resulting effective decay time obtained from fitting experimental data will approach a constant value, see (10.11'),

$$\tau_1 = \frac{2k_B\kappa}{g_n\mu_n B} \tag{12.48}$$

instead of being $\tau_1 = \kappa/T_e$, because now the relaxation rate depends on the magnetic rather than on the thermal energy. In this situation τ_1 decreases with spin I according to

$$\tau_1(T=0; I) = \frac{1}{2I}\tau_1(T=0; I=1/2) . \qquad (12.49)$$

In Table 10.1 I have summarized the properties of several metallic isotopes which may also be suitable for NMR. From these properties and the experience of several groups it turns out that Pt seems to be the most suitable thermometric probe at very low temperatures. It has only one isotope, [195]Pt, with nuclear spin I = 1/2; therefore we have no problems with nuclear quadrupole interaction. It has a short τ_1; this means, that electrons and nuclei quickly attain thermal equilibrium. Its nuclear spin-spin relaxation time τ_2 is long; therefore the decay of the signal takes a long time, simplifying observation of the signal.

Pulsed NMR on thin Pt wires (or Pt powder immersed in liquid [3]He) at fields of 6÷60 mT and correspondingly at frequencies of about 55÷550 kHz is now the standard thermometric method for the microkelvin temperature range [12.47, 79, 89, 104-106, 109-111, 118-122]. A bundle of several hundred or, better, thousand thin (e.g., 25 μm), annealed (but see [12.79, 111]) wires and not too high frequencies are chosen to keep eddy current heating low and to let the RF field penetrate the sample wires (the skin depth is of order 10 μm at ν = 250 kHz for Pt with RRR $\simeq$ 100). Successful

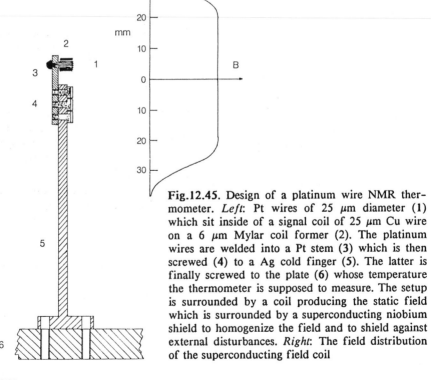

Fig.12.45. Design of a platinum wire NMR thermometer. *Left*: Pt wires of 25 μm diameter (1) which sit inside of a signal coil of 25 μm Cu wire on a 6 μm Mylar coil former (2). The platinum wires are welded into a Pt stem (3) which is then screwed (4) to a Ag cold finger (5). The latter is finally screwed to the plate (6) whose temperature the thermometer is supposed to measure. The setup is surrounded by a coil producing the static field which is surrounded by a superconducting niobium shield to homogenize the field and to shield against external disturbances. *Right*: The field distribution of the superconducting field coil

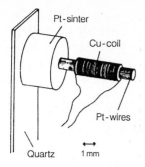

Pt-sinter

Cu-coil

Pt-wires

Quartz

↔ 1 mm

Fig.12.46. Platinum wire NMR thermometer for measuring the temperature of liquid helium. The Pt wires (e.g. 25 μm diameter) are pressed into a platinum black sinter of 0.25 g. The latter provides a large surface area of 4 m^2 to make thermal contact with the liquid. It is preferable to do the NMR on the Pt wires rather than on the very fine Pt powder directly because the latter usually contains a large fraction of impurities and its NMR resonance may also be more strongly influenced by size and strain effects. The thermometer is held by a quartz sheet and a copper signal coil is wound around the Pt wires [12.122])

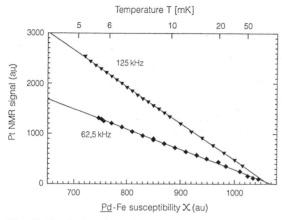

Fig.12.47. Calibration of the NMR signal of a platinum wire NMR thermometer versus electronic paramagnetic susceptibility of PdFe (Sect.12.8) in the temperature range between 5 and 50 mK at the two frequencies shown. The vertical scale is different for the two frequencies [12.79]

designs of Pt wire NMR thermometers are shown in Figs.12.45,46 [12.47, 79, 122]. These thermometers have a signal-to-noise ratio of 1 at about 0.1 K. Figure 12.47 shows the calibration of a Pt wire thermometer with PdFe susceptibility thermometer (Sect.12.8), which in turn had been calibrated by a superconducting fixed point device (Sect.11.3.2). Such a NMR thermometer and the described calibration is believed to give the temperature at 1 mK (20μK) to $\pm$ 2% ($\pm$5%), assuming the fixed point device temperatures to be correct [12.47,79,89]. The data in Fig.12.47 also demonstrate that χ_n(Pt) $\propto$ χ(PdFe) to within 10^{-3}, or that both susceptibilities follow a Curie (or Curie-Weiss law) to that accuracy in the investigated temperature range. Usually the accuracy of a NMR thermometer is limited by the accuracy of the calibration and by heating effects [12.102].

The validity of the ^{195}Pt NMR temperature scale has been confirmed to at least 70 μK by the observation that B/T_{Pt} = const. in the adiabatic nuclear demagnetization experiments of [12.79], and to at least 100 μK by the observation that the relative change of the velocity of sound of polycrystalline Ag is propertional to $\ell n T_{Pt}$ [12.66]. In addition, in [12.47] it was shown that T_n (from χ_n) and T_e (from τ_1) agree to within 2% from 48 to 306 μK (Fig. 12.43). These as well as other observations [12.89] provide convincing evidence that the Pt-NMR temperature scale is correct to at least 50 μK. However, NMR on ^{195}Pt has exclusively been used up till now in all experiments for T < 1 mK. This indicates the urgent need for the development of alternative thermometric methods for this temperature range to substantiate the obtained temperatures. Deviations from the Curie law and time constant problems may limit the present thermometric methods to T > 1 μK anyway.

Even though electronic magnetic impurities have no direct influence on the signal in nuclear resonance methods, they may have an indirect influence by changing the local magnetic field seen by neighbouring host nuclei or by influencing the relaxation rate. This may have a pronounced effect on the data if the investigated temperature range includes characteristic temperatures like the Kondo temperature for Kondo alloys [12.112] or the spin-glass freezing temperature for spin glasses.

12.10 Magnetic Thermometry via Anisotropy of Gamma Rays (Nuclear Orientation Thermometry)

Nuclear magnetic thermometry relies on the detection of the Boltzmann population of magnetic sublevels, that is, of the nuclear magnetic polarization. The detection is via measurement of the resulting magnetization or via measurement of the change in magnetization due to resonant RF radiation (see preceding section). In this section I will discuss another way to detect nuclear polarization which can be applied if radioactive nuclei are used.

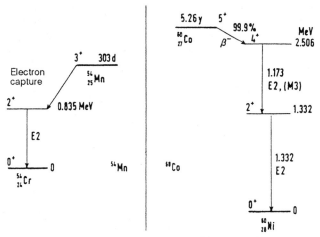

Fig. 12.48. Energy level diagrams for ^{54}Mn and ^{60}Co (slightly simplified). These are the two favorite decay schemes used for nuclear orientation thermometry

Radioactive long-lived nuclei suitable for nuclear orientation thermometry usually show a $\beta^{\pm}$-decay feeding a short-lived excited state which then decays by emission of γ-rays (Fig.12.48). If the long-living $\beta^{\pm}$-emitters are polarized, the polarization is transferred to the excited, γ-ray emitting state. This γ-ray then has an emission probability with a spatial anisotropy that differs for each of the $(2I+1)$ sublevels in a magnetic field. The spatial anisotropy is a result of the conservation of angular momentum. The γ-radiation field carries an angular momentum which is the difference of the angular momenta of the two nuclear sublevels involved. The angular momentum of the emitted radiation determines the multipole character of the radiation.

If we have an ensemble of radioactive nuclei, the mean value for the emission probability is equal in all directions. We have to orient the nuclei to be able to detect the spatial anisotropy of the emitted γ-ray intensity, which is a result of the Boltzmann population of the sublevels and therefore of the temperature. The anisotropy depends on the parameters of the nuclear transition and on the polarization of the nucleus. The anisotropic emission of γ-rays from an assembly of oriented nuclei can be used for thermometry if all other parameters determining the γ-ray intensity are known.

The intensity of the γ-radiation emitted from axially symmetric nuclei and detected at an angle θ, which is the angle betwen the direction of orientation of the nuclei (or of the magnetic field) and the detection or observation of the radiation, is given by [12.3, 4, 7, 123-128]

$$W(T,\theta) = 1 + \sum_{k=2,4,6,\ldots}^{k_{max}} Q_k U_k F_k B_k(T) P_k(\cos\theta) ; \qquad (12.50)$$

this value has been normalized to the intensity at high temperatures, where the probability is equal in all directions. In the summation we have only to consider even k-values because γ-quanta have a spin 1, and the interaction which determines the transition between two nuclear levels resulting in emission of a γ-ray is parity conserving. The parameter k will run to k_{max} = 2 I or 2 L, whichever is smaller, where L is the multipolarity of the emitted radiation. The parameters in the above equation are:

Q_k Geometry parameter (detector properties, finite size of source, finite angle of detection, etc.); often the experiment can be designed so that the Q_k's are of order "1", but they have to be determined for each experiment (see, e.g., [12.123])

U_k Influence of polarization of the former nuclear transitions on the polarization to be used for thermometry; this is "algebra" and can be taken from tables in the literature [Ref.12.128, App.5]

F_k Angular momentum coupling coefficients of the nuclear transition; again this can be taken from tables [Ref.12.128, App.5]

B_k Population of nuclear magnetic sublevels [Ref.12.128, App.6]

P_k Legendre polynomials expressing the angular dependence of the γ-ray distribution

θ Angle between γ-ray emission and axis of orientation.

The essential parameter for our thermometric purpose is

$$B_k = I^k \frac{(2k)!}{(k!)^2} \frac{(2I+1)(2k+1)(2I-k)!}{\sqrt{(2I+k+1)}} f_k(I) ,$$ (12.51)

with

$$f_2 = I^{-2} \sum_{m=-I}^{+I} m^2 P(m) - \frac{I(I+1)}{3} ,$$ (12.52)

and

$$f_4 = I^{-4} \sum_{m=-I}^{+I} m^4 P(m) - \frac{I^2(6I^2+6I-5)f_2}{7} - \frac{(3I^2+3I-1)I(I+1)}{15} .$$ (12.53)

In these equations $P(m)$ is the Boltzmann population probability of the sub-level with the magnetic quantum number m; these $P(m)$ are given in (9.9). They are the only T-dependent parameters in the above equations.

The nuclear decay level schemes of the two most commonly used isotopes, ^{60}Co and ^{54}Mn, are shown in Fig. 12.48. These two isotopes are attractive because all the necessary nuclear parameters are known, the lifetime of the intermediate state is short so that reorientation effects can be neglected, and they are pure E2 transitions giving a purely electric quadrupole radiation pattern with multipolarity L = 2 (2) and nuclear spin I = 3 (5) for ^{54}Mn (^{60}Co), therefore k_{max} = 4. Figure 12.49 shows the angular radiation pattern for ^{60}Co for various values of $k_B T/\Delta m g_n \mu_n B$. For the mentioned isotopes the relevant parameters are

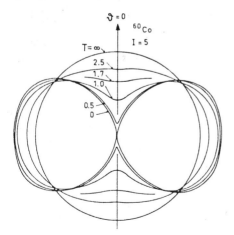

Fig.12.49. Angular radiation patter of ^{60}Co for several values of $k_B T/\mu\mu_B B$. The figure demonstrates that the highest sensitivity for temperature changes is obtained when the detector is in the θ = 0 direction

$$U_2F_2 = -0.49486 \; ; \quad U_4F_4 = -0.44669 \quad \text{for} \quad {}^{54}\text{Mn} \, ,$$

$$U_2F_2 = -0.42056 \; ; \quad U_4F_4 = -0.24280 \quad \text{for} \quad {}^{60}\text{Co} \, ,$$

$$P_2(\cos\theta) = (3\cos^2\theta - 1)/2 \, ,$$

$$P_4(\cos\theta) = (35\cos^4\theta - 30\cos^2\theta + 3)/8 \, .$$

With these parameters we find eventually for E2 radiation detected at an angle $\theta = 0$ [12.3]:

$$W(T,0) = 1 + 0.38887 \, Q_2 \sum_m m^2 \, P(m) - 0.55553 \, Q_4 \sum_m m^4 \, P(m)$$

for ^{54}Mn, and

$$W(T,0) = 1 + 0.04333 \, Q_2 \sum_m m^2 \, P(m) - 0.00333 \, Q_4 \sum_m m^4 \, P(m)$$

for ^{60}Co .

In order for the nuclei to be polarized or oriented they have to experience a magnetic field. This can be an externally applied field, or as has been done in most cases, we can implant the radioactive isotope into a ferromagnetic host matrix (deposit radioactive material on a host metal and then let it diffuse at high T). In this matrix the nuclei experience a large internal hyperfine field which can be of the order of $10 \div 30$ T if the isotope is implanted in a ferromagnetic 3d host. If we use this latter method we only have to apply a small field ($0.1 \div 1$T) to orient the magnetic domains for saturation of the matrix and to define a quantization axis.

The γ-ray detector should be in a direction where the change of the γ-ray intensity is a maximum as a function of temperature. As Fig.12.49 demonstrates, this is the case for an angle $\theta = 0$, if we have an E2 transition. We have to correct for any background contributions to the radiation, for geometry effects, and for the intensity of our source by performing a measurement at high temperatures where $W(T,\theta) = 1$.

Using radioactive nuclei for thermometry one has to be careful not to produce too large a self-heating of the source due to radioactive transitions. Typical values are for

1 μCurie ^{60}Co : 0.57 nW   due to the β-emission ,

and 1 μCurie ^{54}Mn: 0.03 nW   due to the 5 keV radiation from radioactive ^{54}Cr after electron capture [12.3, 4, 7, 123–128].

In an appropriate experimental set-up the high-energy γ-rays used for thermometry can leave the source without noticeable heating effects. If the source is too strong it will heat; if it is too weak, counting times may get excessive. In any case the source has to be in good thermal contact to its surrounding. This can usually even be achieved by soldering because the polarizing field will keep the solder normal-conducting.

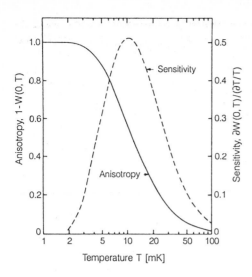

Fig.12.50. Temperature dependence of the anisotropy of the γ-radiation of ^{54}Mn in a Ni host along $\theta = 0$. The quantity dW/dT is a measure of the temperature sensitivity of the thermometer which, in this case, has its maximum value at about 10 mK

One of the disadvantages of nuclear orientation thermometry is that the sensitivity T(dW/dT) is limited to a certain temperature range at around a value of T $\simeq \Delta m \mu_n g_n B/k_B$, which is usually between 1 and 100 mK (Fig.12.50). For the above-mentioned isotopes we have $\Delta E_m/k_B$ = 9.14 mK for ^{54}Mn in Fe and 7.97 mK for ^{60}Co in Fe (corresponding to internal fields of -22.7 and -29.0 T, respectively). Therefore for these transitions the useful range is a few millikelvin to about 40 mK, whereas at higher and lower temperatures W(T, θ) is independent of T because all levels are either equally populated or only the lowest level is populated. - Because this method is a statistical method we need a certain counting time to obtain the desired accuracy. The error of the measurement due to statistics is $\Delta T/T = (2/n)^{1/2}$ if we count n pulses. One typically needs a measuring time of several minutes to get the required accuracy, because the source must not be too strong in order to avoid self-heating. Low-temperature physicists sometimes unjustifiably avoid this method because they do not have the counting and detecting electronics on hand, which is more common in nuclear physics laboratories (the basic equipment consists of a γ-ray detector, like GeLi, a preamplifier, gate, and a multichannel analyser with a microcomputer).

An advantage of this method is that we can use a metal to make good thermal contact to the point whose temperature we want to measure and to have a good nuclear spin-lattice coupling. The γ-energy is very often large enough that we do not need special windows to get the γ-rays out of the cryostat. We do not need any leads to the sample because we only measure the electromagnetic field of the γ-rays. And, finally, nuclear orientation is a primary thermometric method because the theory is well established, and we do not need any extra calibration except that we have to normalize the counting rate or the intensity of the radioactive source at high temperatures. Therefore this method has very often been applied for calibration purposes [12.118, 119, 128, 129].

Detailed and instructive comparisons between various nuclear orientation and other thermometric methods are described in [12.123-129]. In some
of these papers as well as in other relevant work discrepancies observed between the various temperature scales were reported, with many of them
originating from self-heating effects or from incomplete magnetic saturation (aligning of domains) of the γ-ray source; in some cases fields in excess of even 1 T seem to be necessary for complete magnetization. Some of
the observed discrepancies are not yet fully understood. Agreement to better than 0.5% at $10 \div 50$ mK has been found in [12.129] for a Josephson noise
thermometer and a ^{60}Co γ-ray anisotropy thermometer. The main usefulness of a γ-ray anisotropy thermometer may remain as a primary thermometer for calibration purposes in a restricted temperature range and for
nuclei with well-understood decay schemes.

Another method relying on the Boltzmann population of nuclear sublevels of radioactive nuclei is the Mössbauer effect. This method has not
often been applied and, for more details, the literature cited in [12.3,4]
should be consulted. A disadvantage of it is that one can only use low-ener-
gy γ-rays ($E \leq 100$ keV) requiring in most cases special thin windows to let
the γ-rays escape from the cryostat. In addition, corrections for finite sample thickness, long counting times, specialized equipment and motion of
source or absorber are necessary.

12.11 Summary

Table 12.4 summarizes the most important thermometric methods for determination of temperatures below 1 K. They are resistance measurements on
a thin sheet of a carbon sample and susceptibility measurements of the
electronic parmagnetism, for the temperature range above a few millikelvin.
Below this temperature one has to resort to nuclear magnetism where the
nuclear susceptibility in most cases is measured either directly or more appropriately via one of the discussed nuclear magnetic resonance methods.
Here one relies on the applicability of the Curie law.

The result of each temperature measurement has an error and it deviates more or less from the absolute thermodynamic temperature. Very often

Table 12.4. The most commonly used thermometric techniques at T < 1 K

Measured property	Function	Material	Temperature range
Electrical Resistance	$\ell n R = \sum_{n=0}^{m} \alpha_n (\ln T)^n$	Carbon composite	> 10 (5) mK
Electronic param. suscept.	$\chi_e = \chi_0 + \lambda_e / (T_e - \Delta)$	CMN; PdFe	> 1 mK
Nuclear paramag. suscept.	$\chi_n = \chi_0 + \lambda_n / T_n$	Pt	$1\ \mu K \div 0.1$ K
Nuclear orientation	$I_\gamma = f(\mu B / k_B T)$	^{60}Cu; ^{54}Mn	1 mK $\div 0.1$ K

it is difficult to estimate the uncertainty of the measured "temperature". In cases where temperature is a very important parameter, such as in measurements of heat capacities, it is sometimes advisable to use two different thermometric methods and compare the results if possible to get a feeling for the uncertainty in T. In any case, it is very important to write up the obtained results with all relevant experimental details so that future researchers can reconstruct the used temperature scale, and, if necessary, later corrections are possible. A low-temperature physicist should always remember that the quality of his data depends on the quality of his thermometry!

13. Miscellaneous Cryogenic Design Aids

This chapter deals with various cryogenic tools, design details and measuring techniques, which have turned out to be very useful in the construction and operation of a cryogenic apparatus.

13.1 Cryogenic Capacitive Transducers for Thermometry and Manometry

In the last two decades low-temperature capacitive transducers have gained in importance for thermometry, for pressure measurements and for investigations of the properties of liquid and solid helium. They can measure the parameter of interest in situ, they are very sensitive and reproducible, and the simple capacitance measurement is performed with no or at most very low dissipation.

The successful career of capacitive transducers for low-temperature experiments began with the description of a capacitive melting pressure gauge by *Straty* and *Adams* [13.1]. This gauge is shown schematically in Fig.13.1. All later gauges (see Figs.13.2,3, for example) are only slight vari-

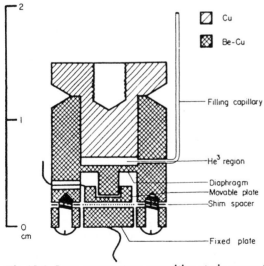

Fig.13.1. Low-temperature capacitive strain gauge for ^{3}He melting pressure measurements of [13.1,2]. The bottom of the ^{3}He chamber flexes with ^{3}He pressure variations, changing the capacitance measured between the movable and fixed plates

ations of this successful original design [13.1-10]. In the capacitive ^{3}He melting pressure gauges a diaphragm is one wall of a compartment containing a solid/liquid mixture whose pressure is to be measured. The ^{3}He is kept at nearly constant volume because a solid block is formed at the point of the filling capillary where the temperature is at the temperature of the minimum of the ^{3}He melting line (Fig. 8.1). The flexing diaphragm moves an electrically isolated plate which is connected to (but electrically isolated from) a pin at its centre. The plate moves relative to a fixed plate glued into a guard ring at electrical ground. Pressure changes are then monitored as capacitance changes when the conducting diaphragm is deflected, moving the two capacitor plates relative to each other.

To determine the expected behaviour of such a capacitor we consider the model of a circular membrane with fixed edges. This gives a deflection

$$y(r) = \frac{3P}{16Ed^3}(r^4 - 2R^2r^2 + R^4) . \tag{13.1}$$

The deflection of the centre of the membrane is then

$$y(0) = \frac{3R^4P}{16Ed^3} , \tag{13.2}$$

where R is the membrane radius, E is Young's modulus of elasticity and d is the membrane thickness. The actual performance will be somewhat worse because the central post carrying the capacitor plate has to be subtracted form the active diameter of the plate. The deflection is maximum for the minimum membrane thickness for which its deformation is still elastic at the maximum pressure. To stay clearly in the elastic limit, the stress on the membrane should be kept below about 20% of the yield stress S of the membrane material, which is usually hardened Be-Cu because of its favourable elastic properties (E $\simeq$ 1.3·10^6 bar; S $\simeq$ 1.2·10^4 bar, torsion (shear) modulus G = 0.53·10^6 bar, all at room temperature but depend on composition and treatment; a hardening treatment of 2÷3 hours at 320÷310° C in vacuum seems to work well). The maximum radial stress on the membrane is given by

$$S_m = \frac{3R^2P}{4d^2} . \tag{13.3}$$

Typical values are d ~ 0.1 (0.5) mm for P_{max} ~ 0.5 (50) bar and a membrane diameter of 4÷10 mm.

Two criteria distinguish a good capacitive manometer. Firstly, its capacitance should show no or at most a very small temperature dependence; for example, 10% change for T = 300 to 4 K and less than 10^{-5} below 4 K. For that reason the electric field by which the capacitance is measured should "see" only the metal electrodes, and not the epoxy, for example, which has a T-dependent dielectric constant (Sect. 12.7), see Fig. 13.2. Se-

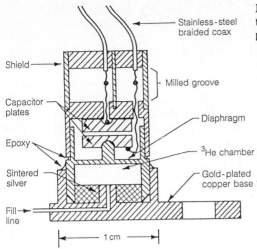

Fig.13.2. Low-temperature capacitive strain gauge for ^{3}He melting pressure thermometry of [13.4]

Stainless-steel braided coax

Shield

Milled groove

Capacitor plates

Diaphragm

Epoxy

^{3}He chamber

Sintered silver

Gold-plated copper base

Fill line

$\vert\longleftarrow\ 1\ cm\ \longrightarrow\vert$

condly the polished or lapped (to $\leq 1\,\mu$m) electrodes should be coplanar, to give a linear relation between their distance and capacitance over a wide pressure range, and they should have a gap as small as possible at the maximum working pressure to increase the capacitance and the sensitivity of the gauge. For this purpose the epoxy on the movable capacitor plate should cure while the latter is in contact with and therefore parallel to the fixed plate, with the gauge kept at a pressure slightly above the maximum working pressure. This should result in a gap of some tens of micrometres at ambient pressure if the maximum working pressure is about 50 bar. Another possibility is to glue both plates, perform a final matching operation to bring the surfaces flat and parallel, and then adjust the gap by shimming. The helium filled volume of the gauge should contain some metal sinter (Sect.13.6) for thermal contact if the gauge is required to have a small time constant in the millikelvin temperature range.

For a parallel plate capacitor, the relation between pressure P and capacitance C is given by

$$P \propto (1/C_0 - 1/C), \tag{13.4}$$

where C_0 is the zero-pressure capacitance; for higher accuracy more terms in $(1/C_0-1/C)^n$ have to be used. Typical values are C ~ $10\div100$ pF, $\Delta C/\Delta P$ ~ $0.1\div1$ pF/bar, $\Delta y/\Delta P$ ~ $0.1\div1$ μm/bar.

Various designs of cryogenic capacitive manometers for melting pressure [13.1-6] or vapour pressure thermometry [13.7-9] as well as for other pressure measurements [13.10] have been described in the literature. The capacitive transducer for vapour pressure thermometry of [13.8] shown in Fig.13.3 uses a gold-plated 0.015 mm thick electro-deposited Cu diaphragm. It has a 30 μm gap and C $\simeq$ 43 pF. The achieved resolution of 10^{-6} pF allows changes of 0.3 mK (0.04μK) at 0.3 K (2K) to be detected, corre-

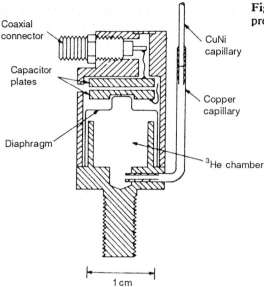

Coaxial
connector

Capacitor
plates

Diaphragm

CuNi
capillary

Copper
capillary

^{3}He chamber

Fig.13.3. Low-temperature vapour pressure capacitive gauge of [13.8]

|← 1 cm →|

sponding to a vapour pressure of 2 μbar (0.2 bar) of ^{3}He. The vapour pressure gauge of [13.7] gave a resolution of $\Delta T/T = 10^{-9}$ from 1.6 to 2.2 K, corresponding to a deflection of y ~ 10^{-3} nm at a capacitor plate spacing of 10 μm. An ultrasensitive low-temperature pressure transducer has been described in [13.11]. The diaphragm is a 7.5 μm thick, 8 mm diameter Kapton foil (E = $6 \cdot 10^4$ bar; S = $3.4 \cdot 10^3$ bar) coated with 60 nm aluminium. Its motion is sensed by a flat coil connected to an RF SQUID. Displacements of $5 \cdot 10^{-4}$ nm and pressure changes of $3 \cdot 10^{-11}$ bar could be resolved. A differential capacitive manometer using an 8 μm thick Kapton diaphragm has given a sensitive of $6 \cdot 10^{-11}$ bar using a conventional electronic detection scheme [13.12,13]. This sensitivity has recently almost been reached in a differential gauge using a 0.8 μm thick aluminium diaphragm [13.14].

A capacitive gauge is an indirect-reading device and has to be calibrated in the operating pressure range. For a melting pressure gauge the calibration is best performed with a gas lubricated, controlled-clearance deadweight tester [13.15]. Well-calibrated and stable mechanical, piezoelectric, or capacitive manometers at room temperature often do well as secondary standards. A low-pressure gauge can be calibrated via a measurement of the vapour pressure of one of the helium isotopes. For these calibrations with the standard at room temperature one may have to take into account the possible problems discussed in Sect.12.2. Because Be-Cu behaves hysteretic, the calibration has to be checked or repeated in each cooldown.

A successful design of a bridge circuit for capacitance measurements using an inductive voltage divider ("ratio transformer") was described in [13.16]. It is essentially identical to the bridge shown in Fig.12.33 with the inductances replaced by capacitors. In such a design the lead capacitances should be kept small to keep stray capacitances low and to avoid degrading the sensitivity or introducing errors. If the reference capacitor is kept at room temperature it usually has to be temperature stabilized. Of course, it is much better to keep it at a low, constant temperature, for example at 4.2 K, if high stability is required. If a home-made reference capacitor is used, one should make it as similar to the working capacitor as possible, again avoiding that the electrical field "sees" dielectric, glassy materials (Sect. 12.7). Otherwise, mica capacitors are appropriate. With a driving voltage of some volts such a bridge with a capacitance gauge allows a ratio (capacitance) resolution of 10^{-8}, corresponding to a pressure resolution of about 10^{-6} bar at 10 bar, for instance. At balance the ratio in the bridge is given by

$$R = \frac{C}{C + C_{Ref}},$$

$$\frac{dR}{dT} = R \frac{1 - R}{C} \frac{dC}{dT},$$

(13.5)

and for a maximum sensitivity, with $C \simeq C_{Ref}$,

$$\frac{dR}{dT} \simeq \frac{1}{4C} \frac{dC}{dT}.$$

(13.6)

One has to keep in mind that the reading C of a bridge can depend on excitation voltage V and frequency ν with values of

$$\frac{\Delta C}{C} \sim \text{several } 10^{-6} \left(\frac{\Delta V}{V} \right) \quad \text{or} \quad \left(\frac{\Delta \nu}{\nu} \right)$$

(13.7)

for a symmetric bridge [13.3].

A pressure gauge whose off-balance signal is amplified and used to regulate the temperature of a ballast volume (for example, at low temperatures and filled with ^{4}He, weakly coupled to the bath at 4.2K) connected to an experiment can be used for high-precision pressure regulation, see Fig. 13.4 [13.5, 10, 17].

13.2 Cold Valves

Valves at low temperature are often necessary for experiments with liquid or solid helium. They confine the helium sample to a constant volume to avoid thermomechanical pressure gradients in the fill line, and eliminate heat leaks or fractionation of a helium mixture along the fill capillary. Successful designs of bellows sealed valves are described in [13.18-20]. The

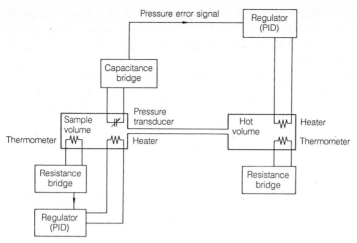

Fig.13.4. Setup to measure and regulate pressures at low temperatures (see text) [13.10]

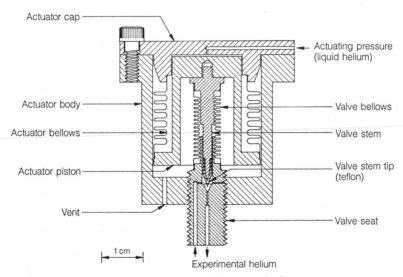

Fig.13.5. Hydraulically actuated cryogenic valve [13.18]

principle of their design is to select an appropriate combination of soft and hard material for the needle tip and the seat.

The tip of the valve stem is usually covered by plastic, e.g., Teflon. The seat and the Teflon-covered stem can be made of Cu or brass. Another variant of a cryogenic valve uses a soft metal seat (e.g., German silver, non-hardened Be-Cu) with a 1 mm hole and a hard needle (e.g., stainless steel, hardened Be-Cu) with a small, ~ 3° taper [13.10]. The bellows sealed design used in our laboratory is very similar to the original design by *Roach* et al. [13.18] (Fig.13.5). Its essential design feature to ensure that it is leak tight at low temperatures even after repeated use is a 38° angle on the Teflon cov-

272

ered brass needle (1.4mm thread with 0.3mm pitch) to be fitted into a 60° angle of the brass seat, which has a 0.4 mm diameter hole. These valves should never be cooled down in the closed position, and should be tested at LN_2 or lower temperatures.

A superleak-tight valve with a hardened and polished Be-Cu tip (30° angle) and an Ag seat (50° angle pressed by a hardened and polished steel jig) has been described in [13.20]. This valve can be tested at room temperature, contrary to earlier designs.

These cryogenic valves are usually actuated hydraulically using a helium mixture or ^{4}He at pressures of 3÷5 bar as the medium to operate the valve, of course requiring a second capillary in the cryostat. The valve should be at or at least close to the temperature of the experimental cell.

13.3 Coaxial Cables and Feedthroughs

The appropriate materials for single leads transmitting electrical signals to and from the cold parts of a cryostat have already been discussed in Sect. 4.1. Coaxial cables and appropriate miniature connectors suitable for Kelvin temperatures can be obtained commercially. For lower temperatures home-made coaxial cables seem to be more appropriate. The best design with the lowest heat leak seems to be twisted pairs of 0.1 mm Manganin or Constantan or, even better, superconducting NbTi wires (do not use Cu-clad superconducting wires at $T < 0.1$ K! because of the possible influences due to the temperature-dependent superconducting proximity effect) inside of a thin-walled CuNi tube or of a superconducting capillary. The capillary can be commercial Nb tubing or it can be home-made by leaching out the resin core from a commercial Pb-Sn solder. This can be accomplished by putting several 50÷80 cm long pieces of a Pb-Sn solder in a glass tube filled with some alcohol or gasoline and heating it to a temperature between 120 and 160° C for 1÷3 hours, for example by means of a heater around the glass tube. The process is accelerated if the lower end of the glass tube is kept in an ultrasonic bath. Afterwards the solder capillaries should be cleaned with acetone. Another simple choice is a thin-walled Cu-Ni tube coated with a superconducting solder. Figure 13.6 shows how one can easily make shielded pin connections for such a superconductor shielded coaxial lead.

Often coaxial cables and simple leads (as well as capillaries for helium experiments) have to be vacuum enclosed so that they are guarded against the effects of bath level changes. Then thermal anchoring at 4.2 K and, if they go to lower temperatures, at further points with successively lower temperatures is essential [13.21, 22]. This can be achieved by winding a considerable length of them tightly around a Cu post, where they should be fixed by an adhesive. Another possibility is to clamp leads between Cu plates using grease for improved thermal contact.

If leads run through the ^{4}He bath then they are well thermally anchored but mostly they have to be brought into an evacuated can by an electrically isolating, vacuum tight, cold epoxy feedthrough. Appropriate

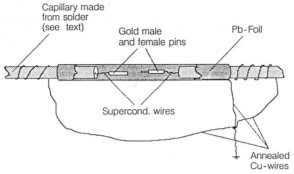

Fig.13.6. Design of detachable connectors for cryogenic coaxial leads

designs are described in [13.3,21-25] and shown in Fig.3.15. The performance of such a feedthrough can be improved by using a filler, for example Al_2O_3 or metal powder, in the epoxy so that its thermal expansion
coefficient is better matched to that of metals. Leads for superconducting
magnets will be discussed in the following section.

13.4 Small Superconducting Magnets and Magnet Leads

Because the cost of the wire is a large fraction of the price of a superconducting magnet and because considerable experience is needed to design
and wind a powerful superconducting magnet, such magnets are better
bought than home-made. For many purposes, for example NMR experiments or thermometry, specially designed small superconducting solenoids
for moderate fields are necessary; here do-it-yourself is in order. These
magnets are designed using computer programs [13.3,26-32].

Very frequently such solenoids sit in the vacuum space of the cryostat.
And when they are in close proximity to other equipment, their fields have
to be shielded by a superconducting cylinder (Sect.13.5.2) or they must be
isolated from the stray fields of other coils. This is a typical situation in a
nuclear demagnetization cryostat with a main, typically 8 T, solenoid for
refrigeration and small coils and field-free regions for heat switches, NMR
thermometry, and experiments. The superconducting shield reduces the
field-to-current ratio of the solenoid and smoothes the central field but it
complicates calculations. The design and behaviour of a shielded NMR
solenoid operated in vacuum and thermally anchored to the mixing chamber of a dilution refrigerator at 20 mK are described in [13.31]. This coil
with 14 mm inside diameter has 30 layers of 0.1 mm diameter Cu-clad
monofilamentary Nb-Ti wire inside a Nb shield. It can produce an axial
field of 0.45 T at a current of 1.75 A with $5\cdot10^{-4}$ homogeneity over 1 cm.
A small superconducting magnet with a central field of 3 T and an active
and a passive superconducting shield is described in [13.32]; its design is
shown in Fig.13.7.

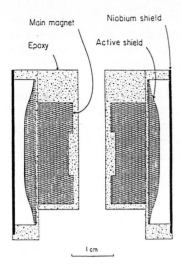

Main magnet Niobium shield

Epoxy Active shield

Fig.13.7. Superconducting solenoid for operation in vacuum. Besides the main solenoid the design contains an active shield produced by a second solenoid as well as a passive superconducting shield of Nb [13.32]

1 cm

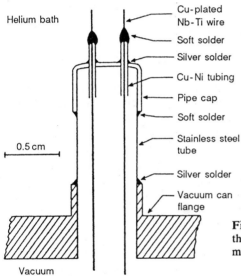

Helium bath

Cu-plated
Nb-Ti wire

Soft solder

Silver solder

Cu-Ni tubing

Pipe cap

Soft solder

0.5 cm

Stainless steel
tube

Silver solder

Vacuum can
flange

Fig.13.8. Leak-tight vacuum feed-throughs for leads to a superconducting magnet; for details see text [13.33]

Vacuum
enclosure

The leads to a superconducting magnet sitting inside the vacuum can of the cryostat have to be fed from the ^{4}He bath into this can. A reliable, easy to make, all-metal feedthrough for this purpose is discussed in [13.33] (Fig.13.8). Such a feedthrough can be used when normal-conducting connections between the leads and to the cryostat can be tolerated. The Cu or Cu-Ni cladding on commercial superconducting wires allows easy, vacuum-tight soldering to the tube through which the lead is fed into the vacuum space. In addition, this shunt provides a desired low resistance path on the power supply output for filtering of abrupt field or current changes, so that in the case of a quench of the magnet the current does not have to go through the resistive cladding of the magnet wire. The L/R time constant in the loop may even have to be further adjusted by a parallel shunt across the leads. The use of a superconducting shunt as a persistent switch for a superconducting solenoid is discussed in Sect. 10.2.

Current leads to a large cryogenic magnet may give rise to a high helium consumption, even when the electric current is reduced to zero, because they usually have to be good conductors. They have then to be designed to compromise between low thermal conductivity losses and low Joule heating; often brass is the appropriate compromise for this purpose. The zero-current helium consumption may be greatly reduced by using disconnectable leads which can be removed when the current to the magnet is zero or, especially, when the magnet is operated in the persistent mode with a superconducting shunt in the helium bath (Fig. 10.6) [13.34]. For such leads, design criteria are gold-plated contacts with a low resistance [13.35]. Current leads for cryogenic magnets which are cooled by the vapour of the evaporating cryogenic liquid and designed for currents up to about 100 A were described in [13.3, 36-40].

13.5 Shielding Against Magnetic Fields and Magnetic Fields Inside of Shields

As already mentioned in the preceding section, many low temperature experiments require careful shielding against stray magnetic fields of nearby magnets or even against the earth's magnetic field. This is particularly important if highly homogeneous fields for NMR are needed or if experiments on superconductors with very low transition temperatures (and therefore very low critical magnetic fields) or with DC SQUIDs are to be performed [13.41-43]. The earth's magnetic field can be cancelled to the 1 μT range by three mutually perpendicular pairs of Helmholtz coils. A further step would be a μ-metal shield at room temperature around the cryostat. However, such a shield is bulky and expensive. Therefore cryogenic shields, either normal conducting soft magnets or superconductors, have to be considered.

13.5.1 Normal-Conducting Shields

A soft magnetic material keeping its shielding properties due to a high permeability (up to about 10^5) after cooldown is Cryoperm 10 (Vakuumschmelze, D-6450 Hanau). This material can be bought as sheet and then rolled to tubes of appropriate diameter after annealing for 2 h at 800° C. Welding should be performed without adding other materials. The following heat treatment of a Cryoperm tube has given successful results: 2÷4 h at 1100° C in vacuum; 1 h cooling to 500° C and then with He or Ar gas to room temperature; annealing under vacuum for 0.5 h at about 570° C; slow cooling to 470° C and annealing there for 2 h; fast He gas cooling to room temperature. The Cryoperm (as well as other soft magnetic shields) should be degaussed in situ with an amplitude slowly decreasing from a starting value of about 0.1 mT and a frequency of about 1 Hz to about 1 nT in 1 h. Such a procedure allows shielding to about 0.1 μT, and in the best cases with some effort to 10 nT [13.41-43]. To achieve such small remaining fields, all parts in the setup have to be non-magnetic, and sometimes even low concentrations of magnetic impurities (in brass, for example) have to be considered.

13.5.2 Superconducting Shields

A closed superconducting enclosure is a perfect shield against electromagnetic and, of course, in particular against magnetic fields if the field does not exceed the thermodynamic critical field B_c for a type-I superconductor or the lower critical field B_{c1} for a type-II superconductor. However, a superconducting shield freezes in the field present when it goes through its transition temperature; hence in many cases they have to be surrounded by a μ-metal shield to reduce this field. A superconducting shield can be made from a Nb tube or from Nb sheet; Ti should be used if a lower critical temperature and/or field are required. Another possibility is to coat a Cu, brass or, better, Cu-Ni tube or capillary with a superconducting solder. The latter, a Cu-Ni capillary coated with a Pb-Sn solder ($T_c \simeq 7.2$K) is a suitable shield for the electrical leads (Sects.4.1, 13.3). It should be filled with grease for proper mechanical and thermal anchoring of the leads inside of the shield. Another way to produce a superconducting capillary shield is to leach out the resin core of a commercial flux-core solder, as discussed in Sect.13.3. The shielding factor increases with the length-to-diameter ratio of an open cylindrical shield.

A frequently encountered problem with superconducting shields is that thermal gradients may produce currents and magnetic fields as the shield enters the superconducting state. These fields may be greater than the field which the superconductor was supposed to shield against! Only trial and error can help to eliminate this problem. A well-controlled cool down of the shield with the temperature decreasing from one end of it to the other may solve this problem.

A combination of superconducting and normal conducting shields should be used if the highest performance is required, for example, when very small, constant and homogeneous fields are required [13.41-43]. As mentioned in Sect.13.4, a superconducting shield reduces the field-to-current ratio of a field coil and can homogenize the field profile [13.30,44,45]. However, be careful: A superconducting shield can destroy the homogeneity of the field of a coil designed for free space.

13.5.3 Magnetic Fields Inside of Shields

The central field of an infinitely long solenoid inside of a coaxial cylindrical superconducting shield is given by [13.31]

$$B_i = \frac{B_0}{1 + \dfrac{A_{coil}}{A_{shield} - A_{coil}}} ,$$

where B_0 is the field without the shield and A_{coil} (A_{shield}) is the cross-sectional area of the coil (shield).

The AC field B_i (at angular frequency ω) inside of a conducting cylinder is reduced compared to the external field B due to eddy currents. For an infinitely long cylinder of inner radius r_i with open ends and with conductance σ, the field ratio is [13.46]

$$B_i/B = \frac{2\delta}{i/\pi^2 r_i^2 A}$$

with skin depth $\delta = (2/\mu_0 \sigma \omega)^{1/2}$ and

$$A = J_0(r_0/a) N_2(r_i/a) - J_2(r_i/a) N_0(r_0/a) ,$$

where J_i (N_i) are Bessel (Neumann) functions of order i, r_0 is the outer radius of the cylinder, and $a = \delta(1+i)/2$.

13.6 Sintered Metal Heat Exchangers

As discussed in Sect. 4.3, the limiting factor in the refrigeration of helium by another refrigerant or in the refrigeration of a solid by liquid helium to millikelvin temperatures or even lower is the thermal boundary resistance. To overcome this problem one has to use a heat exchanger with a large surface area, usually a sintered metal powder. In addition to increasing the contact area, metal sinters seem to contain an enhanced density of low frequency vibrational modes which may couple well to helium phonon modes (Sect. 4.3.2) [13.47-51]. A further important result of [13.52] is the observation that the elastic constant of sintered metal powder is only a few percent of the bulk elastic constant. The introduction of sintered metal heat exchangers has been essential in the development of the ^{3}He-^{4}He dilution refrigerator, see [13.53-58]. Therefore the production techniques of such sponges are of great cryotechnical importance and will be discussed in this section.

Sintered metal for heat exchangers operating at very low temperatures is produced by compressing powder or flakes - mostly of Ag or Cu - and then heating it under H_2, a noble gas or in vacuum. Surface diffusion -

even at room temperature - causes the formation of neck connections between the particles in a conducting metal sponge. The important parameters of a sinter heat exchanger are surface area, thermal conductivity and bonding to its container. In producing a metal sinter sponge, a compromise has to be found between a large surface area (low sintering temperature) and a good bond between the particles and the container as well as a high thermal conductivity of the sinter (high sintering temperature). This can only be achieved by a combination of pressing and heating. The bonding of the metal sinter to a bulk metal is usually improved if first a bonding layer of larger grains is sintered to the bulk material at an elevated temperature and then the main sinter is sintered to this "glue".

Systematic studies of the influence of sintering time and temperature, pressure and atmosphere during pretreatment and sintering, on surface area, structure, packing factor, hardness, mechanical contact, elastic constant and electrical conductivity of sinters produced from submicron Ag and Cu powders of typical dimensions of about 0.1 μm and specific starting surface area of $4 \div 7$ m^2/g have been reported in [13.52, 59], see Fig. 13.9. The results

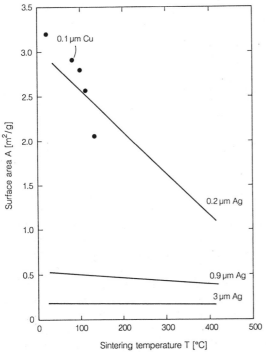

Fig.13.9. Surface area of sinters made from Ag (*solid lines*) and Cu powders (•) with the indicated original grain sizes as a function of the sintering temperature. The Ag powders were sintered for 15 min at the given temperatures after pre-compression to 40% of their bulk densities [13.62]. The Cu powder was first pre-sintered and deoxidized at 120°C for 100 min in 1 bar H$_2$ and then compressed to 47%. The sintering was performed for 30 min in 1 bar H$_2$ at the given temperatures [13.59]

Table 13.1. Sintering conditions and properties of some representative Cu and Ag sinters. (The shorthand "N. part." stand for nominal particle, and own means own work)

Metal	N. part. size [μm]	Particle size [μm]	Compressed to [%]	Treatment	ρ_{300} [μΩ·cm]	RRR	A/m [m²/g]	Refs.
Ag	0.04	--	40÷50	--	(ρ_4=12)	--	1.9	13.60
Ag	0.04	--	40÷50	20 min/200° C	(ρ_4=3.4)	--	1.7	13.60
Ag	0.04/0.07	--	--	45 min/200° C	--	--	2.2/1.8	13.56
Ag	0.04/0.07	--	(75 bar)	12 min/100÷200° C/H$_2$	--	--	0.9	13.61
Ag	0.04/0.07	0.2	27÷47	15 min/100÷400° C	--	2÷5	1.1÷2.8	13.62
Ag	0.07	0.7	35÷54	15 min/200° C/H$_2$	8÷36	2÷3	0.8	13.52
Ag	0.07	0.1÷0.5	45	45 min/160÷265° C/Ar-H$_2$	--	--	1.2÷1.7	13.63
Ag	0.07	0.3	45 (200 bar)	several h/50° C	(ρ_4=12)	--	2.0	13.64
Ag	0.07	--	48	60 min/225° C/H$_2$	(ρ_4=5.8)	2.4	1.9	13.65
Ag	0.08	--	48	50 min/100° C/H$_2$	(ρ_4=17.5)	1.2	4.9	13.65
Ag	0.08	--	48	50 min/125° C/H$_2$	(ρ_4=8.4)	2.1	3.7	13.65
Ag	1	1	45	45 min/160° C/Ar-H$_2$	--	--	0.7	13.63
Ag	3	0.9	28÷52	15 min/100÷400° C	--	6÷12	0.5	13.62
Ag	50	3	36÷55	15 min/100÷400° C	--	8÷20	0.2	13.62
Cu	0.03	0.1	46÷53	30 min/100÷130° C/ 60÷160 bar/H$_2$	10÷20	2÷4	2÷3	13.59
Cu	0.07	0.7	31÷48	15 min/200° C/H$_2$	12÷30	2÷15	0.9	13.56
Cu	--	--	41÷52	2 h/465÷580° C/H$_2$	10÷100	2÷11	0.3÷2.5	13.66
Cu	~20	~20	--	30 min/500° C/H$_2$	--	--	0.15	own
Cu	~50	~50	50	450° C/H$_2$	--	--	0.26	own
Pt	--	--	31	1 h/500° C	--	--	2	13.67
Pt	--	--	37	RT	--	--	16	13.67
Pt	0.01	--	30	120 bar/RT	(ρ_4=560)	--	27	13.68
Pt	0.01	--	30	15 min/320° C	(ρ_4=150)	--	15	13.68

of these references as well as of some further work are given in Table 13.1. Copper powder has the advantage over other noble metal powders that sintering at room temperature is supressed by its oxide layer, so its properties are more stable [13.52,59] than those of Ag powder, which self-sinters at room temperature. But because of its oxide layer, fine Cu powder should be reduced in a H$_2$ atmosphere before sintering. If this is performed at 120° C for 10 min in 1 bar H$_2$, the originally black powder changes its colour and the specific surface area is reduced by 20÷30%. The optimum sintering conditions turned out to be 100÷130° C, 60÷160 bar, in 1 bar H$_2$ atmosphere for 30 min, resulting in a packing fraction of 45÷50%, specific surface areas of at least 2 m²/g, $\rho_{300} \simeq 10$ μΩ·cm, $R_{300}/R_4 \simeq 2÷3$, and good bonding to a Cu foil [13.59]. Similar results were obtained when the powder was first pressed at 1 kbar at room temperature and then sintered at ambient pressure. At the given sintering parameters, the Cu grains lose their spherical structure and build up connections by neck growth.

Further reports on sintering submicrometer- and micrometer-sized Ag powders have been given in [13.60-65], which describe detailed investigations of the influence of temperature on the properties of the sinter (Fig. 13.9 and Table 13.1). From these studies, a sintering temperature of 160÷200° C seems to be favoured for submicron Ag powder. Investigation of sinters made from substantially larger Cu grains have been reported in [13.66]; such coarse sinters are appropriate for use at T > 50 mK. Here higher sintering temperatures are possible, giving a mechanically stronger sinter, and the results, also given in Table 13.1, do not show a strong dependence on the temperature or on the sintering time. - A substantially larger surface area of 10÷15 m^2/g can be obtained by sintering ultrafine, catalytic Pt powder, the so-called "Pt-black", with a starting surface area of 20÷30 m^2/g [13.67,68] (Table 13.1). A successful procedure to produce a well-bound Pt sinter with about 12 m^2/g and 230 $\mu\Omega\cdot$cm has been described in [13.68] (presintering at 150° C, pressing at 2 bar, sintering to a Cu surface coated with a Pt bonding layer at 100° C; the sintering is performed for 30 min in a He-H_2 atmosphere).

As determined qualitatively in [13.62], metal powders shrink during sintering. They therefore break off from walls in a container. To avoid this problem sinters should be allowed to shrink around solid metal posts or onto metal foils with a rough surface. Because of the poor thermal conductivity of the sinter, these bulk metal parts should not be more than 1÷2 mm apart. Similarly, because of the poor thermal conductivity of liquid helium in the sinter pores, there should be channels in the sinter so that the high thermal conductivity of bulk liquid helium can be used. A typical sintered metal heat exchanger for work with helium at very low temperatures therefore contains channels and posts (or foils) of 1 mm diameter and with 2 mm separation.

The surface areas of the sinter samples are usually determined by the volumetric BET gas adsorption technique using N_2 or noble gases at LN_2 temperature [13.69-72]. In this method of isothermal adsorption one determines the volume V of gas (N_2 at 77K, for example) absorbed on the surface of the substrate at a partial pressure P/P_{svp} and applies the equation

$$\frac{P}{V(P_{svp} - P)} = \frac{1 + (P/P_{svp})(C-1)}{V_0 C} , \qquad (13.8)$$

where V_0 is the volume of the adsorbed gas required to form a monolayer and C is a constant related to the heat of adsorption.

A plot of the left hand side of (13.8) against P/P_{svp} gives the unknowns V_0 and C from the intercept and slope of the curve. If N_2 (Ar) is used as the gas, then a value of 16.2 (16.65) $\mathring{A}^2$ for the area of one N_2 (Ar) molecule seems to be correct.

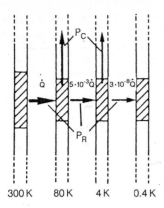

Fig.13.10. Energy flow diagram for light through two ideal windows at 80 K and 4 K indicating the reduction of the radiation power P_R. The absorbed power P_C is conducted along the windows which have to be well heat sunk to their surroundings

300 K   80 K   4 K   0.4 K

13.7 Optical Windows

For optic experiments at low temperatures, light has to be brought into the cryostat with optic fibers or via transparent windows. Usually these windows are transparent not only to visible light but also to heat radiation. To reduce the heat radiated to the cold parts, one has to introduce windows with good thermal contact to the radiation shields at successively lower temperatures. An ideal cryogenic window for the visible should be transparent in the visible range but totally absorbant for infrared heat radiation. The heat load due to an ideal window can then be reduced to negligible values because the radiated power decreases with T^4 (Fig.13.10). Real windows have a finite transmissivity for at least part of the spectrum. Sapphire windows, which are very often used are transparent for a large fraction of the Planck spectrum at 300 and 80 K, whereas "Crownglass" and "Suprasil" quartz windows reduce the transmitted spectrum substantially (Fig.13.11). A black body at 293 K radiates 42 mW/cm^2 into a half sphere. This will be reduced by Crownglass to 0.6 mW/cm^2 at wavelengths $\lambda < 2.7$ μm and to 0.2 mW/cm^2 at $\lambda > 100$ μm. In general, amorphous materials often show a very useful broad and temperature-independent absorption band at $4 \div 150$ μm. Some companies offer special heat (infrared) absorbing "filters" with rather narrow transmitting wavelength ranges in the visible.

Two further aspects of optic experiments have to be borne in mind. The bubbling of a cryogenic fluid may cause problems if the light has to be transmitted through it. This can be avoided by pumping on the bath. Furthermore, one has to make sure that after cooldown the sample has not moved from its required place due to differential thermal contraction of various parts of the apparatus.

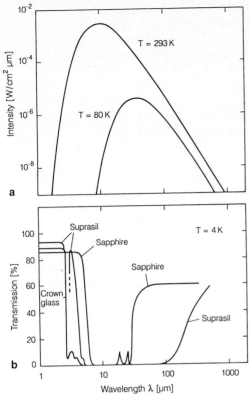

Fig.13.11. (a) Spectral intensity distribution of blackbody radiation at room temperature and at 80 K. (b) Transmission through three different window materials: Crownglass (BK7), sapphire (Al_2O_3) and Suprasil (SiO_2). Crownglass should behave similar to Suprasil for $\lambda > 100$ μm [13.73,74]

Appendix

Magnetic Susceptibilities of Some Selected Materials

This appendix gives data for the magnetic susceptibility of various materials, in particular of weakly magnetic materials often used in the construction of cryogenic apparatus where sensitive magnetic measurements are to be performed. In Table A.1 the parameters B and C of the equation

$$\chi/\rho = B + C/T \qquad\qquad\qquad\qquad (A.1)$$

for the susceptibility χ per mass density ρ are given. One should keep in mind that a rather large variation of χ can be found for some of the listed materials, particularly weakly magnetic, multicomponent materials. The given data are from [A1], measurements from 2 to 10 K; [A2], measurements from 1.6 to 4.2 K; and [A3], measurements from 1.4 to 4.2 K.

Table A.1. Susceptibility of some selected materials

Material	C $[10^{-6}\,cm^3 \cdot K/g]$	B $[10^{-6}\,cm^3/g]$	Refs.
Fused quartz, Suprasil	0.05 ± 0.02	-0.383 ± 0.004	A.1
Macor	24.5 ± 0.06	2.87 ± 0.18	A.1
Stycast 2850 GT	17 ± 1	2.97 ± 0.15	A.1
	26 ± 7	15 ± 4	A.2
Stycast 1266	-0.63 ± 0.03	0.18 ± 0.01	A.1
Epibond 1210 A/9615-10	80 ± 4	7.0 ± 0.4	A.1
GE varnish 7031, cured	2.2 ± 01	-0.54 ± 0.03	A.1
mixed 1:1 with toluene	-7 ± 3	2 ± 1.5	A.2
Apiezon N grease	-2 ± 3	0.1 ± 1.2	A.2
Mylar tape	0.34 ± 0.02	-0.43 ± 0.02	A.1
Teflon tape	0.063 ± 0.003	-0.33 ± 0.02	A.1
	0.05 ± 0.01	-0.33 ± 0.01	A.3
Nylon	-0.06 ± 0.02	-0.63 ± 0.01	A.3
	0.3 ± 3.0	-0.6 ± 1.5	A.2
Manganin wire (low Ni)	(318)	92 ± 5	A.1
Manganin wire, enamel insulated	-13 ± 3	120 ± 1	A.2
$Cu_{0.7}Ni_{0.3}$ (Inconel)	$(-2.3 \pm 0.2) \cdot 10^5$	$(2.6 \pm 0.2) \cdot 10^5$	A.2
Stainless steels	-120 to ± 10	100 to 300	A.2
$Pt_{92}W_8$, alloy 479	0.43 ± 0.02	0.24 ± 0.01	A.1

List of Symbols

In some cases – when there is no danger of confusion – the same symbol is used for different purposes; they are separated by a slash in the following list. In the text the symbols are usually explained when they appear for the first time.

A	Area
a	Interatomic distance
B	Magnetic field
b	Internal magnetic field
C	Heat capacity/capacitance
d	Distance/diameter/thickness
$E; \epsilon(\Delta E); E_F$	Energy; Energy gap; Fermi energy
e	Elementary charge $(4.803 \cdot 10^{-10} \, g^{1/2} \, cm^{3/2}/s; \quad 1.602 \cdot 10^{-19} \, C)$
F	Force
f	Distribution function
g	Density of states/g-factor/acceleration due to gravity $(9.807 \, m/s^2)$
H	Enthalpy/Hamiltonian
h	Height
$h; \hbar = h/2\pi$	Planck constant $(6.626 \cdot 10^{-27} \, erg \cdot s; \; 1.055 \cdot 10^{-27} \, erg \cdot s)$
I	Nuclear spin
J	Rotational quantum number/total angular momentum quantum number
k	Rate constant
k_B	Boltzmann constant $(1.381 \cdot 10^{-16} \, erg/K; \; 1.381 \cdot 10^{-23} \, J/K)$
L	Latent heat of vaporization/orbital angular momentum quantum number/ length/induction
L_0	Lorenz number $(2.45 \cdot 10^{-8} \, W \cdot \Omega/K^2)$
l	Length
M	Magnetization
m	Mass/magnetic quantum number
m^*	Effective mass
m_e	Electron mass $(9.110 \cdot 10^{-28} \, g)$
N_0	Avogadro number $(6.022 \cdot 10^{23} \, atoms/mol)$
n	Number of moles or particles/Occupation number
P	Pressure/polarization
P_m	Melting pressure
$\underline{P}_{vp}$	Vapour pressure
$\underline{P}$	Density of tunneling states in glasses
Q	Quantity of Heat/nuclear electric quadrupole moment
R	Radius/distance/gas constant $(8.134 \, J/mol \cdot K)$
R_K	Thermal boundary (Kapitza) resistance
RRR	Residual resistivity ratio
r	Radius/distance
S	Entropy/spin quantum number
$T; T_F$	Temperature/Fermi temperature

t	Time
U	Internal energy
V	Potential/volume
V_m	Molar volume
V_{zz}	Electric field gradient ($\delta^2 V/\delta z^2$)
v_s	Velocity (of sound)
v_F	Fermi velocity
x	Concentration
Z	Charge/partition function/impedance
α	Polarizibility/van der Waals constant/thermal expansion coefficient
β	Coefficient of lattice specific heat
γ	Sommerfeld constant of electronic specific heat
δ	Skin depth
ϵ	Dielectric constant
η	Viscosity
θ	Moment of Inertia/Angle/Weiss constant
θ_D	Debye temperature
κ	Thermal conductivity/Korringa constant
λ	Mean free path/Curie constant
ν	Frequency
μ	Magnetic moment/chemical potential
μ_B	Bohr magneton ($9.274 \cdot 10^{-21}$ erg/Gauss; $9.274 \cdot 10^{-24}$ J/T)
μ_n	Nuclear magneton ($5.051 \cdot 10^{-24}$ erg/Gauss; $5.051 \cdot 10^{-27}$ J/T)
μ_0	Permeability of vacuum ($4\pi \cdot 10^{-7}$ V·s/A·m)
π	Osmotic pressure
ρ	Electrical resistivity/density
σ	Electrical conductivity
τ	Relaxation time
$\tau_{1/2}$	Half-life time
τ_1	Spin–lattice relaxation time
τ_2	Spin–spin relaxation time
τ_2^*	Effective spin decay time
χ	Susceptibility
ω	Frequency$\times 2\pi$
ω_D	Debye frequency$\times 2\pi$

Conversion Factors

$1\ T\quad = 1\ \text{V·s/m}^2 = 10^4\ \text{G}$
$1\ G\quad = 1\ \text{g}^{1/2}/\text{s·cm}^{1/2}$
$1\ \Omega\text{·cm} = 10^{-11}/9\ \text{s}$
$1\ meV\ = k_B \times 11.60\ K$
$1\ eV\quad = 1.602 \cdot 10^{-12}\ \text{erg}$
$1\ W\quad = 1\ \text{J/s} = 10^7\ \text{erg/s}$
$1\ Pa\quad = 1\ \text{N/m}^2 = 10\ \mu\text{bar} = 10\ \text{dyne/cm}^2 = 7.501\ \text{mtorr}$

References

Chapter 1

1.1 C. Kittel: *Introduction to Solid State Physics*, 6th edn. (Wiley, New York 1986)
1.2 N.W. Ashcroft, N.D. Mermin: *Solid State Physics* (Saunders, Philadelphia, PA 1976)
1.3 J.M. Ziman: *Electrons and Phonons* (Clarendon, Oxford 1972)
1.4 H. Ibach, H. Lüth: *Solid-State Physics, an Introduction to Theory and Experiment* (Springer, Berlin, Heidelberg 1991)
1.5 P.V.E. McClintock, D.J. Meredith, J.K. Wigmore: *Matter at Low Temperatures* (Blackie, London 1984)
1.6 G.K. White: *Experimental Techniques in Low Temperature Physics*, 3rd edn. (Clarendon, Oxford 1979)
1.7 A.C. Rose-Innes: *Low Temperature Laboratory Techniques* (English Univ. Press, London 1973)
1.8 O.V. Lounasmaa: *Experimental Principles and Methods Below 1 K* (Academic, London 1974)
1.9 D.S. Betts: *Refrigeration and Thermometry Below One Kelvin* (Sussex Univ. Press, Brighton 1976)
1.10 D.S. Betts: *An Introduction to Millikelvin Technology* (Cambridge Univ. Press, Cambridge 1989)
1.11 R.C. Richardson, E.N. Smith: *Experimental Techniques in Condensed Matter Physics at Low Temperatures* (Addison-Wesley, Redwood City, CA 1988)
1.12 D.R. Tilley, J. Tilley: *Superfluidity and Superconductivity*, 3rd edn. (Hilger, Bristol 1990)
1.13 R.P. Giffard, R.A. Webb, J.C. Wheatley: J. Low Temp. Phys. **6**, 533 (1972)
1.14 A. Barone, G. Paterno: *Physics and Applications of the Josephson Effect* (Wiley, New York 1982)
1.15 H. Koch, H. Lübbig: *SQUID'91*, Springer Proc. Phys. (Springer, Berlin, Heidelberg 1992)

Chapter 2

2.1 P.V.E. McClintock, D.J. Meredith, J.K. Wigmore: *Matter at Low Temperatures* (Blackie, London 1984)
2.2 G.K. White: *Experimental Techniques in Low Temperature Physics*, 3rd edn. (Clarendon, Oxford 1979)
2.3 R.C. Reid, J.M. Prausnitz, T.K. Sherwood: *The Properties of Gases and Liquids* (McGraw-Hill, New York 1977)
2.4 J. van Krankendonk: *Solid Hydrogen* (Plenum, New York 1983)
2.5 K. Motizuki, T. Nagamiya: J. Phys. Soc. Jpn. **11**, 93 (1956); ibid. **12**, 163 (1957)
2.6 A.J. Berlinsky, W.N. Hardy: Phys. Rev. B **8**, 5013 (1973)
2.7 P. Pedroni, H. Meyer, F. Weinhaus, D. Haase: Solid State Commun. **14**, 279 (1974)
2.8 N.S. Sullivan, D. Zhou, C.M. Edwards: Cryogenics **30**, 734 (1990)

2.9   W.R. Wampler, T. Schober, B. Lengeler: Philos. Mag. **34**, 129 (1976)
2.10 M. Schwark, F. Pobell, W.P. Halperin, Ch. Buchal, J. Hanssen, M. Kubota, R.M. Mueller: J. Low Temp. Phys. **53**, 685 (1983)
2.11 M. Kolac, B.S. Neganov, S. Sahling: J. Low Temp. Phys. **59**, 547 (1985); ibid. **63**, 459 (1986)
2.12 J. Wilks: *The Properties of Liquid and Solid Helium* (Clarendon, Oxford 1967)
2.13 R.J. Donnelly: *Experimental Superfluidity* (Univ. Chicago Press, Chicago 1967)
2.14 W.E. Keller: *Helium-three and Helium-four* (Plenum, New York 1969)
2.15 T. Tsuneto: In *The Structure and Properties of Matter*, ed. by T. Matsubara, Springer Ser. Solid-State Sci., Vol.28 (Springer, Berlin, Heidelberg 1982) Chaps.3,4
2.16 J. Wilks, D.S. Betts: *An Introduction to Liquid Helium*, 2nd edn. (Clarendon, Oxford 1987)
2.17 D.R. Tilley, J. Tilley: *Superfluidity and Superconductivity*, 3rd edn. (Hilger, Bristol 1990)
2.18 I.M. Khalatnikov: *An Introduction to the Theory of Superfluidity* (Benjamin, New York 1965)
2.19 K.H. Bennemann, J. B. Ketterson (eds.): *The Physics of Liquid and Solid Helium*, Vols.1,2 (Wiley, New York 1976, 1978)
2.20 D.S. Greywall: Phys. Rev. B **18**, 2127 (1978); ibid. **21**, 1329 (1979)
2.21 D.S. Greywall: Phys. Rev. B **27**, 2747 (1983); ibid. **33**, 7520 (1986)
2.22 M.J. Buckingham, W.M Fairbank: In *Progress in Low Temperature Physics*, Vol.3, ed. by C.J. Gorter (North-Holland, Amsterdam 1961) p.80
2.23 J.A. Lipa, T.C.P. Chui: Phys. Rev. Lett. **51**, 2291 (1983)
2.24 G. Ahlers: In [Ref.2.19, Vol.1, p.85]
2.25 D.S. Greywall: Phys. Rev. B **23**, 2152 (1981)
2.26 D.F. Brewer: In [Ref.2.19, Vol.2, p.573]
2.27 D.D. Osheroff, R.C. Richardson, D.M. Lee: Phys. Rev. Lett. **28**, 885 (1972)
2.28 D.D. Osheroff, W.J. Gully, R.C. Richardson, D.M. Lee: Phys. Rev. Lett. **29**, 920 (1972)
2.29 A.J. Leggett: Rev. Mod. Phys. **47**, 331 (1975)
2.30 J.C. Wheatley: Rev. Mod. Phys. **47**, 415 (1975)
2.31 J.C. Wheatley: Physica **69**, 218 (1973)
2.32 J.C. Wheatley: In *Progress in Low Temperature Physics*, Vol.7, ed. by D.F. Brewer (North-Holland, Amsterdam 1978) p.1
2.33 W.F. Brinkman, M.C. Cross: In *Progress in Low Temperture Physics*, Vol.7, ed. by D.F. Brewer (North-Holland, Amsterdam 1978) p.105
2.34 P. Wölfle: In *Progress in Low Temperature Physics*, Vol.7, ed. by D.F. Brewer (North-Holland, Amsterdam 1978) p.191
2.35 P.W. Anderson, W.F. Brinkman: In [Ref.2.19, Vol.2, p.177]
2.36 D.M. Lee, R.C. Richardson: In [Ref.2.19, Vol.2, p.287]
2.37 D. Vollhard, P. Wölfle: *The Superfluid Phases of Helium-3* (Taylor and Francis, London 1990)
2.38 W.P. Halperin, L.P. Pitaevskii (eds.): *Helium Three* (North-Holland, Amsterdam 1990)
2.39 L.D. Landau: Sov. Phys. JETP **3**, 920 (1957); **5**, 101 (1957); **8**, 70 (1959)
2.40 A.A. Abrikosov, I.M. Khalatnikov: Rep. Prog. Phys. 22, 329 (1959)
2.41 J.C. Wheatley: In *Progress in Low Temperature Physics*, Vol.6, ed. by C.J. Gorter (North-Holland, Amsterdam 1970) p.77
2.42 G. Baym, C. Pethick: In [Ref.2.19, Vol.2, p.1]
2.43 D.S.Greywall: Phys. Rev. B **29**, 4933 (1984)
2.44 O.V.Lounasmaa: *Experimental Principles and Methods Below 1K* (Academic, London 1974)
2.45 R. König, P. Smeibidl, F. Pobell: To be published (1992)

Chapter 3

3.1   C. Kittel: *Introduction to Solid State Physics*, 6th edn. (Wiley, New York 1986)
3.2   N.W. Ashcroft, N. D. Mermin: *Solid State Physics* (Saunders, Philadelphia, PA 1976)
3.3   J.M. Ziman: *Electrons and Phonons* (Clarendon, Oxford 1972)
3.4   H. Ibach, H. Lüth: *Solid-State Physics, an Introduction to Theory and Experiment* (Springer, Berlin, Heidelberg 1991)
3.5   P.V.E. McClintock, D.J. Meredith, J.K. Wigmore: *Matter at Low Temperatures* (Blackie, London 1984)
3.6   E.S.R. Gopal: *Specific Heats at Low Temperatures* (Plenum, New York 1966)
3.7   P. Brüesch: *Phonons: Theory and Experiments I*, Springer Ser. Solid-State Sci., Vol.34 (Springer, Berlin, Heidelberg 1982)
3.8   J.R. Clement, E.H. Quinnell: Phys. Rev. **92**, 258 (1953)
3.9   M.L. Klein, G.K. Horton, J.L. Feldman: Phys. Rev. **184**, 968 (1969)
3.10 L. Finegold, N.E. Philips: Phys. Rev. **177**, 1383 (1969)
3.11 F.L. Battye, A. Goldmann, L. Kasper, S. Hüfner: Z. Phys. B **27**, 209 (1977)
3.12 D.R. Tilley, J. Tilley: *Superfluidity and Superconductivity*, 3rd edn. (Hilger, Bristol 1990)
3.13 M. Tinkham: *Introduction to Superconductivity* (McGraw-Hill, New York 1975)
3.14 A.C. Rose-Innes, E.H. Rhoderick: *Introduction to Superconductivity* (Pergamon, London 1977)
3.15 W. Buckel: *Supraleitung*, 4. Aufl. (VCH, Weinheim 1990)
3.16 N.E. Philips: Phys. Rev. **114**, 676 (1959)
3.17 N.E. Philips, M.H. Lambert, W.R. Gardner: Rev. Mod. Phys. **36**, 131 (1964)
3.18 M.A. Biondi, A.T. Forrester, M.P. Garfunkel, C.B. Satterthwaite: Rev. Mod. Phys. **30**, 1109 (1958)
3.19 J. Bardeen, L.N. Cooper, J.R. Schrieffer: Phys. Rev. **108**, 1175 (1957)
3.20 W.A. Philips (ed.): *Amorphous Solids*, Topics Curr. Phys., Vol.24 (Springer, Berlin, Heidelberg 1981)
3.21 S. Hunklinger, K. Raychaudhuri: In *Progress Low Temperature Physics*, Vol.9, ed. by D.F. Brewer (North-Holland, Amsterdam 1986) p.265
3.22 R.C. Zeller, R.O. Pohl: Phys. Rev. B **4**, 2029 (1971)
3.23 R.B. Stephens: Phys. Rev. B **8**, 2896 (1973)
3.24 S. Hunklinger, W. Arnold: In *Physical Acoustics* **12**, 155 (Academic, New York 1976)
3.25 J.C. Lasjaunias, A.Ravex, M. Vandorpe, S. Hunklinger: Solid State Commun. **17**, 1045 (1975)
3.26 J.H. Ho, N.E. Philips: Rev. Sci. Instrum. **35**, 1382 (1985)
3.27 D.L. Martin: Rev. Sci. Instrum. **38**, 1738 (1967)
3.28 G. Ahlers: Rev. Sci. Instrum. **37**, 477 (1966)
3.29 N. Waterhouse: Can. J. Phys. **47**, 1485 (1969)
3.30 Y. Hiki, T. Maruyama, Y. Kogure: J. Phys. Soc. Jpn. **34**, 723 (1973)
3.31 J. Bevk: Philos. Mag. **28**, 1379 (1973)
3.32 G.J. Sellers, A.C. Anderson: Rev. Sci. Instrum. **45**, 1256 (1974)
3.33 D.S. Greywall: Phys. Rev. B **18**, 2127 (1978)
3.34 E.J. Cotts, A.C. Anderson: J. Low Temp. Phys. **43**, 437 (1980)
3.35 D.J. Bradley, A.M. Guénault, V. Keith, C.J. Kennedy, J.E. Miller, S.B. Musset, G.R. Pickett, W.P. Pratt,Jr.: J. Low. Temp. Phys. **57**, 359 (1984)
3.36 K. Gloos, P. Smeibidl, C. Kennedy, A. Singsaas, P. Sekovski, R.M. Mueller, F. Pobell: J. Low Temp. Phys. **73**, 101 (1988)
3.37 G.K. White: *Experimental Techniques in Low Temperature Physics*, 3rd edn. (Clarendon, Oxford 1979)

3.38 O.V. Lounasmaa: *Experimental Principles and Methods Below 1 K* (Academic, London 1974)

3.39 R.J. Corruccini, J.J. Gniewek: *Specific Heat and Enthalpies of Technical Solids at Low Temperatures*, NBS Monograph 21 (US Govt. Print. Office, Washington, DC 1960)

3.40 K. Schäfer, E. Lax (eds.): *Kalorische Zustandsgrößen*, Landolt-Börnstein, 2. Band, 4. Teil, 6. Aufl. (Springer, Berlin, Heidelberg 1961)

3.41 Y.S. Touloukian, E.H. Buyco (eds.): *Thermophysical Properties of Matter (Specific Heat)* (Plenum, New York 1970, 1971) Vols.4,5

3.42 D.A. Ackerman, A.C. Anderson: Rev. Sci. Instrum. **53**, 1657 (1982)

3.43 Leybold-Heraeus: Kryotechnisches Arbeitsblatt Nr.5, Leybold AG, D-5000 Köln 1, FR Germany

3.44 R.F. Seligmann, R.E. Sarwinski: Cryogenics **12**, 239 (1972)

3.45 G.W. Swift, R.E. Packard: Cryogenics **19**, 362 (1979)

3.46 D.A. Ackerman, A.C. Anderson, E.J. Cotts, J.N. Dobbs, W.M. MacDonald, F.J. Walker: Phys. Rev. B **29**, 966 (1984); see also "Quarzglas and Quarzgut", Q-A1/112.2 from Heraeus Quarzschmelze, D-6450 Hanau 1, FR Germany

3.47 R.J. Corruccini, J.J. Gniewek: *Thermal Expansion of Technical Solids at Low Temperatures*, NBS Monograph 29 (US Govt. Print. Office, Washington, DC 1961)

3.48 Y.S. Touloukian, P.K. Kirby, R.E. Taylor, P.D. Desai, T.Y.R. Lee (eds.): *The Thermophysical Properties of Matter (Thermal Expansion)* (Plenum, New York 1975, 1977) Vols.12,13

3.49 P.G. Klemens: *Solid State Physics* **7**, 1 (Academic, New York 1958)

3.50 R. Berman: *Thermal Conduction in Solids* (Clarendon, Oxford 1976)

3.51 E.C. Crittenden, Jr.: *Cryogenic Technology*, ed. by R.W. Vance (Wiley, New York 1963) p.60

3.52 Leybold-Heraeus: Kryotechnisches Arbeitsblatt Nr.1, Leybold AG, D-5000 Köln 1, FR Germany

3.53 R.L. Powell, W.A. Blaupied: Thermal Conductivity of Metals and Alloys at Low Temperatures, Nat. Bureau of Standards Circular 556 (US Govt. Print. Office, Washington, DC 1954)

3.54 G.E. Childs, R.L. Ericks, R.L. Powell: *Thermal Conductivity of Solids*, NBS Monograph 131 (US Govt. Printing Office, Washington, DC 1973)

3.55 Y.S. Touloukian, R.W. Powell, C.Y. Ho, P.G. Klemens (eds.): *The Thermophysical Properties of Matter (Thermal Conductivity)* (Plenum, New York 1970, 1971) Vols.1,2

3.56 C.Y. Ho, R.W. Powell, P.E. Liley: Thermal conductivity of the elements. J. Phys. Chem. Ref. Data **1**, 279 (1972)

3.57 M. Locatelli, D. Arnand, M. Routin: Cryogenics **16**, 374 (1976)

3.58 J.J. Freeman, A.C. Anderson: Phys. Rev. B **34**, 5684 (1986)

3.59 D.T. Corzett, A.M. Keller, P. Seligmann: Cryogenics **16**, 505 (1976)

3.60 C. Schmidt: Rev. Sci. Instrum. **50**, 454 (1979)

3.61 H.A. Fairbank, D.M. Lee: Rev. Sci. Instrum. **31**, 660 (1960)

3.62 D.S. Greywall: Phys. Rev. B **29**, 4933 (1984)

3.63 A.C.Anderson, W. Reese, J.C. Wheatley: Rev. Sci. Instrum. **34**, 1386 (1963)

3.64 K. Gloos, C. Mitschka, F. Pobell, P. Smeibidl: Cryogenics **30**, 14 (1990)

3.65 G. Armstrong, A.S. Greenberg, J.R. Sites: Rev. Sci. Instrum. **49**, 345 (1978)

3.66 C.L. Tsai, H. Weinstock, W.C. Overton, Jr.: Cryogenics **18**, 562 (1978)

3.67 T. Scott, M. Giles: Phys. Rev. Lett. **29**, 642 (1972)

3.68 D.A. Zych: Cryogenics **29**, 758 (1989)

3.69 D.O. Edwards, R.E. Sarwinski, P. Seligmann, J.T. Tough: Cryogenics **8**, 392 (1968)

3.70 J. Bardeen, G. Rickayzen, L. Tewordt: Phys. Rev. **113**, 982 (1959)

3.71 T. Matsubara (ed.): *The Structure and Properties of Matter*, Springer Ser. Solid-State Sci., Vol.28 (Springer, Berlin, Heidelberg 1982) Chap.5

3.72 A.C. Anderson, R.E. Peterson, J.E. Robichaux: Phys. Rev. Lett. **20**, 459 (1968)

3.73 E.R. Rumbo: J. Phys. F **6**, 85 (1976)

3.74 G.J. v.d. Berg: In *Progress Low Temperature Physics*, Vol.4, ed. by C.J. Gorter (North-Holland, Amsterdam 1964) p.194

3.75 J. Kondo: *Solid State Physics* **23**, 183 (Academic, New York 1969)

3.76 T. Murao: In *The Structure and Properties of Matter*, ed. by T. Matsubara, Springer Ser. Solid-State Sci., Vol.28 (Springer, Berlin, Heidelberg 1982) Chap.9

3.77 J.P. Franck, F.D. Manchester, D.L. Martin: Proc. R. Soc. London A **263**, 494 (1961)

3.78 F.R. Fickett: J. Phys. F **12**, 1753 (1982)

3.79 J. Peterseim, G. Thummes, H.H. Mende: Z. Metallkd. **70**, 266 (1979)

3.80 S.S. Rosenblum, W.A. Steyert, F.R. Fickett: Cryogenics **17**, 645 (1977)

3.81 Y. Yaeli, S.G. Lipson: J. Low Temp. Phys. **23**, 53 (1976)

3.82 A.C. Ehrlich: J. Mater. Sci. **9**, 1064 (1974)

3.83 Z.S. Basinski, J.S. Dugdale: Phys. Rev. B **32**, 2149 (1985)

3.84 B.N. Aleksandrov: Sov. J. Low Temp. Phys. **10**, 151 (1984)

3.85 H. Wenzl, J.M. Welter: Metallkd. **65**, 205 (1974)

Chapter 4

4.1 G.K. White: *Experimental Techniques in Low Temperature Physics*, 3rd. edn. (Clarendon, Oxford 1979)

4.2 A.C. Rose-Innes: *Low Temperature Laboratory Techniques* (English Univ. Press, London 1973)

4.3 R. McFee: Rev. Sci. Instrum. **30**, 98 (1959)

4.4 J.E.C. Williams: Cryogenics **3**, 324 (1963)

4.5 Yu.L. Buyanov, A.B. Fradkov, I.Yu. Shebalin: Cryogenics **15**, 193 (1975)

4.6 R.C. Richardson, E.N. Smith: *Experimental Techniques in Condensed Matter Physics at Low Temperatures* (Addison-Wesley, Redwood City, CA 1988)

4.7 D.G. Blair, H. Paik, R.C. Taber: Rev. Sci. Instrum. **46**, 1130 (1975)

4.8 S.A.J. Wiegers, P.E. Wolf, L. Puech: Physica B **165** & **166**, 165 (1990) (Proc. 19th Int'l Conf. on Low Temp. Phys.)

4.9 O.V. Lounasmaa: *Experimental Principles and Methods Below 1K* (Academic, London 1974)

4.10 N.E. Philips: Phys. Rev. **114**, 676 (1959)

4.11 R.W. Hill, G.R. Pickett: Ann. Acad. Sci. Fenn. Ser. A6, **210**, 40 (1966)

4.12 J.H. Colwell: Rev. Sci. Instrum. **40**, 1182 (1969)

4.13 J.A. Birch: J. Phys. C **8**, 2043 (1975)

4.14 P.R. Roach, J.B. Ketterson, B.M. Abraham, P.D. Roach, J. Monson: Rev. Sci. Instrum. **46**, 207 (1975)

4.15 R.M. Mueller, C. Buchal, T. Oversluizen, F. Pobell: Rev. Sci. Instrum. **49**, 515 (1978); see also R.M. Mueller, C. Buchal, H.R. Folle, M. Kubota, F. Pobell: Cryogenics **20**, 395 (1980)

4.16 V.P. Peshkov, A.Yu. Parshin: Sov. Phys.-JETP **21**, 258 (1965)

4.17 R.H. March, O.G. Symko: Proc. Grenoble Conf. (Int'l Inst. Refrigeration, Paris 1965) Annexe 2, p.57

4.18 J.M. Cotignola, F. de la Cruz, M.E. de la Cruz, R.P. Platzeck: Rev. Sci. Instrum. **38**, 87 (1967)

4.19 Yu.M. Bunkov: Cryogenics **29**, 938 (1989)

4.20 N.S. Lawson: Cryogenics **22**, 667 (1982)

4.21 K.W. Wittekers, W.A. Bosch, F. Mathu, H.C. Meijer, H. Postma: Cryogenics **29**, 904 (1989)
4.22 E. Schuberth: Rev. Sci. Instrum. **55**, 1486 (1984)
4.23 M. Krusius, D.N. Paulson, J.C. Wheatley: Rev. Sci. Instrum. **49**, 396 (1978)
4.24 K. Gloos, C. Mitschka, F. Pobell, P. Smeibidl: Cryogenics **30**, 14 (1990)
4.25 S.G. O'Hara, A.C. Anderson: Phys. Rev. B **9**, 3730 (1974); ibid. B **10**, 574 (1974)
4.26 A.C. Anderson, C.B. Satterthwaite, S.C. Smith: Phys. Rev. B **3**, 3762 (1971)
4.27 P.G. Klemens: *Solid State Physics* 7, 1 (Academic, New York 1958)
4.28 R. Berman: *Thermal Conduction in Solids* (Clarendon, Oxford 1976)
4.29 T. Okamoto, H. Fukuyama, H. Ishimoto, S. Ogawa: Rev. Sci. Instrum. **61**, 1332 (1990) (this paper provides references to former publications on the problem of thermal contact between two metals)
4.30 J. Landau, R. Rosenbaum: Rev. Sci. Instrum. **43**, 1540 (1972)
4.31 H.C. Meijer, G.J.C. Bots, G.M. Coops: Proc. 6th Int'l Cryogenic Engineering Conf., Grenoble (1976)
4.32 W.H. Warren Jr., W.G. Bader: Rev. Sci. Instrum. **40**, 189 (1968)
4.33 R.G. Gylling: Acta Polytechn. Scand. Physics **81**, 1 (1971)
4.34 H.C. Meijer, C. Beduz, T. Mathu: J. Phys. E 7, 424 (1974)
4.35 D. Dummer, P. Anderson, W. Weyhmann: Cryogenics **31**, 388 (1991)
4.36 I.M. Khalatnikov: *An Introduction to the Theory of Superfluidity* (Benjamin, New York 1965)
4.37 J.P. Harrison: J. Low Temp. Phys. **37**, 467 (1979)
4.38 T. Nakayama: In *Progress in Low Temperature Physics*, Vol.7, ed. by D.F. Brewer (North-Holland, Amsterdam 1989) p.155 and references therein
4.39 A.C. Anderson, J.I. Connolly, J.C. Wheatley: Phys. Rev. A **135**, 910 (1964)
4.40 A.C. Anderson, W.L. Johnson: J. Low Temp. Phys. 7, 1 (1972)
4.41 J.T. Folinsbee, A.C. Anderson: J. Low. Temp. Phys. **17**, 409 (1974)
4.42 J.D. Siegwarth, R. Radebaugh: In *Proc. 13th Int'l Conf. Low Temp. Phys.*, ed. by K.D. Timmerhaus, W.J. O'Sullivan, E.F. Hammel (Plenum, New York 1973) p.398, 401
4.43 W.E. Braun (ed.): *Nonequilibrium Phonon Dynamics* (Plenum, New York 1985)
4.44 A.R. Rutherford, J.P. Harrison, M.J. Stott: J. Low Temp. Phys. **55**, 157 (1984)
4.45 M.C. Maliepard, J.H. Page, J.P. Harrison, R.J. Stubbs: Phys. Rev. B **32**, 6261 (1985)
4.46 C.J. Lambert: J. Low Temp. Phys. **59**, 123 (1985)
4.47 D. Burton, C.J. Lambert: J. Low. Temp. Phys. **64**, 21 (1986)
4.48 K. Andres, W. Sprenger: In *Proc. 14th Int'l Conf. Low Temp. Phys.*, Vol.1, ed. by M. Krusius, M. Vuorio (North-Holland, Amsterdam 1975) p.123
4.49 W.R. Abel, A.C. Anderson, W.C. Black, J.C. Wheatley: Phys. Rev. Lett. **16**, 273 (1966)
4.50 W.C. Black, A.C. Mota, J.C. Wheatley, J.H. Bishop, P.M. Brewster: J. Low Temp. Phys. 4, 391 (1971)
4.51 J.H. Bishop, D.W. Cutter, A.C. Mota, J.C. Wheatley: J. Low Temp. Phys. **10**, 379 (1973)
4.52 M. Jutzler, A.C. Mota: J. Low Temp. Phys. **55**, 439 (1984)
4.53 D. Marek, A.C. Mota, J.C. Weber: J. Low Temp. Phys. **63**, 401 (1986)
4.54 A.J. Leggett, M. Vuorio: J. Low Temp. Phys. 3, 359 (1970)
4.55 D.L. Mills, M.T. Beal-Monod: Phys. Rev. A **10**, 343, 2473 (1974)
4.56 O. Avenel, M.P. Berglund, R.G. Gylling, N.E. Philips, A. Vetleseter, M. Vuorio: Phys. Rev. Lett. **31**, 76 (1973)
4.57 A.I. Ahonen, P.M. Berglund, M.T. Haikala, M. Krusius, O.V. Lounasmaa, M. Paalanen: Cryogenics **16**, 521 (1976)

4.58 A.J. Ahonen, O.V. Lounasmaa, M.C. Veuro: J. Physique **39**, Suppl.8 (C6), 265 (1978)
4.59 O.E. Vilches, J.C. Wheatley: Rev. Sci. Instrum. **37**, 819 (1988)
4.60 H. Franco, J. Bossy, H. Godfrin: Cryogenics **24**, 477 (1984)
4.61 G. Frossati: J. Physique **39** (C6), 1578 (1978); J. Low Temp. Phys. (to be published 1992)
4.62 D.D. Osheroff, L.R. Corruccini: Phys. Lett A **82**, 38 (1981)
4.63 G.H. Oh, M. Nakagawa, H. Akimoto, O. Ishikawa, T. Hata, T. Kodama: Physica B **165 & 166**, 527 (1990) (Proc. 19th Int'l Conf. on Low Temp. Phys.)
4.64 H. Chocholacs: Dissertation, KFA Jülich (1984) (JÜL-Report 1901)
4.65 D.A. Ritchie, J. Saunders, D.F. Brewer: In *Proc. 17th Int'l Conf. Low Temp. Phys.*, Vol.2, ed. by U. Eckern, A. Schmid, W. Weber, H. Wühl (North-Holland, Amsterdam 1984) p.743
4.66 D.D. Osheroff, R.C. Richardson: Phys. Rev. Lett. **54**, 1178 (1985)
4.67 T. Perry, K. de Conde, J.A. Sauls, D.L. Stein: Phys. Rev. Lett. **48**, 1831 (1982)
4.68 G.J. Stecher, Y. Hu, T.J. Gramila, R.C. Richardson: Physica B **165 & 166**, 525 (1990) (Proc. 19th Int'l Conf. on Low Temp. Phys.)

Chapter 5

5.1 G.K. White: *Experimental Techniques in Low Temperature Physics*, 3rd edn. (Clarendon, Oxford 1979)
5.2 A.C. Rose-Innes: *Low Temperature Laboratory Techniques* (English Univ. Press, London 1973)
5.3 P.V.E. McClintock, D.J. Meredith, J.K. Wigmore: *Matter at Low Temperatures* (Blackie, London 1984)
5.4 R.M. Mueller, G.G. Ihas, E.D. Adams: Rev. Sci. Instrum. **53**, 373 (1982)
5.5 L.E. De Long, O.G. Symco, J.C. Wheatley: Rev. Sci. Instrum. **42**, 147 (1971)
5.6 J.v.d. Maas, P.A. Probst, R. Studi, C. Rizzuto: Cryogenics **26**, 471 (1986)
5.7 R.C. Richardson, E.N. Smith: *Experimental Techniques in Condensed Matter Physics at Low Temperatures* (Addison-Wesley, Redwood City, CA 1988)
5.8 E.T. Swartz: Rev. Sci. Instrum. **57**, 2848 (1986)
5.9 B.N. Engel, G.G. Ihas, E.D. Adams, C. Fombarlet: Rev. Sci. Instrum. **55**, 1489 (1984)
5.10 K.P. Jüngst, E. Süss: Cryogenics **24**, 429 (1984)
5.11 Y.S. Kim, J.S. Park, C.M. Edwards, N.S. Sullivan: Cryogenics **27**, 458 (1987)
5.12 I.V. Velichkov, V.M. Drobin: Cryogenics **30**, 538 (1990)

Chapter 6

6.1 G.K. White: *Experimental Techniques in Low Temperature Physics*, 3rd edn. (Clarendon, Oxford 1979)
6.2 A.C. Rose-Innes: *Low Temperature Laboratory Techniques* (English Univ. Press, London 1973)
6.3 O.V. Lounasmaa: *Experimental Principles and Methods Below 1 K* (Academic, London 1974)
6.4 D.S. Betts: *Refrigeration and Thermometry Below One Kelvin* (Sussex Univ. Press, Brighton 1976)
6.5 K.W. Taconis: In *Prog. in Low Temperature Physics*, Vol.3, ed. by C.J. Gorter (North-Holland, Amsterdam 1961) p.153
6.6 B.N. Eselson, B.G. Lazarev, A.D. Svets: Cryogenics **3**, 207 (1963)

6.7 C.F. Mate, R. Harris-Lowe, W.L. Davis, J.G. Daunt: Rev. Sci. Instrum. **36**, 369 (1965)
6.8 D. Walton: Rev. Sci. Instrum. **37**, 734 (1966)
6.9 A.D. Svets: Cryogenics **6**, 333 (1966)
6.10 M. Fruneau, A. Lacaze, L. Weil: Cryogenics **7**, 135 (1967)
6.11 W. Wiedemann, E. Smolic: In Proc. 2nd Int'l Cryogenics Eng. Conf., Brighton 1968, p.559
6.12 D. Walton, T. Timusk, A.J. Sievers: Rev. Sci. Instrum. **42**, 1265 (1971)
6.13 J.P. Torre, G. Chanin: Rev. Sci. Instrum. **56**, 318 (1985)
6.14 R.C. Richardson, E.N. Smith: *Experimental Techniques in Condensed Matter Physics at Low Temperatures* (Addison-Wesley, Redwood City, CA 1988)
6.15 E.T. Swartz: Rev. Sci. Instrum. **58**, 881 (1987)
6.16 C.J. Hoffmann, F.J. Edeskuty, E.F. Hammel: J. Chem. Phys. **24**, 124 (1956)

Chapter 7

7.1 References to the early work on ^{3}He-^{4}He dilution refrigeration can be found in [7.8,9]
7.2 G. Frossati: J. de Phys. **39**(C6), 1578 (1978); J. Low Temp. Phys. (to be published 1992)
7.3 G.A. Vermeulen, G. Frossati: Cryogenics **27**, 139 (1987)
7.4 J.C. Wheatley: Am. J. Phys. **36**, 181 (1968); and in *Progress in Low Temperature Physics*, Vol.6, ed. by C.J. Gorter (North-Holland, Amsterdam 1970) p.77
7.5 J.C. Wheatley, O.E. Vilches, W.R. Abel: Physics **4**, 1 (1968)
7.6 J.C. Wheatley, R.E. Rapp, R.T. Johnson: J. Low Temp. Phys. **4**, 1 (1971)
7.7 R. Radebaugh, J.D. Siegwarth: Cryogenics **11**, 368 (1971)
7.8 O.V. Lounasmaa: *Experimental Principles and Methods Below 1K* (Academic, London 1974)
7.9 D.S. Betts: *Refrigeration and Thermometry Below one Kelvin* (Sussex Univ. Press, Brighton 1976)
7.10 D.S. Betts: *An Introduction to Millikelvin Technology* (Cambridge Univ. Press, Cambridge 1989)
7.11 C. Ebner, D.O. Edwards: Phys. Rep. **2C**, 77 (1971)
7.12 G. Baym, C. Pethick: In *The Physics of Liquid and Solid Helium*, ed. by K.H. Bennemann, J.B. Ketterson (Wiley, New York 1978) Vol.2, p.123
7.13 J. Bardeen, G. Baym, D. Pines: Phys. Rev. **156**, 207 (1967)
7.14 I.M. Khalatnikov: *An Introduction to the Theory of Superfluidity* (Benjamin, New York 1965)
7.15 J. Wilks: *The Properties of Liquid and Solid Helium* (Clarendon, Oxford 1967)
7.16 J. Wilks, D.S. Betts: *An Introduction to Liquid Helium*, 2nd edn. (Clarendon, Oxford 1987)
7.17 W.E. Keller: *Helium-Three and Helium-Four* (Plenum, New York 1969)
7.18 G.E. Watson, J.D. Reppy, R.C. Richardson: Phys. Rev. **188**, 384 (1969)
7.19 L.D. Landau: Sov. Phys.-JETP **3**, 920 (1957); ibid. **5**, 101 (1957); ibid. **8**, 70 (1959)
7.20 A.A. Abrikosov, I.M. Khalatnikov: Rep. Prog. Phys. **22**, 329 (1959)
7.21 D. Pines, P. Nozières: *The Theory of Quantum Liquids* (Benjamin, New York 1966) Vol.1
7.22 A.C. Anderson, W.R. Roach, R.E. Sarwinski, J.C. Wheatley: Phys. Rev. Lett. **16**, 263 (1966)
7.23 E. Polturak, R. Rosenbaum: J. Low. Temp. Phys. **43**, 477 (1981)
7.24 H.C. Chocholacs, R.M. Mueller, J.R. Owers-Bradley, Ch. Buchal, M. Kubota, F. Pobell: Proc. 17th Int'l Conf. Low Temp. Phys., Vol.2, ed. by U. Eckern, A.

Schmid, W. Weber, W. Wühl (North-Holland, Amsterdam 1984) p.1247
7.25 H. Chocholacs: Dissertation, KFA Jülich (1984) (JÜL Report 1901)
7.26 D.S. Greywall: Phys. Rev. B 27, 2747 (1983); ibid. B 33, 7520 (1986)
7.27 J.G.M. Kuerten, C.A.M. Castelijns, A.T.A.M. de Waele, H.M. Gijsman: Cryogenics 25, 419 (1985)
7.28 J. Landau, J.T. Tough, N.R. Brubaker, D.O. Edwards: Phys. Rev. A 2, 2472 (1970)
7.29 A. Ghozlan, E.J.-A. Varoquaux: C. R. Acad. Sci. Paris B 280, 189 (1975)
7.30 S.G. Sydoriak, T.R. Roberts: Phys. Rev. 118, 901 (1960)
7.31 J.v.d. Maas. P.A. Probst, R. Stubi, C. Rizzuto: Cryogenics 26, 471 (1986)
7.32 W.P. Kirk, E.D. Adams: Cryogenics 14, 147 (1974)
7.33 Y. Oda, G. Fujii, H. Nagano: Cryogenics 18, 73 (1978)
7.34 Y. Oda, G. Fujii, T. Ono, H. Nagano: Cryogenics 23, 139 (1983)
7.35 D.I. Bradley, T.W. Bradshaw, A.M. Guénault, V. Keith, B.G. Locke-Scobie, I.E. Miller, G.R. Pickett, W.P. Pratt, Jr.: Cryogenics 22, 296 (1982)
7.36 J.D. Siegwarth, R. Radebaugh: Rev. Sci. Instrum. 42, 1111 (1971); ibid. 43, 197 (1972)
7.37 F. A. Staas, K. Weiss, A.P. Severijns: Cryogenics 14, 253 (1974)
7.38 K. Neumaier: as described in G. Eska: Hyperfine Interact. 22, 221 (1985)
7.39 R. Wagner, G. Frossati: Physica B 165 & 166, 165 (1990) (Proc. 19th Int'l Conf. on Low Temp. Phys.)
7.40 E. Suaudeau, E.D. Adams: Cryogenics 30, 77 (1990)
7.41 A. Sawada, S. Inoue, Y. Masuda: Cryogenics 26, 486 (1986)
7.42 R.C. Richardson, E.N. Smith: *Experimental Techniques in Condensed Matter Physics at Low Temperatures* (Addison-Wesley, Redwood City, CA 1988)
7.43 V.S. Edel'man: Cryogenics 12, 385 (1972)
7.44 N.H. Pennings, R. de Bruyn-Ouboter, K.W. Taconis: Physica B 84, 101 (1976); ibid 84B, 102 (1976)
7.45 V.A. Mikheev, V.A. Maidanov, N.P. Mihkin: Cryogenics 24, 190 (1984)
7.46 K. Uhlig: Cryogenics 27, 454 (1987)

Chapter 8

8.1 Yu.D. Anufriev: Sov. Phys. - JETP Lett. 1, 155 (1965)
8.2 R.T. Johnson, R. Rosenbaum, O.G. Symco, J.C. Wheatley: Phys. Rev. Lett. 22, 449 (1969)
8.3 R.T. Johnson, J.C. Wheatley: J. Low Temp. Phys. 2, 423 (1970)
8.4 D.D. Osheroff, R.C. Richardson, D.M. Lee: Phys. Rev. Lett. 28, 885 (1972)
8.5 D.D. Osheroff, W.J. Gully, R.C. Richardson, D.M. Lee: Phys. Rev. Lett. 29, 920 (1972)
8.6 W.P. Halperin, F.B. Rasmussen, C.N. Archie, R.C. Richardson: J. Low Temp. Phys. 31, 617 (1978)
8.7 E.R. Grilly: J. Low Temp. Phys. 4, 615 (1971); ibid. 11, 243 (1973)
8.8 D.S. Greywall, P.A. Busch: J. Low Temp. Phys. 46, 451 (1982)
8.9 D.S. Greywall: Phys. Rev. B 31, 2675 (1985)
8.10 D.S. Greywall: Phys. Rev. B 27, 2747 (1983); ibid B33, 7520 (1986)
8.11 M. Roger, J. Hetherington, J.M. Delrieu: Rev. Mod. Phys. 55, 1 (1983)
8.12 O.V. Lounasmaa: *Experimental Principles and Methods Below 1K* (Academic, London 1974)
8.13 D.S. Betts: *An Introduction to Millikelvin Technology* (Cambridge Univ. Press, Cambridge 1989)
8.14 J.R. Sites, D.D. Osheroff, R.C. Richardson, D.M. Lee: Phys. Rev. Lett. 23, 836 (1969)

8.15 L.R. Corruccini, D.D. Osheroff, D.M. Lee, R.C. Richardson: J. Low Temp. Phys. **8**, 229 (1972)

8.16 G. Frossati: J. Physique **41** (C7), 95 (1980); Jpn. J. Appl. Phys. **26**, 1833 (1987) (Proc. 18th Int'l Conf. Low Temp. Phys.)

8.17 G.A. Vermeulen, S.A.J. Wiegers, C.C. Kranenburg, R. Jochemsen, G. Frossati: Can. J. Phys. **65**, 1560 (1987); Jpn. J. Appl. Phys. **26**, 215 (1987) (Proc. 18th Int'l Conf. Low Temp. Phys.)

8.18 D.D. Kranenburg, L.P. Roobol, R. Jochemsen, G. Frossati: J. Low Temp. Phys. **77**, 371 (1989)

8.19 E.N. Smith, H.M. Bozler, W.S. Truscott, R. Gianetta, R.C. Richardson, D.M. Lee: Proc. 14th Int'l Conf. Low Temp. Phys., Vol.4, ed. by M. Krusius, M. Vuorio (North-Holland, Amsterdam 1975) p.9

8.20 R.B. Kummer, R.M. Mueller, E.D. Adams: J. Low Temp. Phys. **27**, 319 (1977)

Chapter 9

9.1 O.V. Lounasmaa: *Experimental Principles and Methods Below 1K* (Academic, London 1974)

9.2 D.S. Betts: *Refrigeration and Thermometry Below One Kelvin* (Sussex Univ. Press, Brighton 1976)

9.3 R.P. Hudson: *Principles and Application of Magnetic Cooling* (North-Holland, Amsterdam 1972)

9.4 D.S. Betts: *An Introduction to Millikelvin Technology* (Cambridge Univ. Press, Cambridge 1989)

9.5 B.I. Bleaney, B. Bleaney: *Electricity and Magnetismus*, 3rd ed. (Oxford Univ. Press, Oxford 1976)

9.6 W.F. Giauque, R.A. Fisher, E.W. Hornung, G.E. Brodale: J. Chem. Phys. **58**, 2621 (1973)

 R.A. Fisher, E.W. Hornung, G.E. Brodale, W.F. Giauque: J. Chem. Phys. **58**, 5584 (1973)

9.7 O.E. Vilches, J.C. Wheatley: Rev. Sci. Instrum. **37**, 819 (1966); Phys. Rev. **148**, 509 (1966)

9.8 W.R. Abel, A.C. Anderson, W.C. Black, J.C. Wheatley: Physics **1**, 337 (1965)

9.9 M. Kolac, K. Svec, R.S. Safrata, J. Matas, T. Tethal: J. Low Temp. Phys. **11**, 297 (1973)

9.10 D.N. Paulson, M. Krusius, J.C. Wheatley, R.S. Safrata, M. Kolac, T. Tethal, K. Svec, J. Matas: J. Low Temp. Phys. **34**, 63 (1979); ibid. **36**, 721 (E) (1979)

 R.S. Safrata, M. Kolac, J. Matos, M. Odehnal, K. Svec: J. Low Temp. Phys. **41**, 405 (1980)

9.11 J.M. Parpia, W.P. Kirk, P.S. Kobiela, Z. Olejniczak: J. Low Temp. Phys. **60**, 57 (1985)

9.12 J.H. Bishop, D.W. Cutter, A.C. Mota, J.C. Wheatley: J. Low Temp. Phys. **10**, 379 (1973)

9.13 G.K. White: *Experimental Techniques in Low Temperature Physics*, 3rd edn. (Clarendon, Oxford 1979)

9.14 A.C. Rose-Innes: *Low Temperature Laboratory Techniques* (English Univ. Press, London 1973)

Chapter 10

10.1 M.T. Huiku, T.A. Jyrkkiö, J.M. Kyynäräinen, M.T. Loponen, O.V. Lounasmaa, A.S. Oja: J. Low Temp. Phys. **62**, 433 (1986)

10.2 N. Kurti, F.N. H. Robinson, F.E. Simon, D.A. Spohr: Nature 178, 450 (1956)

10.3 N. Kurti: Cryogenics 1, 2 (1960)

10.4 E.B. Osgood, J.M. Goodkind: Cryogenics 6, 54 (1966); Phys. Rev. Lett. 18, 894 (1967)

10.5 O.G. Symco: J. Low Temp. Phys. 1, 451 (1969)

10.6 R.G. Gylling: Acta Polytech. Scand., Phys. 81, 1 (1971)
P.M. Berglund, G.J. Ehnholm, R.G. Gylling, O.V. Lounasmaa, R.P. Sovik: Cryogenics 12, 297 (1972)
P.M. Berglund, H.K. Collan, G.J. Ehnholm, R.G. Colling, O.V. Lounasmaa: J. Low Temp. Phys. 6, 357 (1972)

10.7 O.V. Lounasmaa: *Experimental Principles and Methods Below 1 K* (Academic, London 1974)

10.8 D.S. Betts: *Refrigeration and Thermometry Below One Kelvin* (Sussex Univ. Press, Brighton 1976)

10.9 K. Andres, O.V. Lounasmaa: In *Progress in Low Temperature Physics*, Vol.8, ed. by D.F. Brewer (North-Holland, Amsterdam 1982) p.221

10.10 G.R. Pickett: Rep. Prog. Phys. 51, 1295 (1988)

10.11 T. Uchiyama, T. Mamiya: Rev. Sci. Instrum. 58, 2192 (1987)

10.12 J.P. Harrison: J. Low Temp. Phys. 37, 467 (1979)

10.13 A.C. Anderson, R.E. Peterson: Phys. Lett. 38 A, 519 (1972)

10.14 A. Abragam, M. Goldman: *Nuclear Magnetism - Order and Disorder* (Clarendon, Oxford 1982)

10.15 A. Abragam: *Principles of Nuclear Magnetism* (Clarendon, Oxford 1983)

10.16 M. Goldman: *Spin Temperature and Nuclear Magnetic Resonance in Solids* (Clarendon, Oxford 1970)

10.17 C.P. Slichter: *Principles of Magnetic Resonance*, 3rd edn., Springer Ser. Solid-State Sci., Vol.1 (Springer, Berlin, Heidelberg 1990)

10.18 F. Bacon, J.A. Barclay, W.D. Brewer, D.A. Shirley, J.E. Templeton: Phys. Rev. B5, 2397 (1972)

10.19 F. Shibata, Y. Hamano: J. Phys. Soc. Jpn. 52, 1410 (1983)

10.20 E. Klein: In *Low Temperature Nuclear Orientation*, ed. by N.J. Stone, H. Postma (North-Holland, Amsterdam 1986) p.579

10.21 G. Eska: J. Low Temp. Phys. 73, 207 (1988); in (4) of this reference x should be replaced by x/I

10.22 G.C. Carter, L.H. Bennett, D.J. Kahon: Metallic shifts in NMR, Pt.I; in *Progr. Mater. Science*, Vol.20 (Pergamon, Oxford 1977)

10.23 D.J. Bradley, A.M. Guénault, V. Keith, C.J. Kennedy, J.E. Miller, S.G. Musset, G.R. Pickett, W.P. Pratt, Jr.: J. Low Temp. Phys. 57, 359 (1984)

10.24 F. Pobell: Physica 109,110 B,C, 1485 (1982) (Proc. 16th Int'l Conf. Low Temp. Phys.); J. Low Temp. Phys. (To be published 1992)

10.25 R.M. Mueller: Hyperfine Interact. 22, 211 (1985)

10.26 R.M. Mueller, C. Buchal, H.R. Folle, M. Kubota, F. Pobell: Cryogenics 20, 395 (1980)

10.27 H. Ishimoto, N. Nishida, T. Furubayashi, M. Shinohara, Y. Takano, Y. Miura, K. Ono: J. Low Temp. Phys. 55, 17 (1984)

10.28 K. Gloos, P. Smeibidl, C. Kennedy, A. Singsaas, P. Sekovski, R.M. Mueller, F. Pobell: J. Low Temp. Phys. 73, 101 (1988)

10.29 G.A. Vermeulen, G. Frossati: Cryogenics 27, 139 (1987)

10.30 Y. Oda, G. Fujii, H. Nagano: Cryogenics 18, 73 (1978)

10.31 Y. Oda, G. Fujii, T. Ono, H. Nagano: Cryogenics 23, 139 (1983)

10.32 R.C. Richardson, E.N. Smith: *Experimental Techniques in Condensed Matter Physics at Low Temperatures* (Addison-Wesley, Redwood, CA 1988)

10.33 W.P. Kirk, M. Twerdochlib: Rev. Sci. Instrum. 49, 765 (1978)

10.34 D.I. Bradley, T.W. Bradshaw, A.M.Guénault, V. Keith, B.G. Locke-Scobie, I.E. Miller, G.R. Pickett, W.P. Pratt, Jr.: Cryogenics 22 296 (1982)
10.35 A.C. Tims, R.L. Davidson, R.W. Timme: Rev. Sci. Instrum. 46, 554 (1975)
10.36 U. Angerer, G. Eska: Cryogenics 24, 515 (1984)
G. Eska, E. Schuberth: Jpn. J. Appl. Phys., Suppl. 26-3, 435 (1987) (Proc. 18th Conf. Low Temp. Phys.)
G. Eska: In Quantum Fluids and Solid-1989, AIP Conf. Proc. No.194, ed. by G.G. Ihas, Y. Tahovo (AIP, New York 1989) p.316
10.37 B. Schröder-Smeibidl, P. Smeibidl, G. Eska, F. Pobell: J. Low Temp. Phys. 85 (1991)
10.38 S.Y. Shen, J. B. Ketterson, W.P. Halperin: J. Low Temp. Phys. 31, 193 (1978)
10.39 R.C.M. Dow, A.M. Guénault, G.R. Pickett: J. Low Temp. Phys. 47, 477 (1982)
10.40 I.A. Gachechiladze, D.V. Pavlov, A.V. Pantsulaya: Cryogenics 26, 242 (1986)
10.41 M. Schwark, F. Pobell, W.P. Halperin, Ch. Buchal, J. Hanssen, M. Kubota, R.M. Mueller: J. Low Temp. Phys. 53, 685 (1983)
10.42 M. Kolac, B.S. Neganov, S. Sahling: J. Low Temp. Phys. 59, 547 (1985); ibid. 63, 459 (1986)
10.43 R. Lässer: Tritium and Helium-3 in Metals, Springer Ser. Mater. Sci., Vol.9 (Springer, Berlin, Heidelberg 1989)
10.44 M. Schwark, M. Kubota, R.M. Mueller, F. Pobell: J. Low Temp. Phys. 58, 171 (1985)
10.45 W.A. Phillips (ed.): Amorphous Solids, Topics Cur. Phys., Vol.24 (Springer, Berlin, Heidelberg 1981)
10.46 J. Zimmermann, G. Weber: Phys. Rev. Lett. 46, 661 (1984)
J. Zimmermann: Cryogenics 24, 27 (1984)
10.47 M. Scherl: Diploma Thesis, University of Bayreuth (1991)
10.48 Y.H. Tang, E.D. Adams, K. Uhlig, D.N. Bittner: J. Low Temp. Phys. 60, 351 (1985)
10.49 K. Andres, B. Millimill: J. de Phys. 39(C6), 796 (1978)
10.50 K. Gloos, R. König, P. Smeibidl, F. Pobell: Europhys. Lett. 12, 661 (1990)
10.51 W. Heeringa, R. Aures, R. Maschuw, F.K. Schmidt: Cryogenics 25, 369 (1985)
10.52 K. Andres, E. Bucher: J. Appl. Phys. 42, 1522 (1971); J. Low Temp. Phys. 9, 267 (1972)
10.53 K. Andres: Cryogenics 18, 473 (1973)
10.54 K. Andres, S. Darak: Physica 86-88B,C, 1071 (1977)
10.55 H.R. Folle, M. Kubota, Ch. Buchal, R.M. Mueller, F. Pobell: Z. Phys. B41, 223 (1981)
M. Kubota, H.R. Folle, Ch. Buchal, R.M. Mueller, F. Pobell: Phys. Rev. Lett. 45, 1812 (1980)
10.56 J. Babcock, J. Kiely, T. Manley, W. Weyhmann: Phys. Rev. Lett. 43, 380 (1979)
10.57 Th. Herrmannsdörfer, R. König, P. Smeibidl, F. Pobell: Univ. Bayreuth (1991)
10.58 M. Reiffers, K. Flachbart, S. Janos, A.B. Beznosov, G. Eska: Phys. Status Solidi B109, 369 (1982)
10.59 H.C. Meijer, G.J.C. Bots, H. Postma: Physica 107B, 607 (1981)
10.60 S.N. Ytterboe, P.D. Saundry, L.J. Friedman, M.D. Daybell, C.M. Bould, H.M. Bozler: Phys. Rev. B 42, 4752 (1990)
10.61 J.P. Carney, A.M. Guénault, G.R. Pickett, G.F. Spencer: Phys. Rev. Lett. 62, 3042 (1989)
10.62 P.J. Hakonen, S. Yin, O.V. Lounasmaa: Phys. Rev. Lett. 64, 2707 (1990)
P.J. Hakonen, S. Yin: J. Low Temp. Phys. 85, (1991)
10.63 D.S. Greywall: Phys. Rev. B31, 2675 (1985)
10.64 S.A. Wiegers, T. Hata, C.C. Kranenburg, P.G. van de Haar, R. Jochemsen, G. Frossati: Cryogenics 30, 770 (1990)
10.65 P.G. van de Haar, G. Frossati: J. Low Temp. Phys. (to be published 1992)

10.66 H. Yano, T. Uchiyama, T. Kato, Y. Minamide, S. Inoue, Y. Miura, T. Mamiya: J. Low Temp. Phys. **78**, 165 (1990)
10.67 G. Frossati: J. Physique **39**(C6), 1578 (1978); J. Low Temp. Phys. (to be published 1992)
10.68 G. Bernstein, S. Labov, D. Landis, N. Madden, J. Millett, E. Silver, P. Richards: Cryogenics **31**, 99 (1991)
10.69 R. König, P. Smeibidl, F. Pobell: J. Low Temp. Phys. (to be published 1992)
10.70 T. Mamiya, H. Yano, H. Kondo, T. Suzuki, T. Kato, Y. Minamide, Y. Miura, S. Inoue: Physica B**165** & **166**, 837 (1990) (Proc. 19th Int'l Conf. Low Temp. Phys.)

Chapter 11

11.1 IPTS-68: Metrologia **12**, 1 (1976)
11.2 EPT-76: Metrologia **15**, 65 (1979)
11.3 M. Durieux, D.N. Astrov, W.R.G. Kemp. C.A. Swenson: Metrologia **15**, 57 (1979)
11.4 H. Preston-Thomas: Metrologia **27**, 3 (1990)
11.5 B.W. Magnum: J. Res. Nat. Inst. Stand. Technol. **95**, 69 (1990)
11.6 B.W. Magnum, G.T. Furukawa: Nat. Inst. Stand. Technol., Technical Note 1265 (1990)
11.7 R.J. Soulen, R.B. Dove: *Standard Reference Materials: SRM 768: Temperature Reference Standard for Use Below 0.5 K.* National Bureau of Standards, US Department of Commerce; Special Publication 260-62 (1979)
11.8 J.H. Colwell, W.E. Fogle, R.J. Soulen, Jr.: *Proc. 17th Int'l Conf. on Low Temp. Phys.*, ed. by E. Eckern, A. Schmid, W. Weber, H. Wühl (North-Holland, Amsterdam 1984) p.395
11.9 R.J. Soulen, Jr., H. Marshak: Cryogenics **20**, 408 (1980)
11.10 D.S. Greywall: Phys. Rev. B**27**, 2747 (1983); ibid. B**33**, 7520 (1986)
11.11 W.E. Fogle: Private communication
11.12 D.S. Greywall, P.A. Busch: J. Low Temp. Phys. **46**, 451 (1982)
11.13 D.S. Greywall: Phys. Rev. B **31**, 2675 (1985)
11.14 W.P. Halperin, F.B. Rasmussen, C.N. Archie, R.C. Richardson: J. Low Temp. Phys. **31**, 617 (1978)
11.15 E.R. Grilly: J. Low Temp. Phys. **4**, 615 (1971); ibid. **11**, 243 (1973)

Chapter 12

12.1 G.K. White: *Experimental Techniques in Low Temperature Physics*, 3rd edn. (Clarendon, Oxford 1979)
12.2 A.C. Rose-Innes: *Low Temperature Laboratory Techniques* (English Universities Press, London 1973)
12.3 O.V. Lounasmaa: *Experimental Principles and Methods Below 1 K* (Academic, London 1974)
12.4 D.S. Betts: *Refrigeration and Thermometry Below One Kelvin* (Sussex Univ. Press, Brighton 1976)
12.5 D.S. Betts: *An Introduction to Millikelvin Technology* (Cambridge Univ. Press, Cambridge 1989)
12.6 R.C. Richardson, E.N. Smith: *Experimental Techniques in Condensed Matter Physics at Low Temperatures* (Addison-Wesley, Redwood City, CA 1988)
12.7 Review articles on thermometry below 0.3 K:
R.P. Hudson, H. Marshak, R.J. Soulen, Jr, D.B. Utton: J. Low Temp. Phys. **20**, 1 (1975);

D.S. Parker, L.R. Corruccini: Cryogenics **15**, 499 (1975);
R.C. Richardson: Physica B **90**, 47 (1977)

12.8   Many thermometric techniques discussed in this chapter are described in various articles in:
H.H. Plumb (ed.): *Temperature: Its Measurement and Control in Science and Industry*, Vol.4, Parts 2,3 (Instrument Society of America, Pittsburgh, PA 1972)

12.9   W. Weyhmann: In *Methods of Experimental Physics*, Vol.11, ed. by R.V. Coleman (Academic, New York 1974) p.485

12.10 F.X. Eder: *Arbeitsmethoden der Thermodynamik*, Band 1: *Temperaturmessung* (Springer, Berlin, Heidelberg 1981)

12.11 T.R. Roberts, S.G. Sydoriak: Phys. Rev. **102**, 304 (1956)

12.12 A. Freddi, I. Modena: Cryogenics **8**, 18 (1968)

12.13 V. Steinberg, G. Ahlers: J. Low Temp. Phys. **53**, 255 (1983)

12.14 D.S. Greywall, P.A. Busch: Rev. Sci. Instrum. **51**, 509 (1980)

12.15 K.H. Mueller, G. Ahlers, F. Pobell: Phys. Rev. B **14**, 2096 (1976)

12.16 D.S. Greywall: Phys. Rev. B **27**, 2747 (1983); ibid. B **33**, 7520 (1986)

12.17 W.P. Halperin, F.B. Rasmussen, C.N. Archie, R.C. Richardson: J. Low Temp. Phys. **31**, 617 (1978)

12.18 D.S. Greywall, P.A. Busch: J. Low Temp. Phys. **46**, 451 (1982)

12.19 D.S. Greywall: Phys. Rev. B **31**, 2675 (1985)

12.20 G.S. Straty, E.D. Adams: Rev. Sci. Instrum. **40**, 1393 (1969)

12.21 R.A. Scribner, E.D. Adams: Rev. Sci. Instrum. **41**, 287 (1970)

12.22 H. Fukuyama, H. Ishimoto, T. Tazaki, S. Ogawa: Phys. Rev. B **36**, 8921 (1987)

12.23 G. Schuster, D. Hechtfischer, W. Buck, A. Hoffmann: Physica B **165** & **166**, 31 (1990) (Proc. 19th Int'l Conf. Low Temp. Phys.)

12.24 W.E. Fogle, J.H. Colwell, R.J. Soulen, Jr.: Physica B **165** & **166**, 33 (1990) (Proc. 19th Int'l Conf. Low Temp. Phys.)

12.25 E.R. Grilly: J. Low Temp. Phys. **4**, 615 (1971); ibid. **11**, 243 (1973)

12.26 G. Frossati: J. Physique **41** (C7), 95 (1980); Jpn. J. Appl. Phys. **26**, 1833 (1987) (Proc. 18th Int'l Conf. Low Temp. Phys.)

12.27 C.C. Kranenburg, S.A.J. Wiegers, P.G. v. d. Haar, R. Jochemsen, G. Frossati: Jpn. J. Appl. Phys. **26**, 215 (1987) (Proc. 18th Int'l Conf. Low Temp. Phys.)

12.28 R. Rosenbaum: Rev. Sci. Instrum. **39**, 890 (1968)

12.29 Y. Maeno, H. Hauck, J.C. Wheatley: Rev. Sci. Instrum. **54**, 946 (1983)

12.30 H. Armbrüster, W. Kirk, D. Chesire: In *Temperature: Its Measurement and Control in Science and Industry*, Vol.5, ed. by J.F. Schooley (American Institute of Physics, New York 1982) p.1025

12.31 P.A. Schroeder, C. Uher: Phys. Rev. B **18**, 3884 (1978)

12.32 D.J. Bradley, A.M. Guénault, V. Keith, G.R. Pickett, W.P. Pratt, Jr.: J. Low Temp. Phys. **45**, 357 (1981)

12.33 R.P. Peters, Ch. Buchal, M. Kubota, R.M. Mueller, F. Pobell: Phys. Rev. Lett. **53**, 1108 (1984)

12.34 L.J. Neuringer, A.J. Perlman, L.G. Rubin, Y. Shapira: Rev. Sci. Instrum. **42**, 9 (1971)

12.35 H.H. Sample, L.G. Rubin: Cryogenics **17**, 597 (1977)

12.36 A.C. Andersson: In *Temperature: Its Measurement and Control in Science and Industry*, Vol.4, ed. by H.H. Plumb (Instrument Society of America, Pittsburgh, PA 1972) p.773; Rev. Sci. Instrum. **44**, 1475 (1973)

12.37 T. Saito, T. Sato: Rev. Sci. Instrum. **46**, 1226 (1975)

12.38 S. Kobayashi, M. Shinohara, K. Ono: Cryogenics **16**, 597 (1976)

12.39 Y. Koike, T. Fukase, S. Morita, M. Okamura, N. Mikoshiba: Cryogenics **25**, 499 (1985)

12.40 W.C. Black, W.R. Roach, J.C. Wheatley: Rev. Sci. Instrum. **35**, 587 (1964)

12.41 Y. Oda, G. Fujii, H. Nagano: Cryogenics **14**, 84 (1974)

12.42 J.S. Lasjaunias, B. Picot, A. Ravex, D. Thoulouze. M. Vandorpe: Cryogenics **17**, 111 (1977)

12.43 R.B. Stephens: Phys. Rev. B **8**, 2896 (1973)

12.44 B. Andraka, G.R. Stewart: Rev. Sci. Instrum. **62**, 837 (1971)

12.45 S. Alterovitz, M. Gershenson: Cryogenics **14**, 618 (1974)

12.46 M. Steinback, P.J. Anthony, A.C. Andersson: Rev. Sci. Instrum. **49**, 671 (1978)

12.47 R.M. Mueller, C. Buchal, H.R. Folle, M. Kubota, F. Pobell: Cryogenics **20**, 392 (1980)

12.48 K. Neumaier, G. Eska: Cryogenics **23**, 84 (1983)

12.49 E. Polturak, M. Rappaport, R. Rosenbaum: Cryogenics **18**, 27 (1978)

12.50 J.E. Robichaux, Jr., A.C. Anderson: Rev. Sci. Instrum. **40**, 1512 (1969)

12.51 M.J. Naughton, S. Dickinson, R.C. Samaratunga, J.S. Brooks, K.P. Martin: Rev. Sci. Instrum. **54**, 1529 (1983)

12.52 H.H. Sample, B.L. Brandt, L.G. Rubin: Rev. Sci. Instrum. **53**, 1129 (1982); *Adv. Cryogenic Eng.* **31**, 1221 (Plenum, New York 1986)

12.53 W.A Bosch, F. Mathu, H.C. Meijer, R.W. Willekers: Cryogenics **26**, 3 (1986)

12.54 Q. Li, C.H. Watson, R.G. Goodrich, D.G. Haase, H. Lukefaler: Cryogenics **26**, 467 (1986)

12.55 M.W. Meisel, G.R. Stewart, E.D. Adams: Cryogenics **29**, 1168 (1989)

12.56 R.W. Willekers, F. Mathu, H.C. Meijer, H. Postma: Cryogenics **30**, 351 (1990)

12.57 C. Kittel: *Elementary Statistical Physics* (Wiley, New York 1961) Chaps.29,30

12.58 F. Reif: *Fundamentals of Statistical and Thermal Physics* (McGraw-Hill, New York 1965) Chaps.15-17

12.59 R.P. Giffard, R.A. Webb, J.C. Wheatley: J. Low Temp. Phys. **6**, 533 (1972)

12.60 R.A. Webb, R.P. Giffard, J.C. Wheatley: J. Low Temp. Phys. **13**, 383 (1973)

12.61 W.A. Phillips (ed.): *Amorphous Solids*, Topics Curr. Phys., Vol.24 (Springer, Berlin, Heidelberg, 1981)

12.62 M.V. Schickfus, S. Hunklinger, L. Piché: Phys. Rev. Lett. **35**, 867 (1975)

12.63 P.J. Reijntjis, W. van Rijswijk, G.A. Vermeulen, G. Frossati: Rev. Sci. Instrum. **57**, 1413 (1986)

12.64 S.A.J. Wiegers, R. Jochemsen, C.C. Kranenburg, G. Frossati: Rev. Sci. Instrum. **58**, 2274 (1987)

12.65 M.C. Foote, A.C. Anderson: Rev. Sci. Instrum. **58**, 130 (1987)

12.66 P. Esquinazi, R. König, F. Pobell: To be published (1992)

12.67 D. Bakalyar, R. Swinehart, W. Weyhmann, W.N. Lawless: Rev. Sci. Instrum. **43**, 1221 (1972)

12.68 R.P. Hudson: *Principles and Application of Magnetic Cooling* (North-Holland, Amsterdam 1972)

12.69 M. Kolac, K. Svec, R.S. Safrata, J. Matas, T. Tethal: J. Low Temp. Phys. **11**, 297 (1973)

12.70 D.N. Paulson, M. Krusius, J.C. Wheatley, R.S. Safrata, M. Kolac, T. Tethal, K. Svec, J. Matas: J. Low Temp. Phys. **34**, 63 (1979); ibid. **36**, 721 (E) (1979)

12.71 G. Fujii, Y. Oda, K. Kosuge, H. Nagano: Proc. Int'l Cryogen. Eng. Conf. **6**, 209 (1976)

12.72 J.M. Parpia, W.P. Kirk, P.S. Kobiela, Z. Olejniczak: J. Low Temp. Phys. **60**, 57 (1985)

12.73 J.C. Wheatley: In *Progress in Low Temperature Physics*, Vol.6, ed. by C.J. Gorter (North-Holland, Amsterdam 1970) p.77

12.74 W.R. Abel, A.C. Anderson, J.C. Wheatley: Rev. Sci. Instrum. **35**, 444 (1964)

12.75 D.S. Greywall, P.A. Busch: Rev. Sci. Instrum. **60**, 471 (1989); Physica B **165** & **166**, 23 (1990) (Proc. 19th Int'l Conf. Low Temp. Phys.)

12.76 T.A. Alvesalo, T. Haavasoja, P.C. Main, L.M. Rehn, K.H. Saloheimo: J. Physique Lett. **39**, L459 (1978)

12.77 M. Jutzler, B. Schröder, K. Gloos, F. Pobell: Z. Phys. B **64**, 115 (1986)

12.78   E.C. Hirschkoff, O.G. Symco, J.C. Wheatley: J. Low Temp. Phys. **5**, 155 (1971)

12.79   K. Gloos, P. Smeibidl, C. Kennedy, A. Singsaas, P. Sekowski, R.M. Mueller, F. Pobell: J. Low Temp. Phys. **73**, 101 (1988)

12.80   D.S. Greywall: Phys. Rev. B **18**, 2127 (1978)

12.81   H. Yano, T. Uchiyama, T. Kato, Y. Minamide, S. Inoue, Y. Miura, T. Mamiya: J. Low Temp. Phys. **78**, 165 (1990)

12.82   T.C.P. Chui, J. Lipa: Proc. 17th Int'l Conf. Low Temp. Phys., ed. by U. Eckern, A. Schmid, W. Weber, H. Wühl (North-Holland, Amsterdam 1984) p.931

12.83   D. Marek: Jpn. J. Appl. Phys., Suppl. **26-3**, 1684 (1987) (Proc. 18th Int'l Conf. Low Temp. Phys.)

12.84   A. Abragam, M. Goldman: *Nuclear Magnetism - Order and Disorder* (Clarendon, Oxford 1982)

12.85   A. Abragam: *Principles of Nuclear Magnetism* (Clarendon, Oxford 1983)

12.86   M. Goldman: *Spin Temperature and Nuclear Magnetic Resonance in Solids* (Clarendon, Oxford 1970)

12.87   C.P. Slichter: *Principles of Magnetic Resonance*, 3rd edn. (Springer, Berlin, Heidelberg 1990)

12.88   E. Fukushima, S.B.W. Roeder: *Experimental Pulse NMR* (Addison-Wesley, New York 1981)

12.89   F. Pobell: J. Low Temp. Phys. (to be published 1992)

12.90   K. Gloos, R. König, P. Smeibidl, F. Pobell: Europhys. Lett. **12**, 661 (1990)

12.91   U. Angerer, G. Eska: Cryogenics **24**, 515 (1984)
        G. Eska, E. Schuberth: Jpn. J. Appl. Phys., Suppl. **26-3**, 435 (1987) (Proc. 18th Int'l Conf. Low Temp. Phys.)

12.92   P.M. Andersen, N.S. Sullivan, M. Rall, J.P. Brison: Physica B **169**, 453 (1991) (Proc. 19th Int'l Low Temp. Phys.)

12.93   R.A. Buhrman, W.P. Halperin, S.W. Schwenterly, J. Reppy, R.C. Richardson, W.W. Webb: Proc. 12th Int'l Conf. Low Temp. Phys., ed. by E. Kanda (Acadmic Press Japan, Tokyo 1971) p.831

12.94   E.C. Hirschkoff, O.G. Symco, L.L. Vant-Hull, J.C. Wheatley: J. Low Temp. Phys. **2**, 653 (1970)

12.95   J.H. Bishop, E.C. Hirschkoff, J.C. Wheatley: J. Low Temp. Phys. **5**, 607 (1971)

12.96   K. Andres, J.H. Wernick: Rev. Sci. Instrum. **44**, 1186 (1973)

12.97   D.J. Meredith, G.R. Pickett, O.G. Symko: J. Low Temp. Phys. **13**, 607 (1973)

12.98   H. Ahola, G.J. Ehnholm, S.T. Islander, P. Östman, B. Rantala: Cryogenics **20**, 277 (1980)

12.99   L.J. Friedman, A.K.M. Wennberg, S.N. Ytterboe, H.M. Bozler: Rev. Sci. Instrum. **57**, 410 (1986)

12.100   N. Bloembergen: J. Appl. Phys. **23**, 1383 (1952)

12.101   L.R. Corruccini, D.D. Osheroff, D.M. Lee, R.C. Richardson: J. Low Temp. Phys. **8**, 229 (1972)

12.102   G. Eska: J. Low Temp. Phys. **73**, 207 (1988); in Eq.(4) of this reference x should be replaced by x/I

12.103   R.E. Walstedt, E.L. Hahn, C. Froidevaux, E. Geissler: Proc. R. Soc. London **A284**, 499 (1965)

12.104   D. Bloyet, P. Piejus, E.J.-A. Varoquaux, O. Avenel: Rev. Sci. Instrum. **44**, 383 (1973)

12.105   M.I. Aalto, P.M. Berglund, H.K. Collan, G.J. Ehnholm, R.G. Gylling, M. Krusius, G.R. Pickett: Cryogenics **12**, 184 (1972)

12.106   M.J. Aalto, H.K. Collan, R.G. Gylling, K.O. Nores: Rev. Sci. Instrum. **44**, 1075 (1973)

302

12.107 R.E. Walstedt, M.W. Dowley, E.L. Hahn, C. Froidevaux: Phys. Rev. Lett. **8**, 406 (1962)

12.108 M.T. Huiku, T.A. Jyrkkiö, J.M. Kyynäräinen, M.T. Loponen, O.V. Lounasmaa, A.S. Oja: J. Low Temp. Phys. **62**, 433 (1992)

12.109 O. Avenel, P.M. Berglund, E. Varoquaux: as quoted by D.O. Edwards, J.D. Feder, W.J. Gully, G.G. Ihas, J. Landau, K.A. Muething: In *Physics at Ultralow Temperatures*, Proc. Int'l Symp. Hakone, ed. by T. Sugawara, S. Nakajima, T. Ohtsuka, T. Usui (Phys. Soc. Jpn., Tokyo, 1978) p.280

12.110 R. Ling, E.R. Dobbs, J. Saunders: Phys. Rev. B **33**, 629 (1986)

12.111 P.G. v.d.Haar, G. Frossati: J. Low Temp. Phys. (to be published 1992)

12.112 W.A. Roshen, W.F. Saam: Phys. Rev. B **22**, 5495 (1980)

12.113 H. Ishimoto, N. Nishida, T. Furubayashi, M. Shinohara, Y. Takano, Y. Miura, K. Ono: J. Low Temp. Phys. **55**, 17 (1984)

12.114 F. Bacon, J.A. Barclay, W.D. Brewer, D.A. Shirley, J.E. Templeton: Phys. Rev. B **5**, 2397 (1972)

12.115 F. Shibata, Y. Hamano: J. Phys. Soc. Jpn. **52**, 1410 (1983)

12.116 E. Klein: In [Ref.12.128, p.579]

12.117 O.G. Symco: J. Low Temp. Phys. **1**, 451 (1969)

12.118 A.I. Ahonen, M. Krusius, M.A. Paalanen: J. Low Temp. Phys. **25**, 421 (1976)

12.119 A.I. Ahonen, P.M. Berglund, M.T. Haikala, M. Krusius, O.V. Lounasmaa, M.A. Paalanen: Cryogenics **16**, 521 (1976)

12.120 C. Buchal, J. Hanssen, R.M. Mueller, F. Pobell: Rev. Sci. Instrum. **49**, 1360 (1978)

12.121 D. Candela, D.R. McAllaster: Cryogenics **31**, 94 (1991)

12.122 H. Chocholacs: Dissertation, KFA Jülich (1984) (JÜL-Report 1901)

12.123 S.R. de Groot, H.A. Tolhoek, W.J. Huiskamp: In *Alpha-, Beta-, and Gamma-Ray Spectroscopy*, Vol.2, ed. by K. Siegbahn (North-Holland, Amsterdam 1985) p.1199

12.124 H.J. Rose, D.M. Brink: Rev. Mod. Phys. **39**, 306 (1967)

12.125 H. Marshak: In [Ref.12.128, p.769]

12.126 P.M. Berglund, H.K. Collan, G.J. Ehnholm, R.G. Gylling, O.V. Lounasmaa: J. Low Temp. Phys. **6**, 357 (1972)

12.127 J.R. Sites, H.A. Smith, W.A. Steyert: J. Low Temp. Phys. **4**, 605 (1971)

12.128 N.J. Stone, H. Postma (eds.): *Low Temperature Nuclear Orientation* (North-Holland, Amsterdam 1986)

12.129 R.J. Soulen, Jr., H. Marshak: Cryogenics **20**, 408 (1980)

Chapter 13

13.1 G.S. Straty, E.D. Adams: Rev. Sci. Instrum. **40**, 1393 (1969)

13.2 R.A. Scribner, E.D. Adams: Rev. Sci. Instrum. **41**, 287 (1970)

13.3 R.C. Richardson, E.N. Smith: *Experimental Techniques in Condensed Matter Physics at Low Temperatures* (Addison-Wesley, Redwood City, CA 1988)

13.4 D.S. Greywall, P.A. Busch: J. Low Temp. Phys. **46**, 451 (1982)

13.5 W.P. Halperin, F.B. Rasmussen, C.N. Archie, R.C. Richardson: J. Low Temp. Phys. **31**, 617 (1978)

13.6 A.S. Greenberg, G. Guerrier, M. Bernier, G. Frossati: Cryogenics **22**, 144 (1982)

13.7 V. Steinberg, G. Ahlers: J. Low Temp. Phys. **53**, 255 (1983)

13.8 D.S. Greywall, P.A. Busch: Rev. Sci. Instrum. **51**, 509 (1980)

13.9 R. Gonano, E.D. Adams: Rev. Sci. Instrum. **41**, 716 (1970)

13.10 K.H. Mueller, G. Ahlers, F. Pobell: Phys. Rev. B **14**, 2096 (1976)

13.11 D. Avenel, E. Varoquaux: Phys. Rev. Lett. **55**, 2704 (1985); Physica Scripta B **19**, 445 (1987)

13.12 G.F. Spencer, G.G. Ihas: Physica B,C 109 & 110, 270 (1982) (Proc. 17th Int'l Conf. Low Temp. Phys.)
13.13 G.F. Spencer: Ph.D. Thesis, University of Florida (1988)
13.14 P.D. Saundry, L.J. Friedman, C.M. Gould, H.M. Bozler: Physica B 165 & 166, 615 (1990) (Proc. 19th Int'l Conf. Low Temp. Phys.)
13.15 D.H. Newhall, I. Ogawa, V. Zilberstein: Rev. Sci. Instrum. 50, 964 (1979)
13.16 M.C. Foote, A.C. Anderson: Rev. Sci. Instrum. 58, 130 (1987)
13.17 R.B. Kummer, R.M. Mueller, E.D. Adams: J. Low Temp. Phys. 27, 319 (1977)
13.18 P.R. Roach, J.B. Ketterson, M. Kuchnir: Rev. Sci. Instrum. 43, 898 (1972)
13.19 G.C. Bischoff, L.I. Piskovski: Rev. Sci. Instrum. 48, 934 (1977)
13.20 T. Tsuda, Y. Mori: Rev. Sci. Instrum. 62, 841 (1991)
13.21 G.K. White: *Experimental Techniques in Low Temperature Physics*, 3rd edn. (Clarendon, Oxford 1979)
13.22 A.C. Rose-Innes: *Low Temperature Laboratory Techniques* (English Universities Press, London 1973)
13.23 J.C. Wheatley: Rev. Sci. Instrum. 35, 765 (1964)
13.24 A.C. Anderson: Rev. Sci. Instrum. 39, 605 (1968)
13.25 F. Mathu, H.C. Meijer: Cryogenics 22, 428 (1982)
13.26 D.B. Montgomery: *Solenoid Magnet Design* (Wiley, New York 1969)
13.27 M.N. Wilson: *Superconducting Magnets* (Oxford Univ. Press, Oxford 1983)
13.28 T.J. Smith: J. Appl. Phys. 44, 852 (1973)
13.29 D.G. Schweitzer, M. Garber: Phys. Rev. B 1, 4326 (1970)
13.30 D. Hechtfischer: Cryogenics 27, 503 (1987)
13.31 K.A. Muething, D.O. Edwards, J.D. Feder, W.J. Gully, H.N. Scholz: Rev. Sci. Instrum. 53, 485 (1982)
13.32 U.E. Israelsson, C.M. Gould: Rev. Sci. Instrum. 55, 1143 (1984)
13.33 R.M. Mueller, E.D. Adams: Rev. Sci. Instrum. 45, 1461 (1974)
13.34 T. Uchiyama, T. Mamiya: Rev. Sci. Instrum. 58, 2192 (1987)
13.35 J. Chassy, P. Gianese: Cryogenics 29, 1169 (1989)
13.36 K.R. Efferson: Rev. Sci. Instrum. 38, 1776 (1967)
13.37 J.W. Thomasson, D.M. Ginsberg: Rev. Sci. Instrum. 47, 387 (1976)
13.38 P. Grassmann, T.V. Hoffmann: Cryogenics 14, 349 (1974)
13.39 Yu.L. Buyanov, A.B. Fradkoo, J.Yu. Shebalin: Cryogenics 15, 193 (1975)
13.40 R.F. Berg, G.G. Ihas: Cryogenics 23, 438 (1983)
13.41 Ch. Buchal, R.M. Mueller, F. Pobell, M. Kubota, H.R. Folle: Solid State Commun. 42, 43 (1982)
13.42 R.F. Hoyt, H.N. Scholz, D.O. Edwards: Phys. Lett. A 84, 145 (1981)
13.43 B. Xu, W.O. Hamilton: Rev. Sci. Instrum. 58, 311 (1987)
13.44 K. Grohmann, D. Hechtfischer: Cryogenics 17, 579 (1977)
13.45 D. Hechtfischer: J. Phys. E20, 143 (1987)
13.46 H. Yano, T. Uchiyama, T. Kato, Y. Minamide, S. Inoue, Y. Miura, T. Mamiya: J. Low Temp. Phys. 78, 165 (1990)
13.47 T. Nakayama: In *Progress in Low Temperature Physics* Vol.7, ed. by D.F. Brewer (North-Holland, Amsterdam 1989) p.155, and references therein
13.48 A.R. Rutherford, J.P. Harrison, M.J. Stott: J. Low Temp. Phys. 55, 157 (1984)
13.49 M.C. Maliépard, J.H. Page, J.P. Harrison, R.J. Stubbs: Phys. Rev. B 32, 6261 (1985)
13.50 C.J. Lambert: J. Low Temp. Phys. 59, 123 (1985)
13.51 D. Burton, C.J. Lambert: J. Low Temp. Phys. 64, 21 (1986)
13.52 R.J. Robertson, F. Guillon, J.P. Harrison: Can. J. Phys. 61, 164 (1983)
13.53 J.C. Wheatley, O.E. Vilches, W.R. Abel: Physics 4, 1 (1968)
13.54 J.C. Wheatley, R.E. Rapp, R.T. Johnson: J. Low Temp. Phys. 4, 1 (1971)
13.55 R. Radebaugh, J.D. Siegwarth: Cryogenics 11, 368 (1971)

13.56 G. Frossati: J. de Phys. **39** (C6), 1578 (1978); J. Low Temp. Phys. (to be published 1992)

13.57 G.A. Vermeulen, G. Frossati: Cryogenics 27, 139 (1987)

13.58 Y. Oda, G. Fujii, T. Ono, H. Nagano: Cryogenics 23, 139 (1983)

13.59 K. Rogacki, M. Kubota, E.G. Syskakis, R.M. Mueller, F. Pobell: J. Low Temp. Phys. **59**, 397 (1985)

13.60 H. Ishimoto, H. Fukuyama, N. Nishida, Y. Miura, Y. Takano, T. Fukuda, T. Tazaki, S. Ogawa: J. Low Temp. Phys. 77, 133 (1989)

13.61 V. Keith, M.G. Ward: Cryogenics 24, 249 (1984)

13.62 P.A. Busch, S.P. Cheston, D.S. Greywall: Cryogenics 24, 445 (1984)

13.63 H. Franco, J. Bossy, H. Godfrin: Cryogenics 24, 477 (1984)

13.64 D.D. Osheroff, R.C. Richardson: Phys. Rev. Lett. **54**, 1178 (1985)

13.65 W. Itoh, A. Sawada, A. Shinozaki, Y. Inada: Cryogenics 31, 453 (1991)

13.66 M. Krusius, D.N. Paulson, J.C. Wheatley: Cryogenics **18**, 649 (1978)

13.67 H. Chocholacs: Dissertation, KFA Jülich (1984) (Jül-Report 1901)

13.68 P.R. Roach, Y. Takano, R.O. Hilleke, M.L. Urtis, D. Jin, B.K. Sarma: Cryogenics **26**, 319 (1986)

13.69 S. Brunauer, P.H. Emmett, E. Teller: J. Am. Chem. Soc. **60**, 309 (1938)

13.70 E.A. Flood: *The Solid-Gas Interface* (Dekker, New York 1967)

13.71 D.M. Young, A.D. Crowell: *Physical Adsorption of Gases* (Butterworth, London 1962)

13.72 S.J. Gregg, K.S.W. Sing: *Adsorption, Surface Area, and Porosity*, 2nd edn. (Academic, New York 1982)

13.73 W. Breinl: Dissertation, University of Bayreuth (1989)

13.74 A.S. Baker, A.J. Sievers: Rev. Mod. Phys. **47**, Suppl.2 (1975)

Appendix

A.1   J.M. Lockhart, R.L. Fagaly, L.W. Lombardo, B. Muhlfelder: Physica B **165** & **166**, 147 (1990) (Proc. 19th Int'l Conf. Low Temp. Phys)

A.2   G.L. Salinger, J.C. Wheatley: Rev. Sci. Instrum. 32, 872 (1961)

A.3   R.J. Commandor, C.B.P. Flinn: J. Phys. E 3, 78 (1969)

Subject Index

Absolute zero 199
Accommodation coefficient 84,85
Acoustic mismatch (impedance) 73–80
Adiabatic demagnet. of paramag. salts
  148–157
- cooling power 151; Fig.9.1
- heat of magnetization 150; Fig.9.1
- history 148
- minimum temperature 151,153,157
- paramagetic salts 154,155; Figs.9.1,2
- principle 148–150
- refrigerators 155,156; Fig.9.3
- thermodynamics 150–154
Adiabatic nuclear demagnetization 158–
  197
- cooling power 171
- double stage nuclear refrigerator 190,
  192–195; Figs.10.3,19,23
- experimental procedure 163–165
- heat leaks 174–181; Fig.10.10
- history 160; Fig.10.26
- influence of heat load 171–174;
  Figs.10.7,8
- minimum (final) temperature 158,162,
  185,187,193; Figs.10.10,17,25,26;
  Table 10.2
- nuclear refrigerators 186–195;
  Figs.10.3,14,15,18–21,23,24
- optimum demagnet. field 171–173
- precooling 163–165,186; Fig.10.16
- requirements on refrigerants 181
- temperature regulation 193
- warming-up time 172,173,193;
  Figs.10.8,25
Adsorption capacity (isotherms) of charcoal 104; Fig.6.5
Adsorption cryostats, ^{3}He 100–104;
  Figs.6.2,3
Adsorption isotherms 104,281; Fig.6.5
Adsorption pump for helium 100–103
Ag
- freezing point Table 11.1
- nuclear specific heat Fig.10.4

- properties Table 10.1
- sintered powder 278–281; Fig.13.9;
  Table 13.1
- thermal conductivity 59; Figs.3.17,18,
  21
- thermal expansion coefficient Fig.3.14
Air, liquid 7
Al
- freezing point Table 11.1
- as a nuclear refrigerant 182
- nuclear specific heat Fig.10.4
- properties 182; Table 10.1
- specific heat Figs.3.5,10.4; Table 10.1
- superconducting transition temperature
  Tables 10.1,11.5
- thermal conductivity 68,69;
  Figs.3.16– 18,4.1–3
- thermal expansion coefficient Fig.3.14
Al_2O_3 (sapphire)
- heat release 179
- optical transmissivity 282; Fig.13.11
- thermal conductivity Figs.3.16,18,20;
  Table 3.2
Angular radiation pattern of oriented
  nuclei 261– 264; Figs.12.49
Anisotropy of γ-rays, thermometry 260–
  266; Figs.12.49,50
Araldite, thermal conductivity
  Figs.3.18,20
Atomic potential 30,45; Fig.3.13
Au, properties Table 10.1
$AuIn_2$, properties 183,248,250;
  Fig.12.36; Tables 10.1,11.6
Avogadro number 285

Background temperature in universe 2;
  Table 1.1
Be-Cu, elastic properties 268
Bellows in pumping lines 176; Fig.10.9
BET adsorption technique 281
Blackbody radiation 282,283; Fig.13.11
Bohr magneton 286
Boiling points

- cryoliquids Table 2.1
- ^{3}He and ^{4}He Tables 2.1,3
Boltzmann constant 285
Boltzmann population 152,262
Boundary resistance
- between helium and metal sinters 76, 77; Figs.4.7,9,10
- between helium and solids 73-80; Figs.4.5-10
- between solids 70-72; Fig.4.5
- in dilution refrigerators 125,128,130, 131
- magnetic coupling 77-88; Figs.4.8-10
- magnetic field dependence 80; Fig.4.10
Brass
- thermal conductivity Figs.3.17,18
- thermal expansion coefficient Fig.3.14
Bridge
- capacitance 270,271
- inductance (susceptibility) 245,246; Figs.11.2,12.32-34
- resistance 229-232; Figs.12.20,21
Brillouin function 153; Fig.10.5

Capacitance bridge 270,271
Capacitive strain gauge (manometer; transducer) 267-271; Figs.13.1-3
Carbon resistance thermometers 222-232; Figs.12.7,11-19
- design 228,232; Fig.12.16
- electrical resistance 225; Figs.12.7,11-14
- heat capacity 227; Fig.12.15
- heating effects 227
- magnetoresistance 229; Figs.12.17-19
- thermal time constants 229,232
Carnot cycle 198
Celsius temperature scale 198
Charcoal
- adsorption capacity (isotherms) 103; Fig.6.5
- adsorption cryostats 100-104; Figs.6.2,3
- cold trap 133; Fig.7.22
Clausius-Clapeyron equation 16,139,208
CMN
- adiabatic refrigeration 154,155; Figs.9.1,2
- boundary resistance to ^{3}He 77,78; Fig.4.8
- entropy Figs.9.1,2
- susceptibility thermometry 241-243; Figs.12.27-29
- thermal conductivity Fig.3.18
- thermal time constant 242; Fig.12.28

Coaxial cryogenic leads and connector 273,274; Fig.13.6
Cold trap 133; Fig.7.22
Cold valve 271,272; Fig.13.5
Conductance of pumping tube 100
Conductivity of sintered metals 279-281; Table 13.1
Connector for cryogenic coaxial leads Fig.13.6
Constantan
- electrical resistance 65
- specific heat 41,42; Figs.3.9,12
- thermoelectric power 216; Fig.12.4
Contact resistance between metals 67,70-72; Fig.4.5
Continuous ^{4}He evaporation cryostat see Evaporation cryostats
Continuous heat exchanger 125,126; Fig.7.12
Cooling power
- ^{3}He-^{4}He dilution refrigeration 108, 109,113-116,121; Figs.7.3,19
- ^{4}He evaporation cryostat 17,18
- nuclear refrigerators 171
- paramagnetic electronic refrigeration 151; Fig.9.1
- Pomeranchuk refrigeration 139,143; Fig.8.4
Cosmic rays, heat leak 174
Cost of ^{3}He 97
Critical magnetic fields, superconductors Tables 10.1,11.6
Critical temperature (pressure)
- cryoliquids Table 2.1
- ^{3}He and ^{4}He Tables 2.1,3
- superconductors 72,73,204-207; Fig.11.3; Tables 10.1,11.5,6
Cryogenic coaxial leads and connector 273,274; Fig.13.6
Cryogenic valves 271,272; Figs.13.5
Cryogenic windows 281-283
Cryoliquids, properties Tables 2.1,3
Cryoperm, see Normal-conducting shields
Cryopumping 16,100-103; Fig.6.5
Cryostats
- adsorption 100-104; Figs.6.2,3
- consumption of ^{4}He 82,83
- cool-down period/precooling 82,83
- dipstick 92,103,131; Figs.5.6,6.3,7.20
- evaporation 85-92,98-103
- gas flow 88; Fig.5.3

- glass 85-87; Fig.5.1
- ^{3}He 97-104; Figs.6.1-3
- ^{4}He 85-92; Figs.5.1-4
- heat sources 83-85
- metal 87,88; Fig.5.2
Crystalline structure of metals Table 10.1
Crystallization water in paramagnetic
   salts 157
Cu
- electrical conductivity 60-63;
   Figs.3.22,23; Tables 3.3,4
- freezing point Table 11.1
- heat release 180; Fig.10.11
- internal magnetic field 162,169
- Korringa constant 255; Table 10.1
- nuclear antiferromagnetic ordering
   159,190; Fig.10.1
- nuclear magnetic resonance 251;
   Fig.12.38
- nuclear magnetic spin entropy 159,182;
   Figs.10.1,12,22
- nuclear magnetization 249;
   Figs.10.5,12.35
- nuclear specific heat Fig.10.4
- nuclear Zeeman levels 159; Fig.10.2
- properties 183; Table 10.1
- residual resistivity ratio 61-63; Fig.3.24
- sintered powder 278-281; Fig.13.9;
   Table 13.1
- specific heat 43; Figs.3.4,11,12,10.4
   Table 10.1
- thermal conductivity 58;
   Figs.3.16-18,21; Table 3.2
- thermal expansion coefficient Fig.3.14
Cu-Ni
- susceptibility Table A.1
- thermal conductivity Fig.3.18;
   Table 3.2
- thermal expansion coefficient Fig.3.14
Curie(-Weiss) law (constant)
- electronic 240-242
- nuclear 162,248; Table 10.1
Current leads to supercond. magnets 65,
   66,275,276; Fig.13.8

Dead weight tester 270
Debye model 31-33; Fig.3.1
Debye temperature (frequency) 32,33;
   Fig.3.1; Table 10.1
Decay time in pulsed NMR 257
Demagnetization
- nuclear moments, see Adiabatic nuclear
   demagnetization
- paramagnetic salts, see Adiabatic de-

magnet. of paramag. salts
Demagnetization field (parameter) 240,
   241
Density
- ^{3}He and ^{4}He Table 2.3
- metals Table 10.1
Density of states
- conduction electrons 35
- phonons 32,33; Fig.3.1
Dephasing of nuclear spins (in pulsed
   NMR) 254
Detection of helium 3,11
Deuterium, para-ortho conver-
   sion Fig.2.2
Dewars, see Cryostats
Dielectric constant
- glasses for thermometry 237-239;
   Figs.12.25,26
- ^{3}He and ^{4}He 14
Difference between electr. and nuclear
   temperature 168-174; Figs.10.7,8
Diffusion of ^{4}He through glass 85
Dilution refrigeration 105-137
- alternative designs 136,137
- boundary resistance 125,128,130,131
- cooling power 108,109,113-116,121;
   Figs.7.3,19
- enthalpy balances 113-116,121-124
- examples 131-134; Figs.7.16-18,20
- gas handling system 132,133; Fig.7.21
- general design 118-120; Figs.7.8,9
- heat exchanger 123-131; Figs.7.12-14
- history 105
- impedances 119,130
- minimum temperature 105,121,122,
   130,131
- mixing chamber 119-122
- osmotic pressure 116-118; Figs.7.6,7
- still 122, 123
- viscous heating 130
Dipole-dipole interaction 158
Dipstick cryostats 92,103,131; Figs.5.6,
   6.3,7.20
Double-stage nuclear demagnetization
   refrigerator 190,192-195;
   Figs.10.3.19,23
Dulong-Petit law 31; Fig.3.2
Dynamic nuclear susceptibility 252,253

Eddy current heating 177,178
- in pulsed NMR 257
Effective decay time in pulsed NMR
   257
Effective magnetic field 153

Effective mass
- electrons 36
- ^{3}He 110
Einstein model, specific heat 31; Fig.3.1
Elastic constants
- Be-Cu 268
- Kapton 270
- sintered metals 76,278
Electrical conductivity 57-63
- alloys 65
- carbon as thermometer 225;
  Figs.12.7,11-14
- Cu 60-63; Figs.3.22,23; Tables 3.3,4
- Ge as thermometer Fig.12.7
- Pt as thermometer 202,219,220;
  Figs.12.6,7; Table 12.3
- RhFe as thermometer 219,220;
  Fig.12.7
Electron mass 285
Electron-nucleus coupling 168-171
Electron-phonon coupling 165,166
Electron scattering 49,53,54,57-63;
  Fig.3.22,23
Electronic temperature 160,168-174;
  Figs.10.7,8
Electroplating 66,70
Elementary charge 285
Emissivities of metals 83,84; Table 5.2
Enthalpy, ^{3}He, ^{3}He-^{4}He 114-116,
  121-124
Enthalpy balances
- in ^{3}He-^{4}He dilution refrig.
  113-116,121-124
- ^{4}He gas 82,83
Entropy
- CMN Figs.9.1,2
- Cu nuclei 159,182; Figs.10.1,12,22
- ^{3}He 140-143,208,209; Figs.8.2,11.4
- In, Nb nuclei 182; Fig.10.12
- magnetic 152,153,162;
  Figs.9.1,2,10.1,12,13,22
- paramagnetic salts Figs.9.1,2
- PrNi$_5$ 182,187; Figs.10.12,13,22
Epibond, thermal conductivity
  Figs.3.18,20
EPT-76 temperature scale 199,200,204;
  Table 11.5
Evaporation cryostats 85-92,98-103
Exchange gas 66,67,84-87,180,181
Exchange interaction in solids ^{3}He 141
  142

Feedthrough of leads 273,274; Fig.3.15
- for supercond. magnets 275; Fig.13.8

Fermi-Dirac function 34; Fig.3.3
Fermi energy (temperature)
- ^{3}He and ^{3}He-^{4}He 26,112,115
- metals 33-36; Fig.3.3; Table 10.1
Fermi velocity of electrons 49,58
Film-flow burner in still 123; Fig.7.11
Filter for electrical resistance thermome-
  try 232; Fig.12.21
Final demagnetization temperature
  (field) 162,171,172; Fig.10.7
Fixed point device, superconducting
  204-207; Figs.11.1-3; Table 11.6
Fixed points, temperature 200-209;
  Tables 11.1,5-7
Flow impedance 90,91,98,119,130
Fluxgate magnetometer 250
Formulas (chemical) for paramagnetic
  salts 154
Free-electron model 35,36
Free induction decay (in pulsed NMR)
  254; Fig.12.41
Freezing points, metals Table 11.1

Gas constant 285
Gas-flow ^{4}He cryostat 88; Fig.5.3
Gas handling system for dilution refrig.
  132,133; Fig.7.21
Gas heat switch 66
Gas thermometry 211,212; Fig.12.1
Germanium resistance thermometry 222;
  Figs.12.7-10
Glass, permeability for ^{4}He 85
Glass cryostats 85-87; Fig.5.1
Glasses, see Non-crystalline solids
Gold, see Au
Graphite
- heat release 179
- thermal conductivity
  Figs.3.18,20; Table 3.2
Gyromagnetic ratios of metals Table 10.1

Harmonic approximation (potential) 30
Hartshorn bridge Fig.12.32
Heat capacity, see Specific heat
Heat exchanger in ^{3}He-^{4}He dilution
  refrig. 123-131; Figs.7.12-14
Heat leaks (release)
- due to conduction 64-66,83
- due to cosmic rays 174
- due to eddy currents 177,178,257
- due to gas in vacuum space 84,85
- due to ortho-para conversion of H$_2$
  8-11,179; Fig.2.2
- due to radiation 83,84,281-283;

Fig.13.10
- due to RF radiation 175
- due to structural relaxation 178-180
- due to vibrations 175,176
- from Cu 180; Fig.10.11
- from H_2 in metals 9-11,179; Fig.2.2
- from non-crystalline materials 179;
  Fig.10.11
- from radioactive nuclei 263
- in helium cryostats 83-85
- in nuclear refrigerators 174-181;
  Figs.10.1
- internal time dependent 178-181;
  Figs.10.10,11
Heat of magnetization 150,163,164;
  Fig.9.1
Heat switch
- gaseous 66
- mechanical 67
- superconducting 67-70,161; Figs.4.1-4
Heating from radioactive nuclei 263
Helium
- boundary resistance to solids
  73-80; Figs.4.5-10
- detection 3,11
- isotopes 11,12
- liquefaction 3,6,11
- natural occurrence 11,12
- polarizibility 14
- van der Waals force 14,23,24
Helium gas
- enthalpy 82,83
- thermal conductivity 84,85;
  Figs.2.10,3.17
Helium-3
- adsorption cryostats 100-104; Figs.6.2,3
- boiling point Tables 2.1,3
- cost 97
- critical temperature (pressure)
  Tables 2.1,3
- cryostats 97-104; Figs.6.1-3
- density Table 2.3
- dielectric constant 14
- effective mass 110
- enthalpy 114-116,121-124
- entropy 140-143,208,209; Figs.8.2,11.4
- exchange interaction in solid 141,142
- Fermi energy (temperature) 26,112,115
- Landau theory 26,27
- latent heat of evaporation 15,16;
  Fig.2.5;Table 2.1
- latent heat of freezing 139
- melting pressure (curve) 13,139,214-
  216; Figs.2.3,8.1; Tables 2.1,3,12.2

- molar volume Table 2.3
- molar volume difference 139,208
- phase diagram Figs.2.3,8.1
- Pomeranchuk cooling 138-147;
  Fig.8.4,6
- production 12
- solidification 138
- specific heat 26,27,113;
  Figs.2.8,14,15,3.12,7.5
- superfluid transition 25;
  Tables 2.3,11.7
- thermal conductivity 26,27;
  Figs.2.16,17,3.18
- transition temperatures 25,207;
  Tables 2.3,11.7
- vapour pressure 16-18,201,203;
  Figs.2.6,7;Tables 11.2,3
- viscosity 27; Fig.2.18
- zero-point energy 14
Helium-4
- boiling point Tables 2.1,3
- critical temperature (pressure)
  Tables 2.1,3
- cryostats 85-92; Figs.5.1-4
- density Table 2.3
- dielectric constant 14
- diffusion through glass 85
- enthalpy of gas 82,83
- latent heat of evaporation 15,16;
  Fig.2.5;Table 2.1
- level detectors 94-96; Fig.5.9
- liquefaction 3,6,11
- melting pressure (curve) 13; Fig.2.3;
  Tables 2.1,3
- molar volume Table 2.3
- phase diagram Fig.2.3
- potentials Fig.2.4
- specific heat 18-21; Figs.2.8,9,3.12
- storage vessel 92; Fig.5.7
- superfluid film 23-25,38; Figs.2.12,13
- superfluid transition 19,20; Fig.2.9;
  Table 2.3
- thermal conductivity 21,22;
  Figs.2.10,11,17,3.18
- transfer tube 92; Fig.5.8
- vapour pressure 16-18,201-203;
  Figs.2.6,7; Tables 11.2,4
- viscosity 22
- zero-point energy 14; Fig.2.4
^{3}He/^{4}He
- dilution refrigeration, see Dilution refrigeration
- effective mass of ^{3}He 110
- enthalpy 113-116,121,124

- Fermi temperature (energy) 112,115
- osmotic pressure 116-118; Fig.7.6,7
- phase separation/phase diagram 106, 107,110-112; Figs.7.1,2
- solubility 106,107,110-112; Figs.7.1,2,4
- specific heat 109,110,113-115; Fig.7.5
- thermal conductivity Fig.2.17
- viscosity Fig.2.18
Helium-6 and helium-8 12
High-temperature approximation 162, 163,240
History
- dilution refrigeration 105
- nuclear refrigeration 160; Fig.10.26
- paramagnetic electronic refrigeration 148
- Pomeranchuck refrigeration 138,145
- refrigeration 2; Fig.1.2; Table 1.1
Homogenization of magnetic fields 277
Hydrogen
- heat release 9-11,179; Fig.2.2
- liquefaction 2
- liquid 7-11
- in metals 10,11,179; Fig.2.2
- ortho-para conversion 8-11,179; Fig.2.2
- properties 7-11; Fig.2.1; Tables 2.1,2,11.1,6
- rotational energy states 8,9; Fig.2.1; Table 2.2
- thermal conductivity Fig.3.17
Hyperfine enhanced nuclear refrigeration (refrigerants, paramagnets) 184-186
Hyperfine enhancement factor 184

Impedance
- flow 90,91,98
- in ^{3}He-^{4}He dilution refrigerators 119, 130
- of pumping tube 100
Indium
- as nuclear refrigerant 182; Fig.10.12
- nuclear magnetization Fig.10.5
- properties 182; Table 10.1
Inductance (susceptibility) bridges 245, 246; Figs.11.2,12.32-34
Insulators
- specific heat 31-33,38-40; Figs.3.1,2,7,12
- thermal conductivity 49-53,55;

Figs.3.16-20; Table 3.2
- thermal expansion coefficient 46-48; Fig.3.14
Internal magnetic field 153,162,169,185
- of Cu 162,169
Internal time dependent heat leaks 178-181; Figs.10.10,11
International temperature scales 199-204; Tables 11.1-5
IPTS-68 temperature scale 199,200
Isotherms, adsorption 281; Fig.6.5
Isotopes, helium 11,12
Isotopic abundance of metals Table 10.1
ITS-90 temperature scale 199-203; Tables 11.1-4

Johnson noise 234,235
Joule heating 164

Kapitza resistance, see Boundary resistance
Kapton, elastic constants 270
Kelvin temperature scale 199
Kondo effect (alloys) 60,216,219,255; Figs.3.22,12.4
Korringa law (constant) 168,169,255; Table 10.1
- of Cu 255; Table 10.1
- of metals Table 10.1
- of Pt 255; Figs.12.43,44; Table 10.1

Landau theory for ^{3}He 26,27
Landé factor 152
Latent heat of evaporation
- of cryoliquids Table 2.1
- of ^{3}He and ^{4}He 15,16; Fig.2.5; Table 2.1
- in a ^{4}He cryostat 82
Latent heat of freezing, ^{3}He 139
Lattice specific heat, see Phonon specific heat
Lattice temperature, see Electronic temperature
LCMN
- adiabatic demag. refrig. 155
- susceptibility thermometry 241; Fig.12.27
Leads to supercond. magnets 65,66,275, 276; Fig.13.8
Legendre polynomials (in NO thermometry) 261,262
Level detectors for L^{4}He 94-96; Fig.5.9
Linde rule 59,60; Table 3.3
Liquefaction 6

- of H_2 2
- of ^{4}He 3,6,11
Lorenz number 57,285
Low-pass filter for resistance thermometers 232; Fig.12.21

Magnetic coupling
- between ^{3}He and CMN 77,78; Fig.4.8
- between ^{3}He and metals
  78-80; Figs.4.9,10
Magnetic entropy, see Entropy and Nuclear magnetic entropy
Magnetic field
- critical, of superconductors
  Table 10.1,11.6
- effective (internal) 153,162,169,185
- homogenization 277
- inside of conducting shield 278
Magnetic impurities, passivation 61-63;
  Fig.3.23
Magnetic refrigeration, see Adiabatic
  demag. of paramag. salts and
  Adiabatic nuclear demagnetization
Magnetic scattering of electrons 60-63;
  Figs.3.22,23; Table 3.4
Magnetic specific heat 40-43,153,162;
  Figs.3.8-10,10.4; Table 3.1
Magnetic susceptibility 162,241,248,284;
  Table A.1
- PdFe 244; Fig.12.30,44
Magnetic thermometry
- with nuclear moments, see Nuclear
  magnetic resonance thermometry
- with electronic moments, see Susceptibility thermometry
Magnetization
- heat of 150,163,164; Fig.9.1
- nuclear 162,163,249; Figs.10.5,12.35
- saturation 153
Magnetoresistance Figs.12.10,17-19
Manganin
- electrical resistance 65
- specific heat 41,42; Fig.3.9,12
- susceptibility Table A.1
- thermal conductivity Fig.3.18;
  Table 3.2
Manometer, see Capacitive strain gauge
Mean free path of phonons/electrons
  48-53,58
Mechanical heat switch 67
Melting curve thermometry, ^{3}He 214-
  216,267-271; Figs.13.1,2; Table 12.2
Melting points
- cryoliquids Table 2.1

- solders Table 4.1
Melting pressure
- ^{3}He 13,139,214-216; Figs.2.3,8.1;
  Tables 2.1,3,12.2
- ^{4}He 13; Fig.2.3; Tables 2.1,3
- thermometry 214-216,267-271;
  Figs.13.1,2; Table 12.2
Melting pressure gauge (thermometry)
  267-271; Figs.13.1,2
Metal cryostats 87,88; Fig.5.2
Metal seals 47; Fig.3.15
Metals
- density Table 10.1
- emissivity 83,84; Table 5.2
- freezing points Table 11.1
- isotopic abundance Table 10.1
- Korringa constant Table 10.1
- nuclear Curie constant Table 10.1
- properties Table 10.1
- resistance thermometry 202,219,220;
  Figs.12.6,7; Table 12.3
- sintered, see Sintered metal powder
- specific heat 33-36,43;
  Figs.3.4,9.11,12; Table 10.1
- superconducting transition temperature 72,73,204-207; Fig.11.3;
  Tables 4.1,10.1,11.5,6
- thermal conductivity 53-59;
  Figs.3.16-18,21,4.1-3; Table 3.2
- thermal expansion coefficient 44-48;
  Fig.3.14
Minimum temperatures
- of adiabatic nuclear refrig. 158,162,
  185,187,193; Figs.10.7,10,17,22,
  25,26; Table 10.2
- of adiabatic paramag. refrig. 151,
  153,157
- of dilution refrig. 105,121,122,130,131
Mixing chamber of ^{3}He-^{4}He dilution
  refrig. 119-122
Molar volume
- ^{3}He and ^{4}He Table 2.3
- metals Table 10.1
Molar volume difference, ^{3}He 139,208
Mössbauer effect thermometry 265
Mutual inductance 247
Mutual inductance bridges, see Inductance bridges
μ-metal shields, see Normal conducting
  shields

Natural occurrence of helium 11,12
Nb
- properties Table 10.1

- as nuclear refrig. 182; Fig.10.12
NbTi, thermal conductivity Table 3.2
Nitrogen
- liquid 7
- precooling with 82,83
- thermal conductivity Fig.3.17
Noble gases (except He)
- properties Tables 2.1,11.1
- specific heat Fig.3.2
- thermal conductivity Fig.3.17
Noise, Johnson 234,235
Noise thermometry 234-237;
  Figs.12.23,24
Non-crystalline solids (glasses)
- dielectric constant 237-239;
  Fig.12.20,25
- heat release 179; Fig.10.11
- specific heat 38-40; Figs.3.7,12
- thermal conductivity 52,53;
  Figs.3.16-20; Table 3.2
- thermal expansion coefficient 45-48;
  Fig.3.14
Normal-conducting (μ-metal) shields
  276,277
Nuclear antiferromag. order of Cu 159,
  190; Fig.10.1
Nuclear cooling 169,189,190
Nuclear Curie constant (law) 162,248
- metals Table 10.1
Nuclear decay schemes of [54]Mn, [60]Cu
  262; Fig.12.48
Nuclear demagnetization, see Adiabatic
  nuclear demagnetization
Nuclear demagnetization refrigerators
  186-195; Figs.10.3,14,15,18-21,23,24
- double stage 190,192-195;
  Figs.10.3,19,23
Nuclear electric quadrupole interaction
  43,181,182; Fig.3.11
Nuclear electric quadrupole moments
  Table 10.1
Nuclear magnetic spin entropy 159,
  162,182,184; Figs.10.1,12,13,22
- Cu 159,182; Figs.10.1,12,22
- [3]He 140-143,208,209; Figs.8.2,11.4
- In, Nb 182; Fig.10.12
- PrNi$_5$ 182,184; Figs.10.12,13,22
Nuclear magnetic moments of metals
  Table 10.1
Nuclear magnetic ordering temperatures
  158,185,190
Nuclear magnetic resonance spectrum of
  Cu Fig.12.38
Nuclear magnetic resonance thermome-

ters
- calibration of 259,260; Figs.12.47
- design of 258; Figs.12.45,46
Nuclear magnetic resonance thermometry 250-260; Figs.12.37-47
- CW 252,253; Figs.12.39
- effective decay time 257
- properties of isotopes Table 10.1
- with Pt 255,258,259; Figs.12.41,43-47
- pulsed 253-260; Figs.12.40-47
- repetition rate 257
- SQUID 250,251; Figs.12.37,38
- tipping angle 253
Nuclear magnetic susceptibility thermometry 248-260; Figs.12.35-47
Nuclear magnetization 162,163,249;
  Figs.10.5,12.35
- of Cu, In, Pt, Tl 249; Figs.10.5,12.35
- transverse component 253,254
Nuclear magneton 286
Nuclear orientation thermometry 260-
  266; Figs.12.49,50
- equipment 264
- sensitivity 263,264; Fig.12.50
- statistical error 264
Nuclear refrigerants, requirements 181
Nuclear refrigeration/refrigerators
  186-195; Figs.10.3,14,15,18-21,23,24;
  see also Adiabatic nuclear demagneti-
  zation
Nuclear specific heat 162,163
- Ag,Al,Cu,Pt,Tl Fig.10.4;
Nuclear spin temperature 160,168-174;
  Figs.10.7,8
Nuclear susceptibility 162,248
- of AuIn$_2$ 250; Fig.12.36
- of Cu 249; Fig.12.35
- dynamic 252,253
- of Pt Fig.12.44,47
Nuclear Zeeman energy 162
Nuclear Zeeman levels of Cu 159;
  Fig.10.2
Nucleus-electron coupling 168-171
Nylon
- susceptibility Table A.1
- thermal conductivity Figs.3.17,18,20;
  Table 3.2
Nyquist theorem 234,235

Optical transmissivity, SiO$_2$, Al$_2$O$_3$
  282,283; Fig.13.11
Optimum demagnetization field 171-173
Oriented nuclei, thermometry 260-266;
  Figs.12.49,50

Ortho-para conversion of H_2 8-11,179; Fig.2.2
Osmotic pressure of ^{3}He-^{4}He mixtures 116-118; Figs.7,6,7
Oxygen
- liquid 7
- properties Tables 2.1,11.1

Packing fraction of sintered metals 279, 280; Fig.13.9;Table 13.1
Paramagnetic (electronic) refrigeration, *see* Adiabatic demag. of paramag. salts

Paramagnetic salts
- for adiab. refrig. 154,155
- entropy Figs.9.1,2
- thermometry 239-248; Figs.12.27-29
Paramagnets, Van Vleck 184-186
Para-ortho conversion of deuterium Fig.2.2
Partition function 152
Passivation of magnetic impurities 61-63; Fig.3.23
PdFe
- susceptibility thermometry 244; Figs.12.28,30,31,47
- thermal time constant 242; Fig.12.28
- thermoelectric power 217,218; Fig.12.5
Permeability of glass for helium 85
Permeability of vacuum 286
Persistent mode (switch) of a superconduct. magnet 164,165; Fig.10.6
Phase diagrams
- ^{3}He and ^{4}He Figs.2.3,8.1
- ^{3}He-^{4}He mixtures Fig.7.1
Phase separation of ^{3}He-^{4}He mixtures 106,107,110-112; Figs.7.1,2
Phonon-electron coupling 165,166
Phonon mean free path 49-53
Phonon (lattice) specific heat 31-33,38-40; Figs.3.1,2,7,12
Planck constant 285
PMMA
- heat release Fig.10.11
- thermal conductivity Fig.3.19
- thermal expansion coefficient Fig.3.14
Polarizability of helium 14
Polarization 152,262
- of nuclei in Al,Cu,In,Pt,Tl; Fig.10.5
Polystyrol
- thermal conductivity Fig.3.17
- heat release Fig.10.11
Pomeranchuk cooling 138-147; Fig.8.4,6

- amount of solid 142,143
- cooling power 139,143; Fig.8.4
- heating effects 143,144; Fig.8.5
- history 138,145
- refrigeration cells 145-147; Figs.8.7,8
- techniques 144-147
Population of nuclear sublevels 160,261, 262; Fig.10.2
Potential, atomic 30,45; Fig.3.13
Potentials of ^{4}He Fig.2.4
Precooling
- a dewar with LN_2 82,83
- a nuclear refrigerator 163-165,186; Fig.10.16
Pressure regulation 271; Fig.13.4
Primary thermometers 210
$PrNi_5$
- minimum temperature achievable 193
- nuclear refrigerator (refrigeration) 190-193; Figs.10.20,21,23
- nuclear spin entropy 182,184; Figs.10.12,13,22
- properties 184-186; Figs.10.13,22; Table 10.1
Production of ^{3}He 12
Pt
- electrical resistance thermometry 202, 219,220; Figs.12.6,7;Table 12.3
- Korringa constant 255; Figs.12.43,44; Table 10.1
- nuclear magnetization Fig.10.5
- nuclear specific heat Fig.10.4
- properties Table 10.1
- pulsed NMR thermometry (thermometers) 255,258,259; Figs.12.41,43-47
- sintered 281;Table 13.1
- thermal expansion coefficient Fig.3.14
PtW
- specific heat 41,42; Figs.3.9,12
- susceptibility Table A.1
Pump, adsorption 100-103
Pumping tubes
- bellows 176; Fig.10.9
- conductance 100
Pyrex
- thermal conductivity Table 3.2
- thermal expansion coefficient Fig.3.14

Quadrupole interaction (nuclear electric) 43,181,182; Fig.3.11
- specific heat 43; Fig.3.11
Quadrupole moments, nuclear electric Table 10.1
Quantum liquids (parameter) 15

Radiation pattern of oriented nuclei
261-264; Fig.12.49
Radiation shields/baffles 84,174,175;
Figs.5.1-3
Radioactive nuclei, heating 263
Refrigeration, history 2; Fig.1.2;
Table 1.1
Refrigerators
- adiabatic electronic demag. 155,
156; Fig.9.3
- adiabat. nuclear demag. 186-195;
Figs.10.3,14,15
- Pomeranchuck 145-147; Figs.8.7,8
Regulation
- of pressure 271; Fig.13.4
- of temperature in nuclear refrig. 193
Relaxation time
- spin-lattice 168-171,251,255-257;
Fig.12.41-44
- spin-spin 165,169; Table 10.1
- of Cu 61-63; Fig.3.24
Residual resistivity ratio 58,59,186;
Figs.3.21,24,61-63; Fig.3.24
- of Cu 59,62,63; Fig.3.24
Resistance, electrical
- of Cu 60-63; Figs.3.22,23;
Tables 3.3,4
- of Pt 202,219,220; Figs.12.6,7;
Tables 12.3
Resistance bridges 229-232;
Figs.12.20,21
Resistance thermometry
- carbon 222-232; Figs.12.7-19
- Ge 222; Figs.12.7-10
- metals 202,219,220; Figs.12.6,7
Table 12.3
- *Rh*Fe 219,220; Fig.12.7
- RuO$_2$ 233; Fig.12.22
Rotational energy states of H$_2$ 8,9;
Fig.2.1; Table 2.2

Sapphire (Al$_2$O$_3$)
- heat release 179
- optical transmissivity 282; Fig.13.11
- thermal conductivity Figs.3.16-18,20;
Table 3.2
Saturation magnetization 153
Scattering of electrons 49,53,54,57-63;
Figs.3.22,23; Tables 3.3,4
Scattering of phonons 49-53
Schottky anomaly (specific heat) 40-43;
Figs.3.8-10; Table 3.1
Seals, metal 47, Fig.3.15
Secondary thermometers 210

Seismometer 176
Semiconductor resistance thermometry
220-222; Figs.12.7-10,20,21
Shielded rooms 175,232
Shields
- normal conducting 276,277
- superconducting 273,274,277
Shrinking of sintered metals 281
Silver, *see* Ag
Sintered metal powder 76,127,128,
278-281; Fig.13.9; Table 13.1
- boundary resistance to helium 76,77;
Figs.4.7,9.10
- conductivity 279-281; Table 13.1
- elastic constants 76,278
- heat exchanger 126-128; Figs.7.13;
Table 7.1
- low-frequency vibrational modes
76,278
- packing fraction 279-281; Fig.13.9;
Table 13.1
- shrinking 281
- surface area 278-281; Fig.13.9;
Table 13.1
SiO$_2$
- heat release Fig.10.11
- specific heat Figs.3.7,12
- susceptibility Table A.1
- thermal conductivity Figs.3.16-19
- thermal expansion coefficient 47;
Fig.3.14
- transmissivity 282,283; Fig.13.11
Skin depth 257,278
Sn, properties Fig.3.5; Table 10.1
Solders
- melting points Table 4.1
- superconducting transitions 72,73;
Table 4.1
- thermal conductivity Fig.3.17
- thermal expansion coefficient Fig.3.14
Solidification of ^{3}He 138
Solubility of ^{3}He in ^{3}He-^{4}He mixtures
106,107,110-112; Figs.7.1,2,4
Sommerfeld constant of metals 35;
Table 10.1
Specific heat
- Al,Hg,Sn,V 37,38; Figs.3.5,12
- carbon thermometers 227; Fig.12.15
- Constantan, Manganin, PtW 41,42;
Figs.3.9,12
- Cu 43; Figs.3.4,11,12,10.4; Table 10.1
- Debye model 32,33; Fig.3.1
- Dulong-Petit law 31; Fig.3.2
- Einstein model 31; Fig.3.1

- ^{3}He 26,27,113; Figs.2.8,14,15,
3.12,7.5
- ^{4}He 18-21; Figs.2.8,9,3.12
- ^{3}He-^{4}He mixtures 109,110,113-115;
Fig.7.5
- insulators (phonons, lattice) 31-33,
38-40; Figs.3.1,2,7,12
- magnetic 40-43,153,162; Figs.3.8-10,
10.4;Table 3.1
- metals (conduction electrons) 33-36,43;
Figs.3.4,5,9,11,12;Table 10.1
- noble gases (except He) Fig.3.2
- non-crystalline materials 38-40;
Figs.3.7,12
- nuclear quadrupole interaction 43,182;
Fig.3.11
- nuclei in Ag, Al, Cu, Pt, Tl Fig.10.4
- Schottky anomaly 40-43; Figs.3.8-10;
Table 3.1
- SiO$_2$ Figs.3.7,12
- superconductors 37,38; Figs.3.5,12
Spin-lattice relaxation time 168-171
- in pulsed NMR thermometry 255-257
Figs.12.42-44
- in SQUID NMR thermometry 251
Spin-spin relaxation time 165,169;
Table 10.1
Spin temperature 160,168-174;
Figs.10.7,8
SQUID
- amplifier (bridge) 218,236,237,246;
Figs.12.24,34
- NMR thermometry 250-251;
Figs.12.37,38
Steel
- susceptibility Table A.1
- thermal conductivity Table 3.2
- thermal expansion coefficient Fig.3.14
Stefan-Boltzmann equation 83
Step heat exchanger 126-128;
Figs.7.13,14
Still of ^{3}He-^{4}He dilution refrigerators
118,122,123
- film flow burner 123; Fig.7.11
- pressure 118
Storage vessel for ^{4}He 92; Fig.5.7
Strain gauge, capacitive 267-271;
Figs.13.1-3
Structural relaxation, heat release
178-180
Structure of metals Table 10.1
Stycast
- heat release Fig.10.11
- susceptibility Table A.1

- thermal conductivity Table 3.2
- thermal expansion coefficient
Fig.3.14
Superconducting fixed point device
204-207; Figs.11.1-3;Table 11.6
- field dependence Fig.11.3
Superconducting heat switch 67-70,161;
Figs.4.1-4
- frozen-in flux 70
Superconducting magnets
- leads 65,66,275,276; Fig.13.8
- persistent mode (switch) 164,165;
Fig.10.6
- in vacuum 274; Fig.13.7
Superconducting shields 273,274,277
Superconducting transition temperature
- metals 204-207; Fig.11.3;
Tables 10.1,11.5,6
- solders 72,73;Tables 4.1,10.1
Superconduction leads 65,66,275,276;
Fig.13.8
Superconductors
- critical magnetic fields Tables 10.1,
11.6
- specific heat 37,38; Figs.3.4,12
- thermal conductivity 56,57;
Figs.3.18,4.1-3
- transition temperature 72,73,204-207;
Fig.11.3; Tables 4.1,10.1,11.5,6
Supercooling of supercond. transition
206; Fig.11.2
Superfluid film of ^{4}He 23-25,181;
Figs.2.12,13
Superfluid transition
- ^{3}He 25;Tables 2.3,11.7
- ^{4}He 19,20; Fig.2.9; Table 2.3
Superinsulation 88; Figs.5.2,7
Surface area of sintered metals 278-281;
Fig.13.9;Table 13.1
Susceptibility, *see also* Magnetic suscep-
tibility
- magnetic 162,241,248;
Figs.12.36,44,47; Table A.1
- *Pd*Fe 244; Figs.12.30,47
- thermometry 239-248
Susceptibility bridges 245,246;
Figs.11.2,12.32-34
Susceptibility thermometry
- bridges 245,246; Figs.11.2,12.32-34
- CMN, LCMN 241-243; Figs.12.27-29
- dilute magnetic alloys 242-244;
Figs.12.28,30,31
- electronic magnetic 239-250;
Figs.12.27-33

- nuclear magnetic 248-260;
  Figs.12.35-47
- *Pd*Fe 244; Figs.12.28,30,31
- sensitivity, resolution 242,244,246,247
- thermometer design 242,258; Figs.
  12.27,29,31,45,46
- time constants 242; Fig.12.48
Switching of s.c. heat switch 67-69;
  Fig.4.2

Teflon
- heat release 179
- susceptibility Table A.1
- thermal conductivity Figs.3.17,18;
  Table 3.2
Temperature
- electronic, nuclear spin 160,168-174;
  Figs.10.7,8
- fixed points 200-209; Tables 11.1,5-7
Temperature regulation, nuclear refri-
  geration 193
Temperature scales 199-209;
  Tables 11.1-4
Thermal anchoring of leads 232
Thermal boundary resistance, *see*
  Boundary resistance
Thermal conductivity 46-63,68,69;
  Figs.3.16-21; Table 3.2
- Al_2O_3 (sapphire) Figs.3.16,17,18,20;
  Table 3.2
- alloys Figs.3.17,18; Table 3.2
- CMN Fig.3.18
- Cu 59; Figs.3.16-18,21; Table 3.2
- epoxies, graphite Figs.3.18,20;
  Table 3.2
- H_2 Fig.3.17
- [3]He 26,27; Figs.2.16,17,3.18
- [4]He 21,22; Figs.2.10,11,17,3.18
- [3]He-[4]He Fig.2.17
- [4]He gas 84,85; Figs.2.10,3.17
- insulators (phonons) 49-53,55;
  Figs.3.16-18; Table 3.2
- liquefied gases (except He)
  Figs.3.17,20
- metals 53-59,68,69;
  Figs.3.16-18,21,4.1-3; Table 3.2
- non-crystalline solids 52,53;
  Figs.3.16-20; Table 3.2
- plastics Figs.3.17-20; Table 3.2
- SiO_2 Figs.3.16,17,19
- superconductors 56,57,67-69;
  Figs.3.18,4.1-3
Thermal expansion coefficient 45-48;
  Fig.3.14

Thermal time constant, susceptibility
  thermometers 242; Fig.12.28
Thermodynamic temperature 198,199
Thermoelectric power of various metals
  216-218; Figs.12.4,5
Thermoelectric thermometry 216-219;
  Figs.12.3-5
Thermometers
- general requirements 210,111
- primary and secondary 210
Thermometry
- carbon resistors 222-232;
  Figs.12.7,11-19
- dielectric constant 237-239;
  Figs.12.25,26
- electronic susceptibility 239-248;
  Figs.12.27-34
- gas 211,212; Fig.12.1
- germanium resistors 222; Figs.12.7-10
- [3]He melting pressure 214-216,267-
  271; Figs.13.1,2; Table 12.2
- metal resistors 202,219,220;
  Figs.12.6,7; Table 12.3
- Mössbauer effect 265
- noise 234-237; Figs.12.23,24
- nuclear magnetic resonance 250-260;
  Figs.12.37-47
- nuclear magnetic susceptibility
  248-260; Figs.12.35-47
- nuclear orientation 260-266;
  Figs.12.49,50
- resistance 202,219-233; Figs.12.6-22;
  Table 12.3
- *Rh*Fe 219,200; Fig.12.7
- RuO_2 233; Fig.12.22
- SQUID NMR 250,251; Figs.12.37,38
- susceptibility (electronic) 239-248;
  Figs.12.27-34
- susceptibility (nuclear) 248-260;
  Figs.12.35-47
- thermoelectric 216-219; Figs.12.3-5
- vapour pressure 201-203,212-214,269-
  271; Figs.12.2,13.3; Tables 11.2,4,12.1
Time-dependent heat leaks 9-11,84,85,
  178-181; Figs.2.2,10.10,11
Tin, *see* Sn
Tipping angle in NMR thermometry
  253,256,257
Tl, properties 163,182,248; Figs.10.4,5;
  Table 10.1
Transfer tube for L[4]He 92; Fig.5.8
Transition temperatures
- [3]He 25,207; Tables 2.3,11.7
- superconductors 72,73,204-207;

Fig.11.3; Tables 4.1,10.1,11.5,6
Transmissivity of optical windows 282,
283; Fig.13.11
Transverse component of nuclear mag-
netization 253,254
Trap, LN_2 cooled 133; Fig.7.22
Triple points of cryoliquids Table 2.1
Tunneling model 179
Tunneling transitions
- heat release 179
- specific heat 38-40; Fig.3.7
- thermal conductivity 52

Valve, cold, cryogenic 271,272; Fig.13.5
Van der Waals force, ^{3}He and ^{4}He 14,
23,24
Van Vleck paramagnets 184-186
Vapour pressure
- cryoliquids Fig.2.7
- ^{3}He and ^{4}He 16-18,201-203;
Figs.2.6,7; Tables 11.2-4
- ratio of ^{3}He-^{4}He 118
Vapour pressure thermometry 201-203,
212-214; Figs.12.2,13.3;
Tables 11.2-4,12.1
- with capacitive manometers 269-271;
Fig.13.3
Vespel
- heat release Fig.10.11

- thermal conductivity Fig.3.20;
Table 3.2
- thermal expansion coefficient Fig.3.14
Vibrational heating (vibration isolation)
175, 176; Fig.10.9
Vibrational modes of metal sinters 76,
278
Viscosity
- ^{3}He 27; Fig.2.18
- ^{4}He 22
- ^{3}He-^{4}He mixtures Fig.2.18
Viscous heating in ^{3}He-^{4}He dilution
refrig. 130
Volume percent of cryoliquids in air
Table 2.1

Warming-up time, nuclear refrigerator
172,173,193; Figs.10.8,25
Weiss field 240
Wiedemann-Franz law 57-59; Fig.3.21
Windows, cryogenic 281-289

Yield stress 268
Young's modulus 168,170

Zeeman splitting (levels, energy) 162,
182,205
- Cu 159; Fig.10.2
Zero-point energy of ^{3}He,^{4}He 14;
Fig.2.4

Printing: Mercedesdruck, Berlin
Binding: Buchbinderei Lüderitz & Bauer, Berlin